PREPARING FOR THE CHEMISTRY

AP*EXAM

WITH

CHEMISTRY: THE CENTRAL SCIENCE

BROWN/LEMAY/BURSTEN:

TEXT PLUS TEST

**PEARSON
SERIES
FOR
AP*
SUCCESS**

*AP is a registered trademark of the College Board, which was not involved in the
production of, and does not endorse, this product.

PEARSON

Prentice
Hall

Printed in the United States of America

10   9   8   7   6   5   4   3   2   1

ISBN 0-536-73157-8

BA 999188

JC/NN

Please visit our web site at *www.pearsoned.com*

PEARSON PRENTICE HALL
Upper Saddle River, New Jersey 07458
A Pearson Education Company

Preparing for the AP* Chemistry Examination with Brown/LeMay/Bursten: *Chemistry: The Central Science*

TABLE OF CONTENTS

About Your Pearson Text Plus Test AP* Guide

Pearson Education is the leading publisher of textbooks worldwide. With operations on every continent, we make it our business to understand the changing needs of students at every level, from Kindergarten to college.

This gives us unique insight into what kind of study materials work for students. We talk to teachers every day, soliciting feedback on our books. We think that this makes us especially qualified to offer this series of AP test prep books that are tied to some of our best-selling textbooks.

We know that as you study for your AP course, you're preparing along the way for the AP exam. If you can tie the material in the book directly to AP course goals and exam topics, it helps you to focus your study time most efficiently. And that's a good thing!

The AP exam is an important milestone in your education. A high score will position you optimally for college acceptance—and possibly will give you college credits that put you a step ahead. Our goal at Pearson Education is to provide you with the tools you need to excel on the exam . . . the rest is up to you.

Good luck!

Part I

Introduction to the AP Chemistry Examination*

This section gives an overview of the Advanced Placement program and the AP Chemistry Examination. Part I introduces the types of questions you will encounter on the exam, provides helpful test-taking strategies, and explains the procedures used to grade the exam. Finally, a correlation chart shows where in *Chemistry: The Central Science* you will find key information that commonly appears on the AP Chemistry Examination. Review Part I carefully before trying the sample test items in Part II and Part III.

The Advanced Placement Program*

Probably you are reading this book for a couple of reasons. You may be a student in an Advanced Placement (AP) Chemistry class, and you have some questions about how the whole AP program works and how it can benefit you. Also, perhaps, you will be taking an AP Chemistry Examination, and you want to find out more about *that*. This book will help you in several important ways.

The first part of this book introduces you to the AP Chemistry course and the AP Chemistry Exam. You'll learn helpful details about the different formats—multiple-choice questions and free-response questions—that you'll encounter on the exam. In addition, you'll find dozens of test-taking strategies that will help you prepare for the exam. A correlation chart at the end of Part I shows how to use your textbook, *Chemistry: The Central Science*, to find the information you'll need to know to score well on the AP Chemistry Exam. By the way, this chart is useful, too, in helping you to identify (and then to disregard) any extraneous material that *won't* be tested. Also in Part I, you'll find information that clarifies the criteria that will be used to evaluate your work on the exam. Part II of this book provides an extensive content review, along with sample multiple-choice and free-response questions. Finally, in Part III, you will find two full-length sample tests. These will help you practice taking the exam under real-life testing conditions. The more familiar you are with the AP Chemistry Exam ahead of time, the more comfortable you'll be on testing day. And the more comfortable you are, the better your chances of achieving a high score.

The AP program provides an opportunity for high school students to pursue (and receive credit for) college-level course work at the secondary level. Sponsored by the College Board (a nonprofit organization), the AP program is based on the premise that college-level material can be taught successfully to able and well-prepared high school students. The AP program offers thirty-five college-level courses to qualified high school students. If you receive a grade of 3 or higher on an AP exam, you may be eligible for college credit, depending on the policies of the institution you plan to attend. Approximately 3,000 colleges and universities around the world grant credit to students who have performed well on AP exams. If you are taking several AP courses and score well on multiple exams, you may even be eligible to enter college as a sophomore. Some institutions grant sophomore status to incoming first-year students who have demonstrated mastery of many AP subjects. Additionally, the College Board confers a number of AP Scholar Awards on students who score 3 or higher on three or more AP exams. Additional awards are available to students who receive very high grades on four or five AP exams.

Why Take an AP Course?

You may be taking an AP course because you are hungry for knowledge and because you thrive on challenges. Of course, probably you know also that colleges and universities look favorably on applicants who have AP courses on their secondary school transcripts. AP classes involve rigorous, detailed lessons, a lot of homework, and numerous tests. Your willingness to take AP courses tells college admissions officers that you believe in working hard to get the most from your education. Because AP course work is more difficult than average high school work, many admissions officers evaluate AP grades on a higher academic level. For example, if you receive a *B* in an AP class, it might carry the same weight as an *A* in a regular high school class.

Your AP Chemistry course prepares you for many of the skills you will need in college. For example, your teacher may assign major research papers and may require you to perform several challenging laboratory exercises using proper scientific protocol. AP Chemistry teachers routinely give substantial reading assignments, and AP Chemistry students learn how to take detailed lecture notes and participate vigorously in class discussions. The AP Chemistry course will challenge you to gather and consider information in new—and sometimes unfamiliar—ways. You can feel good knowing that your ability to use these methods and skills will give you a leg up as you enter college.

Each college or university decides whether or not to grant college credit for an AP course, and each institution bases this decision on what it considers satisfactory grades on AP exams. Depending on what college you attend and what area of study you pursue, your decision to take the AP Chemistry Exam could end up saving you lots of tuition money. You can contact schools directly to find out their guidelines for accepting AP credits.

Taking an AP Examination

The AP Chemistry Exam is given annually in May. Your AP teacher or school guidance counselor can give you information on how to register for the exam. Remember, the deadline for registration and payment of exam fees is usually in January, four months before the actual exam date in May. The cost of the exam is subject to change and can differ depending on the number of exams taken. However, in 2004 the cost of a single exam was $82. For students who can show financial need, the College Board will reduce the price by $22 dollars, and your school might also waive its regular rebate of $8, so the lowest possible total price is $52. Moreover, schools in some states are willing to pay the exam fee for the student. If you feel you may qualify for reduced rates, ask your school administrators for more information. If your school does not administer the AP Chemistry Exam, your teacher or guidance counselor can help you find a nearby school that does.

The exams are scored in June. In mid-July (about 6–8 weeks after you take the exam) the results will be sent to you, your high school, and any colleges or universities you've marked down on your answer sheet. If you want to know your score as early as possible, you can find out (for an additional charge of $15) beginning July 1st by calling the College Board at (609)-771-7300. On the phone, you'll be asked to give your AP number or social security number, your birth date, and a credit card number. After you receive your score, if you decide that you want it sent to additional colleges and universities, you can fill out the appropriate information on your AP Grade Report (which you will receive by mail in July) and return it to the College Board. There is an additional charge of $15 for each additional school that will receive your AP score.

If you believe that your performance on an exam was dreadful, you can choose to withhold or cancel your grade. (Withholding is temporary, whereas canceling is permanent.) Each procedure carries a $5 charge per college or university. You'll need to write—or send email—to the College Board and include your name, address, gender, birth date, AP number, the date of the exam, the name of the exam, a check for the exact amount due, and the name, city, and state of the college(s) from which you want the score withheld or cancelled. You should check the College Board website for the deadline for withholding your score, but it is usually in mid-June—that is, before you know your score. Of course, we recommend *not* withholding or canceling your scores. Rather, sit back, relax, and assume that the glass is half full.

The Advanced Placement program encourages students with disabilities to take AP examinations. If you have documented disabilities, you may be eligible for accommodations on the AP exams, such as extended time; nonstandard exam forms; permission to use a Braille device, computer, or magnifying device; and permission to use a reader to dictate questions, a writer to record responses, and/or a sign-language interpreter to give directions. To receive accommodations, your school must submit an eligibility form for you. Your school should have copies of this form.

AP Chemistry: Course Goals

The AP Chemistry course is designed to be the equivalent of a general chemistry course usually taken during a student's first year of college. AP Chemistry courses give students a considerable amount of access to specialized equipment—ranging from calculators with probes to volumetric glassware, pH meters, and analytic balances. Moreover, since chemistry is a central science, AP Chemistry courses can be used as the foundation in building larger frameworks of thought and applications.

Typically, AP Chemistry courses are designed for students to spend a minimum of 290 minutes each week in scheduled class time—including a minimum of 90 minutes in a laboratory, preferably in one session. AP Chemistry must be a second-year course offered to students only after they have successfully completed a first-year chemistry course. As well, students should have experience with the higher thinking skills needed to complete advanced mathematics courses. AP Chemistry courses provide college-level chemistry instruction and college-level laboratory experience; also, they prepare students to have the best possible chance for success on the AP Chemistry Exam.

According to the College Board, AP Chemistry courses are built around five main topic areas—structure of matter, states of matter, chemical reactions, descriptive chemistry, and laboratory chemistry. In fact, the College Board has created an outline to illustrate the topics that make up a typical college chemistry course—and so should form the basis for AP Chemistry courses. The outline below is taken directly from pages 5–10 of the AP Chemistry

Course Description, published by the College Board. The numbers in parentheses show the percentage of multiple-choice questions likely to be devoted to particular topics on the AP Chemistry Exam.

I. Structure of Matter (20%)

A. Atomic theory and atomic structure
1. Evidence for the atomic theory
2. Atomic masses; determination by chemical and physical means
3. Atomic number and mass number; isotopes
4. Electron energy levels: atomic spectra, quantum numbers, atomic orbitals
5. Periodic relationships including, for example, atomic radii, ionization energies, electron affinities, oxidation states

B. Chemical bonding
1. Binding forces
   a. Types: ionic, covalent, metallic, hydrogen bonding, van der Waals (including London dispersion forces)
   b. Relationships to states, structure, and properties of matter
   c. Polarity of bonds, electronegativities
2. Molecular models
   a. Lewis structures
   b. Valence bond: hybridization of orbitals, resonance, sigma and pi bonds
   c. VSEPR
3. Geometry of molecules and ions, structural isomerism of simple organic molecules and coordination complexes; dipole moments of molecules; relation of properties to structure

C. Nuclear chemistry: nuclear equations, half lives, and radioactivity; chemical applications

II. States of Matter (20%)

A. Gases
1. Laws of ideal gases
   a. Equation of state for an ideal gas
   b. Partial pressures
2. Kinetic-molecular theory
   a. Interpretation of ideal gas laws on the basis of this theory
   b. Avogadro's hypothesis and the mole concept
   c. Dependence of kinetic energy of molecules on temperature
   d. Deviations from ideal gas laws

B. Liquids and solids
1. Liquids and solids from the kinetic-molecular viewpoint
2. Phase diagrams of one-component systems
3. Changes of state, including critical points and triple points
4. Structure of solids; lattice energies

C. Solutions
1. Types of solutions and factors affecting solubility
2. Methods of expressing concentration (The use of normalities is not tested.)
3. Raoult's law and colligative properties (nonvolatile solutes); osmosis
4. Non-ideal behavior (qualitative aspects)

III. Reactions (35–40%)

A. Reaction types
1. Acid-base reactions; concepts of Arrhenius, Brønsted-Lowry, and Lewis; coordination complexes; amphoterism
2. Precipitation reactions
3. Oxidation-reduction reactions
   a. Oxidation number
   b. The role of the electron in oxidation-reduction
   c. Electrochemistry: electrolytic and galvanic cells; Faraday's laws; standard half-cell potentials; Nernst equation; prediction of the direction of redox reactions

B. Stoichiometry
1. Ionic and molecular species present in chemical systems: net ionic equations
2. Balancing of equations including those for redox reactions
3. Mass and volume relations with emphasis on the mole concept, including empirical formulas and limiting reactants

C. Equilibrium
1. Concept of dynamic equilibrium, physical and chemical; Le Châtelier's principle; equilibrium constants
2. Quantitative treatment
   a. Equilibrium constants for gaseous reactions: K_p, K_c
   b. Equilibrium constants for reactions in solution
      (1) Constants for acids and bases; pK; pH
      (2) Solubility product constants and their application to precipitation and the dissolution of slightly soluble compounds
      (3) Common ion effect; buffers; hydrolysis

D. Kinetics
1. Concept of rate of reaction
2. Use of differential rate laws to determine order of reaction and rate constant from experimental data
3. Effect of temperature change on rates
4. Energy of activation; the role of catalysts
5. The relationship between the rate-determining step and a mechanism

E. Thermodynamics
1. State functions

2. First law: change in enthalpy; heat of formation; heat of reaction; Hess's law; heats of vaporization and fusion; calorimetry
3. Second law: entropy; free energy of formation; free energy of reaction; dependence of change in free energy on enthalpy and entropy changes
4. Relationship of change in free energy to equilibrium constants and electrode potentials

IV. Descriptive Chemistry (10–15%)

Knowledge of specific facts of chemistry is essential for an understanding of principles and concepts. These descriptive facts, including the chemistry involved in environmental and societal issues, should not be isolated from the principles being studied but should be taught throughout the course to illustrate and illuminate the principles. The following areas should be covered:

1. Chemical reactivity and products of chemical reactions
2. Relationships in the periodic table: horizontal, vertical, and diagonal with examples from alkali metals, alkaline earth metals, halogens, and the first series of transition elements
3. Introduction to organic chemistry: hydrocarbons and functional groups (structure, nomenclature, chemical properties)

V. Laboratory (5–10%)

The differences between college chemistry and the usual secondary school chemistry course are especially evident in the laboratory work. The AP Chemistry Examination includes some questions based on experiences and skills students acquire in the laboratory:

- making observations of chemical reactions and substances
- recording data
- calculating and interpreting results based on the quantitative data obtained
- communicating effectively the results of experimental work

For a complete list of twenty-two suggested laboratories, see the College Board's website at www.apcentral.org.

Chemical Calculations

The list below summarizes the types of problems that appear (either explicitly or implicitly) in the AP Chemistry topic outline. The College Board recommends that students give attention to significant figures, precision of measured values, and the use of logarithmic and exponential relationships. Moreover, students are encouraged to employ critical analysis of the reasonableness of all results.

1. Percentage composition
2. Empirical and molecular formulas from experimental data
3. Molar masses from gas density, freezing-point, and boiling-point measurements

4. Gas laws, including the ideal gas law, Dalton's law, and Graham's law
5. Stoichiometric relations using the concept of the mole; titration calculations
6. Mole fractions; molar and molal solutions
7. Faraday's laws of electrolysis
8. Equilibrium constants and their applications, including their use for simultaneous equilibria
9. Standard electrode potentials and their use; Nernst equation
10. Thermodynamic and thermochemical calculations
11. Kinetics calculations

Understanding the AP Chemistry Examination

The purpose of the AP Chemistry Examination is to allow students to demonstrate mastery of the concepts and skills learned in a general undergraduate chemistry course. The AP Chemistry Exam takes three hours to complete, and it is made up of a multiple-choice section and a free-response section. The two sections are designed to complement each other and to meet the overall course objectives and exam specifications. Inside your examination booklet will be a periodic table of elements, which you are free to use for both sections. A table of mathematical equations and of standard reduction potentials will be available for your use only in the free-response section of the exam. It is important that you memorize solubility rules, as well as the names, formulas and charges of common ions before the exam.

Section I: Multiple-Choice Questions

Section I of the exam consists of 75 multiple-choice questions designed to measure your mastery of the content of the AP Chemistry curriculum. You have 90 minutes to complete Section I, and this section will constitute 45% of your final grade on the exam. No calculators may be used with Section I. This portion of the exam is followed by a five- or ten-minute break—the only official break during the examination.

Throughout the test, certain symbols will indicate standard conditions in thermodynamics—that is, 298 K, 1.00 atmosphere pressure, and 1.00 M. For instance, when the symbol for enthalpy is written $\Delta H°$ rather than ΔH, it means standard conditions. You can assume you are at standard conditions unless otherwise directed. All solutions are aqueous unless noted. You will encounter many symbols on the AP Chemistry Exam, and usually a table of these symbols is printed at the beginning of Section I. For instance, the following table is taken from the AP Chemistry Released Exam 1999, published by the College Board.

T = temperature	M = molar
P = pressure	m = molal
V = volume	L, mL = liter(s), milliliter(s)
S = entropy	g = gram(s)
H = enthalpy	nm = nanometer(s)
G = free energy	atm = atmosphere(s)
R = molar gas constant	J, kJ = joule(s), kilojoule(s)
n = number of moles	V = volts
	mol = mole(s)

Several types of multiple-choice questions commonly appear in Section I of the AP Chemistry Exam. Each is described in detail below.

Factual Multiple-Choice Questions

Factual multiple-choice questions are the most basic type of question in Section I. Here you apply your knowledge of chemistry by choosing the best answer from the five choices presented. Below is an example of such a question, including typical directions.

> **Directions:** Each of the questions or incomplete statements below is followed by five suggested answers or completions. Select the one that is best in each case and then fill in the corresponding oval on the answer sheet.

1. Which of the following is the formula for butanal, an aldehyde?
    (A) $CH_3CH_2CH_2OH$
    (B) $CH_3CH_2CH_2COOH$
    (C) $CH_3CH_2COOCH_3$
    (D) $CH_3CH_2OCH_2CH_3$
    (E) $CH_3CH_2CH_2CHO$

The correct answer is *E*. Butanal is an aldehyde having the general formula R—COH. The names of aldehydes end in *-al*. To answer this question correctly you must know the general formula for different classes of organic compounds. That is, $CH_3CH_2CH_2OH$ (answer *A*) is butanol, an alcohol having the general formula R—OH. Answer *B* is butanoic acid, an organic acid having the general formula R—COOH. Answer *C* is propanoate, an ester having the general formula R′—COOR. Finally, $CH_3CH_2OCH_2CH_3$ (answer *D*) is diethyl ether, an ether having the general formula R′—O—R.

"Reverse" Multiple-Choice Questions

Sometimes the format for factual questions is modified slightly, and the result is a slightly more difficult type of multiple-choice question. This type of question features four answers that are correct and only one that is incorrect, and you are asked to find the *incorrect* choice. Generally these questions contain the capitalized words *NOT* or *EXCEPT*. Be alert for these words in Section I of the exam to avoid making a careless mistake. Here is an example of this type of multiple-choice question.

2. Which of the following sets of quantum numbers is NOT acceptable?
    (A) 2, 1, 0, ½
    (B) 1, 0, 0, ½
    (C) 3, 2, −1, −½
    (D) 4, 4, 3, ½
    (E) 5, 0, 0, −½

D is the correct answer. When n = 4, the second quantum number cannot be higher than 3. Every electron can be described by four quantum numbers.

The first number listed is the principle quantum number (n); it designates the energy level and takes the values 1, 2, 3, and so on. The second number listed designates the type of sublevel (l) and has values of 0, 1, ... $n - 1$. The third number (m or m_l) indicates the orientation of the orbital and takes values of $+$ or $-l$. The fourth number is the spin number (s or m_s) and has values of $+\frac{1}{2}$ or $-\frac{1}{2}$.

Matching Questions

Matching questions usually appear at the beginning of Section I. These questions feature a set of five answer choices followed by a series of numbered test items. For these matching questions, you can use the same letter (that is, the same answer) more than once. Below is an example of how matching questions are presented.

Directions: Each set of lettered choices below refers to the numbered phrases immediately following it. Select the one lettered choice that best fits each phrase and then fill in the corresponding oval on the answer sheet. A choice may be used once, more than once, or not at all in each set.

Questions 1–4 refer to the following compounds.
(A) $Zn(NO_3)_2$
(B) Na_2O
(C) CH_3OH
(D) CO_2
(E) $NiSO_4$

3. Forms colored aqueous solutions

4. Contains double bonds

5. Forms a basic solution

6. Is released when sodium bicarbonate is heated

The correct answer to question 3 is *E*. Nickel usually forms green compounds. Most transition metals form colored compounds (Zn is a notable exception). There are no colored compounds with the group 1 or 2 elements.

The correct answer to question 4 is *D*. The Lewis structure for carbon dioxide will have two double bonds (O=C=O). CH_3OH contains no double bonds.

$$
\begin{array}{c}
\text{H} \\
| \\
\text{H—C—O—H} \\
| \\
\text{H}
\end{array}
$$

The other three compounds are ionic, so they do not form molecules and have neither double nor single bonds.

B is the correct answer to question 5. Metallic oxides are basic anhydrides that will form a base when added to water. CO_2 is a nonmetallic oxide and forms an acid when added to water. CH_3OH is an alcohol forming neutral solutions.

The correct answer to question 6 is *D*. Carbonates and bicarbonates will release carbon dioxide on heating or if treated with an acid.

Computational Questions

As you know, you cannot use a calculator to answer the questions in Section I. Many multiple-choice questions will require simple calculations that should not require a calculator. Here is an example of such a question.

7. What is the freezing point of a solution made by dissolving 9.5 grams of $MgCl_2$ in 100 grams of water? (The value of the molal freezing point is constant for water, $K_f = -1.86°C/m$.)
   (A) $-0.186°C$
   (B) $-1.86°C$
   (C) $-3.72°C$
   (D) $-0.458°C$
   (E) $-4.58°C$

D is the correct answer. The change in the freezing point is calculated using $\Delta T = imK_f$, where $i = 3$—in this case, because when $MgCl_2$ dissolves in water it will form one Mg^{2+} ion and two Cl^- ions. Molality (m) = the moles of solute $(MgCl_2)$/kilogram of solvent (H_2O).

$$\text{molar mass } MgCl_2 = 95 \text{ g/mo} \qquad \frac{9.5 \text{ g solute}}{95 \text{ g/mol}} = 0.10 \text{ mol solute}$$

$$\frac{0.10 \text{ mol solute}}{100 \text{ g } H_2O} \times \frac{1000 \text{ g}}{kg} = 1.0 \text{ } m$$

$$\Delta T = 3(1.0 \text{ } m)(-1.86°C/m) = -4.58°C$$

Note that the math required is very easy to do without a calculator and that the answers are very different in magnitude. Sometimes these computational questions will even ask for the approximate answer, and the values will be rounded off. You should practice working without a calculator so that you can work quickly. You can find other sample multiple-choice questions to answer without a calculator on the College Board's website.

Other computational questions (which would normally require a calculator) are presented along with options that show the numbers necessary to solve the problem. Here is an example of this kind of question.

8. A mixture of 0.4 mole of hydrogen gas and 0.4 mole of oxygen are placed in a 10.0-liter flask and sparked. If the temperature in the flask is 25°C, what is the final pressure in the flask after the reaction is complete?

$$2H_2(g) + O_2(g) \rightarrow 2H_2O(g)$$

(A) $\dfrac{0.8(0.0821)(298)}{10}$ atm

(B) $\dfrac{0.6(0.821)(25)}{10}$ atm

(C) $\dfrac{0.6(0.0821)(298)}{10}$ atm

(D) $\dfrac{0.4(0.0821)(298)}{10}$ atm

(E) $\dfrac{0.4(0.0821)(25)}{10}$ atm

The correct answer is *B*. To answer this question correctly you must recognize that $H_2(g)$ is the limiting reagent. Since you need two moles H_2 for every mole O_2 that reacts, you will use only half of the O_2, or 0.2 moles. All of the hydrogen is consumed, and the balanced equation indicates that 0.4 moles of hydrogen will produce 0.4 moles of water. The flask will contain 0.4 moles $H_2O(g)$ and 0.2 moles $O_2(g)$ after the complete reaction occurs. Total pressure is directly proportional to the total number of moles of gas in the flask (0.6 moles). The appropriate equation is $PV = nRT$ where $R = 0.821$ L $\cdot$ atm/mol $\cdot$ K. Note that temperature (T) is in kelvins for all gas law problems.

$$P = \frac{nRT}{V} \quad \text{or} \quad \frac{0.6 \text{ mol } (0.0821 \text{ L} \cdot \text{atm/mol} \cdot \text{K})(298 \text{ K})}{10} \quad P \text{ in atm}$$

Illustration-Based Questions

Illustration-based questions may refer to a graph or scientific table. In these questions you are asked to make an assessment or evaluation based on the ideas expressed in the image. Be sure to look for titles, numbers, and units to answer the question correctly. Here is an example of such a question.

9. The diagram below shows the titration of a weak monoprotic acid by a strong base.

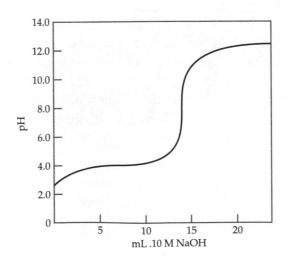

According to the titration curve shown above, the pK_a of this weak acid is approximately

(A) 2
(B) 4
(C) 8
(D) 10
(E) 12

The correct answer is *B*. To answer this question correctly you must recognize that the equivalence point of the titration is signaled by a sharp rise in pH or vertical portion to the curve (approximately 14 mL), and you must know that the pH = pK_a at the ½ equivalence point in the titration of a weak acid with a weak base. At approximately 7 mL, the pH is approximately 4.

Multiple-Answer Questions

Sometimes multiple-choice questions will ask you to identify the correct item or items from a list labeled with Roman numerals. Here is an example.

10. Which of the following experiments led to determining the mass of the electron?
    I. Millikan's oil-drop experiment
    II. Thomson's cathode-ray tube experiment
    III. Rutherford's gold foil experiment
    (A) I only
    (B) II only
    (C) III only
    (D) I and II
    (E) II and III

To answer this question you need to remember the designs of the experiments. J. J. Thomson determined the charge-to-mass ratio of the electron by evaluating cathode ray deflection. Robert Millikan measured the effects of electric fields on charged oil drops and determined the charge of the electron. Though neither scientist measured mass directly, their combined information enabled its value to be calculated. Mathematically, if you know *R* and *c* in R = c/m, you can determine *m*. Rutherford's experiment led to an early hypothetical model of the nucleus, which is a separate atomic entity. The answer, therefore, is *D*.

Section II: Free-Response Questions

Section II of the AP Chemistry Examination usually contains six to eight free-response questions. You have 90 minutes to complete this part of the exam. Free-response questions are presented in two parts (Part A and Part B). Section II constitutes 55% of your final grade on the AP Chemistry Exam.

Free-response questions require you to use your analytical and organizational skills to solve problems, to predict the products of chemical reactions, and to formulate cogent answers to questions. By clearly and precisely answering these questions, you can demonstrate your chemistry skills. Free-response questions give you opportunities not afforded in Section I. In some cases, you may be able to present alternative (yet correct) responses to questions. You may demonstrate your mastery of chemistry concepts by drawing graphs and diagrams. And you may relate different content areas with chemistry as you formulate responses.

Part A: Comprehensive Problems

Part A contains three questions, and you have 40 minutes to answer two of the three problems. You may use a calculator along with the tables of information and equations provided as you work on these problems.

The first question is required, and the score weighting for this question is 20 percent. This question is always an equilibrium problem. There are several types of equilibrium problems: gases, acid-base, and solubility products. Sometimes more than one type of equilibrium will be tested in the same question. Typically this question is scored on a basis of 10 points with the "easy" points early in the problem.

Then you may answer *either* question 2 or question 3, and the score weighting for the question you answer is 20 percent. The topics for these problems could be kinetics, thermodynamics, solutions, gas laws, or any other topic that involves calculations in the course syllabus. These two paired questions are designed to be equal in difficulty, but you may be more familiar with one topic, so it is a good idea to read both problems completely before deciding which will allow you to give a stronger answer. Typically your answer to question 2 or 3 is scored on a basis of 10 points.

As you work on the questions in Part A, remember to show clearly the method you use and the steps involved in arriving at your answers. It is to your advantage to do this, because you may earn partial credit if you do—and you will receive little or no credit if you do not. Remember, also, to pay special attention to units. A maximum of one point per problem is subtracted for errors in the number of significant figures greater than + or −1. Below are examples of the kinds of questions you can expect to see in Part A of Section II of the AP Chemistry Exam.

Question 1

1. In aqueous solution, ammonia [$NH_3(aq)$] reacts with water to form a hydroxide ion [OH^-].

$$NH_3(g) + H_2O(l) = NH_4^+(aq) + OH^-(aq)$$

(a) Write the equilibrium-constant expression.
(b) The hydroxide-ion concentration is 5.60×10^{-4} M at 25°C in a 0.0180 M $NH_3(aq)$ sample. Determine the percent ionization of NH_3 in 0.0180 M $NH_3(aq)$.
(c) Determine the value of the ionization constant, K_b, for $NH_3(aq)$.
(d) Determine the pH of 0.0180 M $NH_3(aq)$. Many metallic hydroxides are insoluble. The K_{sp} of $Ca(OH)_2 = 1.3 \times 10^{-6}$.
(e) Write the solubility-product expression for calcium hydroxide.
(f) Calculate the [Ca^{2+}] in an aqueous solution of pH = 11.72.

Solution for Question 1

Plan and Analyze

Pay close attention to significant figures as well as to mathematical computations.

Solve

(a) $K = \dfrac{[NH_4^+][OH^-]}{[NH_3]}$

(b) % ionization $= \dfrac{\text{amount that ionizes}}{\text{original amount}}$ $\dfrac{5.60 \times 10^{-4}}{0.0180} \times 100$

$= 3.11\%$ **or** 0.0311

(c) or $K_b = \dfrac{(5.60 \times 10^{-4})^2}{0.0180 - 0.000560} = 1.80 \times 10^{-5}$

or

$K_b = \dfrac{(5.60 \times 10^{-4})^2}{0.0180} = 1.74 \times 10^{-5}$ (Frequently we approximate in solving equilibrium problems and assume $1 - x \cong 1$ if the difference is 5% or less.)

(d) $[OH^-] = 5.60 \times 10^{-4}$ ▶ $pOH = 3.252$ or $[H^+] = 1.79 \times 10^{-11}$ ▶ $pH = 10.748$

Note that you have a base, so the pOH is calculated first and then the pH is found, because $14 - pOH = pH$. The significant figures on pH are confusing to some students. You can think of the number in front of the decimal as equivalent to the exponent—the $pH = 10.748$ has three significant figures because the 10 doesn't count.

(e) $K_{sp} = [Ca^{2+}][OH^-]^2$

You must recognize that $Ca(OH)_2(s) = Ca^{2+}(aq) + 2OH^-(aq)$.

(f) $pOH = 14 - 11.72 = 2.28$
$[OH^-] = -\log pOH = 5.2 \times 10^{-3}$ M
$1.3 \times 10^{-6} = [Ca^{2+}][5.2 \times 10^{-3}]^2$
$[Ca^{2+}] = 0.048$ M $\times$ 111 g/mol $= 5.3$ g/L

Question 2

2. A mixture of He and CO_2 is contained in a 2.50-liter vessel at 673 mm Hg and 25°C.
   (a) Calculate the total number of moles of gas in the container.
   (b) Compare the average kinetic energy and velocity of the He and CO_2. Justify your answer.
   (c) If the mixture contains equal masses of He and CO_2, calculate the partial pressure of the He.

The rate law for a certain reaction, A + 2B → C, can be expressed as rate = $k[A]$, where the specific rate constant, $k = 8.3 \times 10^{-4}\ s^{-1}$.

i. Calculate the concentration of [A] after 600.0 seconds if the initial [A] = 1.0 M.

ii. Is the following rate law consistent with the reaction? Explain your answer.

$$A + B = D\ \text{fast}$$
$$D + B \rightarrow C\ \text{slow}$$

Solution for Question 2

(a) $n = RT/PV$ $n = \dfrac{0.0821\ L \cdot atm/mol \cdot K\ (298\ K)}{673/760\ atm\ (2.50\ L)} = 0.090\ moles$

You must remember that R has units of L-atm/mol K. Since you were given pressure in mmHg, you will have to divide the pressure by 760 to covert it to atmospheres. You must also remember to convert the temperature to degrees Kelvin.

(b) The kinetic energy of He = the kinetic energy of CO_2, because both are at the same temperature, and temperature measures the average kinetic energy. The average velocity of He is greater than the average velocity of CO_2 molecules, because $K.E. = \frac{1}{2}\ mv^2$, and in order for the lighter He atoms to have the same $K.E.$ as CO_2 molecules, they must have a higher velocity.

(c) $P_{He} = X_{He}\ P_{total}$ $11/12 \times 673\ mm\ Hg = 617\ mm\ Hg$ is partial pressure of He

The partial pressure of a gas is directly proportional to the mole fraction of that gas in the mixture. Avogadro's hypothesis states that equal volumes of gases at the same temperature and pressure have the same number of particles. Now compare their molar masses. He = 4 and CO_2 = 44—let's say you have 44 grams of each gas—and that would give you 11 moles of He (44 g × 1 mole/4 g) and 1 mole of CO_2. No matter what size the sample is, He and CO_2 are in the same ratio. So He would be 11 moles out of a total of 12 moles.

i. $\ln\,[A]/[A2] = -kt$ $\ln[A]/1.0 = -8.3 \times 10^{-4}\ s^{-1}\ (600.0\ s)$

$$[A] = 0.60\ M$$

This is a first-order reaction, so you need the integrated rate law found on the tables provided with the exam.

ii. No, it is not consistent. The steps add to the overall balanced equation, but the rate for this mechanism = $k[A][B]^2$.

Question 3

3.

(a) Write the equation for the reaction that occurs in each half-cell, and write the overall net ionic equation.
(b) Calculate E° for the electrochemical cell represented above.
(c) Label the anode and cathode on the diagram above, and indicate the direction of electron flow.
(d) How would the voltage be affected if NaCl (*aq*) were added to the silver half-cell? Explain.
(e) Calculate the maximum amount of work that could be done by this electrochemical cell.

Solution for Question 3

(a) $2(Ag^+ + 1e \rightarrow Ag^0)$

$$\frac{Zn^0 \rightarrow Zn^{2+} + 2e}{2Ag^+ + Zn^0 \rightarrow 2Ag^0 + Zn^{2+}}$$

(b) $E^0 = +0.80 + -0.76 = 1.56$ v

	E^0
$2(Ag^+ + 1e \rightarrow Ag^0)$	$+0.80$ V
$Zn^0 \rightarrow Zn^{2+} + 2e$	$+0.76$ V
$2Ag^+ + Zn^0 \rightarrow 2Ag^0 + Zn^{2+}$	1.56 V

You must look up the standard reduction potentials in the table provided on the exam. Since the table lists reduction potentials, the Zn is being oxidized, so that reaction is reversed and the sign of the voltage is changed. You must remember that the voltage for the Ag reduction is not doubled, because voltage is measuring the potential difference between the cells and does not depend on the number of electrons transferred.

(c) You must indicate on the diagram that Zn is the anode (site of oxidation or loss of electrons) and that the Ag is the cathode (site of reduction or gain of electrons). Electrons will flow in the external circuit from anode to cathode.

(d) Adding NaCl to the $AgNO_3$ will form a precipitate of AgCl and reduce the $[Ag^+]$ and the voltage. According to Le Châtelier's principle, reducing the concentration of one of the reactants (Ag^+) will reduce the rate of the forward reaction and thus the voltage.

or

According to the Nernst equation $E = E° - \dfrac{0.0591}{2} \log \dfrac{[Zn^{2+}]}{[Ag^+]^2}$

It is obvious that reducing the $[Ag^+]$ will reduce the voltage, because it will make the term subtracted from E^0 larger.

(e) $\Delta G = -nFE° = -(2)(96500)(1.56\text{ V}) = -3.01 \times 10^5\text{ J} = -301\text{ kJ}$

The maximum work is equal to the change in free energy. Volts = joules/coulombs or the work needed per coulomb of charge, F is the charge on one mole of electrons, and n = the number of moles of electrons gained or lost in the balanced equation.

$\Delta G = -(2\text{ mol electrons})(96500\text{ C/mol electrons})(1.56\text{ J/C})$

Part B: Thematic Questions

For Part B, you will have 50 minutes to answer four questions—one of which requires the determination of products of chemical reactions and one of which is based on laboratory experience. The use of tables is allowed in Part B, but the use of calculators is not permitted. As in Part A, responses should be clear and relevant to the information cited.

Below are some examples of thematic questions, along with sample solutions and explanations.

Answer Question 4 below. The Section II score weighting for this question is 15 percent.

Question 4

4. Write the formulas to show the reactants and the products for any FIVE of the laboratory situations described below. Assume in all cases that reactions occur, solutions are aqueous and represent substances in solution as ions if the substances are ionized. You do not need to balance the equations, and you may omit formulas for ions or molecules that are unchanged by the reaction.

Example: In a solution of silver nitrate, a chemist adds a strip of magnesium.

$$Mg + Ag^+ \rightarrow Mg^{2+} + Ag$$

(a) A barium nitrate solution is added to a potassium chromate solution.
(b) Hydrofluoric acid reacts with sodium hydroxide.
(c) Methylamine gas is bubbled into distilled water.
(d) A mixture of powdered aluminum metal and powdered iron(III) oxide is strongly heated.
(e) A solution of sulfuric acid has solid lead(II) carbonate added to it.
(f) Ethanol is burned in air.
(g) Excess sodium hydroxide is added to a solution of zinc nitrate.
(h) Calcium oxide powder is added to distilled water.

Solution for Question 4
Analyze and Plan

Remember that you do not need to have balanced equations in this problem. As mentioned before, you will need to know solubility rules and common ions, as well as to know how to recognize a strong or weak electrolyte and to give net ionic equations. Typically one point is given for the reactants, and two points are given for the products—with a one-point penalty for including spectator ions or incorrect species. A good strategy would be to identify quickly any options for which you can write both the reactants and products correctly. Then decide if there are others for which you can get either the reactant or the product points. Remember, also, to answer only five, since only the first five will be graded. Clearly cross out any equations you do not want graded.

Solve

(a) $Ba^{2+} + CrO_4^{2-} \rightarrow BaCrO$

(b) $HF + OH^- \rightarrow F^- + H_2O$

(c) $CH_3NH_2 + H_2O \rightarrow CH_3NH_3^+ + OH^-$

(d) $Fe_2O_3 + Al \rightarrow Al_2O_3 + Fe$

(e) $PbCO_3 + H^+ + HSO_4^- \rightarrow PbSO_4 + CO_2 + H_2O$

or $PbCO_3 + H^+ + SO_4^{2-} \rightarrow PbSO_4 + CO_2 + H_2O$

(f) $C_2H_5OH + O_2 \rightarrow CO_2 + H_2O$

(g) $OH^- + Zn^{2+} \rightarrow Zn(OH)_4^{2-}$

(h) $CaO + H_2O \rightarrow Ca(OH)_2$

Answers/Explanations

(a) Since you have solutions, the salts will be completely dissociated. Write the formulas for all the ions that will be found in solution. Check to see if any of the combinations of cations ($+$ ions) and anions ($-$ ions) are insoluble. Remember to eliminate spectator ions from your answer.

(b) This is an acid-base neutralization—acid + base → salt + water. Weak acids (you should learn six strong acids from your text and assume the rest are weak) are written in molecular form because they are only partially ionized. Sodium hydroxide is 100% dissociated in water, and since all sodium salts are soluble, the Na^+ is a spectator ion.

(c) Organic questions can be troublesome. If you do not know how to write the formula for the reactants, then you should skip it. Amines act as proton acceptors (bases) in water.

(d) You should recognize this as a redox problem—whenever you have an element, it will have to lose or gain electrons to react. Aluminum has only two oxidation states (0 when uncombined and $+3$ in compounds). So the Al will be oxidized to the $+3$, and that means that another element will be reduced. Iron is in the $+3$ oxidation state in Fe_2O_3, so it can only be reduced. You should learn activity series: aluminum can replace iron from compounds.

(e) All carbonates react with acids to release CO_2 and water. Solids are always written in molecular form. Remember that sulfuric acid is a strong acid. Consequently, the first H^+ is 100% ionized, and the second H^+ is not easily removed from an already negative HSO_4^- ion. (However, on the AP Chemistry Exam, readers usually give students credit if they write the SO_4^{2-} ion as a reactant.) If you have learned the solubility rules, then you know that lead(II) sulfate is insoluble.

(f) Combustion of any organic compound will produce carbon dioxide and water. You must always add oxygen to the reactants for combustion. All alcohols have the general formula R—OH when R- is a hydrocarbon. Even if you do not know the formula for the reactants, you can get two points for knowing the products are $CO_2 + H_2O$.

(g) The term *excess* should clue you in to the fact that the complex ion is expected. Several metals have amphoteric hydroxides—they will dissolve in excess acid or base. Zn and Al are commonly used as examples.

(h) Metallic oxides are basic anhydrides reacting with water to form a base, and calcium hydroxide is insoluble.

Answer BOTH question 5 AND question 6 below. Both of these questions will be graded. The Section II score weighting for these questions is 30 percent (15 percent each).

Question 5

5.

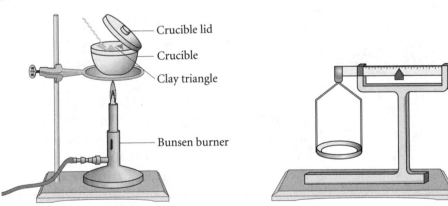

A student performs an experiment to determine the percent by mass of water in a hydrate $BaCl_2 \cdot nH_2O$. Hydrates lose water when heated gently.

Materials
balance
crucible
ring stand
Bunsen burner
glass stirring rod
crystals of $BaCl_2 \cdot nH_2O$

(a) What measurements must the student take? Indicate the units.

(b) What calculations must the student make? Clearly indicate how the calculation is made from the measurements taken.

(c) Suggest how the student can determine if all the water of hydration is driven off.

(d) The theoretical percent of water is 14.8%, and the student obtained a value of 15.4%. Set up the calculations to determine the percent error for the experiment. Do not perform the calculations.

(e) If the student removed some crystals from the crucible while heating by stirring the crystals with a stirring rod, would the value for the percent of water in the crystal be higher, lower, or not affected? Explain.

Solution for Question 5

(a) Measure mass of crucible (g).
Measure mass of crucible plus crystals of hydrate (g).
Measure mass of crucible and crystals after heating (g).

(b) Mass crucible plus crystals of hydrate − mass crucible = mass hydrate
mass crucible plus crystals of hydrate minus mass crucible and crystals after heating = mass of water driven off

$$\% \text{ water} = \frac{\text{mass of water}}{\text{mass of crystals of hydrate}} \times 100$$

(c) If the student does a second heating and finds that the mass of the crystals remains the same, then the student can determine that all the water of hydration was driven off.

(d) $\dfrac{15.4 - 14.8}{14.8} \times 100$

(e) The value for the percent of water in the crystal would be higher. If the student removed any crystals after obtaining the first measurement of the mass of the crystals, then the mass loss would make the difference between the unheated and heated crystals greater. This difference is used as the mass of water in calculations.

Question 6

6. Use chemical principles to explain the following. Be sure to refer to both species in your response.

(a) The second ionization energy of Na is higher that the second ionization energy of Mg.

(b) The melting point of MgO is higher than that of Na_2O.

(c) Br_2 is a liquid at room temperature, whereas Cl_2 is a gas.

(d) The melting point of SiO_2 is much higher than that of CO_2.

Strategy

Make sure you refer to both species explicitly and identify the energy levels, types of bonding, etc., responsible for the differences noted in the question. Tell how that identified property varies based on differences in structure.

Solution for Question 6

(a) The second ionization energy $(X^+(g) \rightarrow X^{2+}(g) + e^-)$ for Na is for removing an electron from the $2p$ sublevel. The second ionization energy for Mg is for removing an electron from the $3s$ sublevel. It requires more energy to remove an electron from a lower energy level.

(b) Both are ionic compounds. The strength of the ionic bond can be predicted from Coulomb's law, $F = kq_1q_2$. Mg^{2+} and O^{2-} charges multiplied $= 4$ for Na^+ and O^{2-} charges multiplied $= 2$.
so you can expect about twice as strong ionic attraction in MgO.

(c) Both bromine and chlorine are nonpolar molecules, so the strength of attraction between molecules is strictly London forces, which are a temporary induced dipole caused by a shift of the electron cloud. Since Br_2 is a larger molecule than Cl_2, it has more electrons and will have stronger induced dipole that results in higher boiling point.

(d) SiO_2 is a covalent network solid, so it has an extremely high melting point—it would require breaking covalent bonds to melt it. CO_2 is a molecular solid consisting of discrete molecules held by weak London forces, so it has a low melting point.

Answer EITHER Question 7 OR Question 8 below. Only one of these two questions will be graded. If you start both questions, be sure to cross out the question you do not want graded. The Section II score weighting for the question you choose is 15 percent.

Question 7

7. Choose the sample of matter that has greater entropy in each pair, and explain your choice.
   (a) 1 mol of NaCl(s) or 1 mol of HCl(g) at 25°C
   (b) 2 mol of HCl(g) or 1 mol of HCl(g) at 25°C
   (c) 1 mol of HCl(g) or Ar(g) at 25°C
   (d) 1 mol of N_2(s) at 24 K or 1 mol of N_2(g) at 298 K

Solution for Question 7

Analyze and Plan

You need to select the system in each pair that has the higher entropy or disorder. To do this you examine the state of the system and the complexity of the molecules that it comprises.

Solve

(a) Gaseous HCl has the higher entropy because gases are more disordered than solids.

(b) The sample containing 2 mol of HCl has twice the entropy of the sample containing 1 mol.

(c) The HCl sample has the higher entropy because the HCl molecule has more atoms (and so more degrees of freedom) than Ar. HCl molecules can rotate and vibrate; Ar atoms cannot.

(d) The gaseous N_2 sample has the higher entropy because the gases are more disordered than solids.

Question 8

8. (a) Draw Lewis electron dot diagrams and name the shape for each of the following.

   SO_3 XeF_2

   (b) Give the hybridization of the central atom for the two structures you drew.

   (c) Use the structural formula shown below to answer the questions that follow.

   (i) Identify the hybridization of each carbon.
   (ii) Identify the bond angle indicated on the diagram.
   (iii) Name the compound.

Solution for Question 8

(a)

$$\overset{\cdot \cdot}{\underset{\cdot \cdot}{O}}$$

                $:\ddot{F}-\ddot{Xe}-\ddot{F}:$

SO_3 is trigonal planar XeF_2 is linear

(b) sp^2 sp^3d or dsp^3

(c)   (i) sp^3, sp^3, sp^2
     (ii) 109.5° the tetrahedral angle
     (iii) Propanoic acid

Organic acids have R—COOH formula. In this case, the R— is three carbons, so *propan-* is the stem and the ending for acids, *-oic*, is added to that stem.

As you review for Section II, keep in mind that the free-response section is typically made up of eight questions whose content often (but not always) follows the following format.

Part A	Question 1 chemical equilibrium	plus EITHER	Question 2 gas laws and kinetics	OR	Question 3 electrochemistry		
Part B	Question 4 chemical reactions	Question 5 determination percent water in a hydrate	Question 6 chemical bonding and atomic structure	plus EITHER	Question 7 thermodynamics	OR	Question 8 molecular structure/ organic

Section II may also include questions on ionic equilibrium in aqueous solutions, gaseous equilibria, acid-base titration, precipitation, thermodynamics, combustion analysis, the electronic structure of atoms, wave nature of light, and rates of chemical reactions under various conditions. In your responses to these questions, you should give not only theory, but also equations that demonstrate applications to appropriate formulas and interpretation of an argument or explanation.

Grading Procedures for the AP Chemistry Examination

The raw scores of the AP Chemistry Exam are converted to the 5-point scale shown below.

5—Extremely Well Qualified
4—Well Qualified
3—Qualified
2—Possibly Qualified
1—No Recommendation

Each of the five points represents a discrete level of achievement designed to correspond with a letter grade. For example, any student who scores a 5 on the AP Chemistry Exam has earned the equivalent of an *A* in college chemistry. Some colleges treat scores of 4 as equivalent to an *A*, as well. Other colleges equate a *4* with the achievement of a typical *B*-level student and a *3* with the achievement of a *C*-level student.

Some colleges give undergraduate course credit to students who achieve scores of 3 or better on AP exams. Other colleges require students to achieve scores of 4 or 5. Remember, if you are considering using your AP Chemistry Exam score for college credit, you should check with individual colleges to find out their specific requirements for credit. Many of the 14,000 college and universities that accept AP credit have their guidelines posted online and in their freshman resource guides.

Below is a breakdown of how the grading of the AP Chemistry Exam works.

Section I: Multiple-Choice Questions

The multiple-choice section of the exam is worth 45% of your total score. The raw score of Section I is determined by crediting one point for each question answered correctly and by deducting $\frac{1}{4}$ point for each question answered incorrectly. No points are gained or lost for questions you do not answer. Consequently, if you can eliminate two or more of the five answer choices, statistically you are better off making an educated guess than you are leaving a blank. Naturally it follows that the more answer choices you can eliminate, the better your chance of guessing the right answer. Moreover, because multiple-choice questions are not weighted with respect to each other—that is, you get as much credit for answering an easy question correctly as you do for answering a difficult question correctly—you should try to identify the easiest questions and answer them first.

Section II: Free-Response Questions

Section II as a whole counts for 55% of your examination grade. The questions in Part A represent 40% of the Section II score, and the questions in Part B represent 60% of the Section II score. Unlike the multiple-choice section of the exam (which is graded by computers), the free-response section is scored by high school and college faculty members, referred to as "readers," who are carefully chosen on the basis of their teaching experience, expertise, gender, ethnicity, and geographic location. The College Board tries to ensure that scoring is done with as little bias as possible. Toward this end, it has developed guidelines to ensure that all readers use exactly the same guidelines for scoring free-response questions. Moreover, a different reader will score each of your answers to free-response questions, and each of your scores (as well as your name and school information) will be covered up as each reader evaluates the next answer. These procedures discourage readers from giving better or worse scores to students based on how well they have performed on other questions—or based on personal or geographical information.

Test-Taking Strategies for the AP Chemistry Examination

Overall, the most important reminder about preparing for the AP Chemistry Exam is that there is absolutely no substitute for studying. Careful review of exam topics and practice with sample questions is the best preparation for the exam. To learn the large quantity of material the exam will cover, you will need to pace yourself. A last-minute studying spree is not enough to prepare you for an exam of this scope. Therefore, you should establish your study routine at the start of the school year.

Clearly your AP Chemistry course work will be a key part of your preparation for the exam in May. However, you must go beyond the class and spend additional time practicing and mastering what you have learned. Outside preparation means rereading sections you've covered in class, practicing problems, and reading ahead in your text. This outside work will sharpen your understanding and your skills, and you will see the effects of this work in class as well as in your performance on the AP Chemistry Exam.

You should begin to focus your preparations between one and two months before exam day. This way, you'll have plenty of time to devote to each of the five main subject areas covered by the test. The more you allow yourself relaxed study time, the more prepared you will be and the better you will do on the exam.

Aim to finish the review sections in Part II of this book a few weeks before the exam. Then take the first practice test in Part III. Treat the practice test exactly like a real AP exam. In other words, find a quiet place where you can work without interruption and give yourself only three hours. This approach will help you become familiar with the actual testing conditions so that you will be less nervous on the day of the exam.

After you have scored your first practice test, take a day to review your answers. Do the questions you got wrong fall under the same content area or areas? If so, you should focus further study on those particular areas for the next few days. How many questions did you skip? If many of them fell fall near the end of Section I, this could mean that you ran out of time. If so, it might be wise to plan ahead of time which kinds of questions you should skip over. You'll need to make sure that you answer the questions you're more likely to know—and that you skip the ones that might slow you down.

Now that you know what adjustments to make to your test-taking strategy, give yourself a few days of extra practice with your problem areas and then take the second practice test about a week before the real exam. Again, analyze your performance. Is there anything you should do differently? Use the last few days to do any fine-tuning and to relax before the exam. Below is a brief list of basic tips to think about during the days just preceding the exam.

- The AP Chemistry Exam is usually scheduled to begin at 8 A.M. Plan to arrive at the exam site thirty minutes before the start time to avoid added anxiety about being late.
- Plan your schedule so that you get *two* good nights of sleep before exam day. On the morning of the exam, make sure that you eat a good protein-based breakfast. If you want your brain to perform well, you must allow your body to be in peak form also.
- Have a photo I.D., such as a driver's license or a student I.D. card, with you to prove your identity when you arrive at the exam site.
- Have at least two pencils for the multiple-choice section, as well as two black or dark blue pens for the free-response section. Take a moment to make sure that your pencils are labeled #2 and that they have good erasers. The machine that grades Section I of the exam cannot recognize marks made by other types of pencils. Also, it cannot read a correct answer if a previous answer has not been erased completely.
- It is helpful to have a watch with you as you take the exam. Though most testing rooms have clocks and test administrators will indicate how much time remains, having your own watch makes it easy to keep close track of your own pace. Avoid watches with a calculator or an alarm, as these are not permitted in the exam room.
- You may wish to purchase and install a new calculator battery a few days before the exam.

The test administrators are very clear and very serious about what is *not* allowed during the examination. Review the list of actions below, as each is grounds for your immediate dismissal from the exam room.

- Do not consult any outside materials during the three hours of the exam period. Remember, the break is technically part of the exam—you are not free to review any materials at that time either.
- Do not bring books of any kind, laptop computers, wireless instant-messaging devices, cameras, portable radios, or cellular phones to the exam site. If you must bring a cellular phone with you, turn it off and give it to the test proctor until you are finished with your exam.
- Do not speak during the exam, unless you have a question for the test proctor. Raise your hand to get the proctor's attention.
- When you are told to stop working on a section of the exam, you must stop *immediately*.
- Do not look forward to another section of the exam before you are told to do so.
- Do not open your exam booklet before the test begins.
- Never tear a page out of your test booklet or try to remove the exam from the test room.
- Do not behave disruptively—even if you are distressed about a difficult test question or because you have run out of time. Stay calm and make no unnecessary noise. Remember, too, the worst-case scenario: if you are displeased with your performance on test day, you can always cancel your exam scores.

Section I: Strategies for Multiple-Choice Questions

Having a firm grasp of chemistry is, of course, the key to your doing well on the AP Chemistry Examination. In addition, being well informed about the exam itself increases your chances of achieving a high score. Below is a list of strategies that you can use to increase your comfort, your confidence, and your chances of excelling on the multiple-choice section of the exam.

▌ Try to approach each problem or question with confidence. Remember that you have been studying over the course of the year, and there is a strong possibility that you have encountered a similar question before.

▌ Pace yourself and keep track of the remaining time as you complete the multiple-choice section of the exam. It's important that you don't get stuck on one question for too long.

▌ Make a light mark in your test booklet next to any questions you can't answer. Return to them after you reach the end of Section I. Sometimes questions that appear later in the test will refresh your memory of a subject area, and you will be able to answer one of those earlier questions.

▌ Always read the entire question carefully, and underline key words or ideas.

▌ Read each of the answer choices carefully before you make your final selection.

▌ Trust your first instinct. Since your first choice is more likely to be correct, you should replace it only if you are completely certain that your second choice is correct.

▌ Use the process of elimination to help you zero in on a correct answer. Cross out the letters of incorrect choices in your test booklet as you eliminate them.

▌ If you are able to eliminate two or more answer choices, it is better to make an educated guess at the correct answer than to leave a blank.

▌ Read the wording of each question carefully. Be careful of distracters— responses that look good at first glance but that have subtle mistakes that make them incorrect.

Section II: Strategies for Free-Response Questions

Section II requires you to demonstrate problem-solving skills and reasoning ability. You may wish to approach each part of Section II by taking a look at the questions, assessing the difficulty of each one, and beginning work on the one about which you feel most confident. Below are additional strategies that will help you succeed in Section II of the AP Chemistry Exam.

▌ It is vital to manage your time carefully, because you have only 90 minutes to answer as many as eight questions in Section II. That means you have around eleven minutes to spend on each question (no matter how many parts it contains).

▌ Be as thorough as possible in your answers to free-response questions. Organize your work logically to maximize your score, and be sure to include any relevant sketches, charts, or graphs that support your explanation.

▌ All of your work must be written clearly and organized in a way that is easy to understand. Since it sometimes takes more than one attempt to arrive at a correct answer, be sure to erase or cross out completely any incorrect attempts you make. Readers may deduct points from your score for incorrect attempts that are not properly crossed out or erased.

■ Remember that partial credit is sometimes awarded to students who answer part of a free-response question correctly.

■ As you write your explanations, remember that your audience is a stranger who is unfamiliar with your skills and your base of knowledge. Clearly show the method you use and the steps involved in arriving at your answer. If you make a mistake in the course of your answer, your presentation of these steps is crucial to your being awarded partial credit.

■ In your responses, try to use key words, such as physical laws, basic concepts, and theories, to clarify your explanations. Always use concise and precise language in answering the questions.

■ Pay close attention to significant figures.

■ Finally, try each part of every question—and no matter what, don't ever leave a blank space beneath a question. If you are uncertain how to answer a question, start by listing what you *do* know about the topic. Then work with that information. Sometimes this process can jumpstart your memory or suggest an approach. At the very least, it makes you a candidate for partial credit.

AP Correlation to Chemistry: The Central Science

The following chart is intended to help you study for the AP Chemistry Exam. The left column includes a series of AP Chemistry topics with which you should be familiar before you take the AP Chemistry Exam. The right column includes a detailed breakdown of chapters in your Brown, LeMay, and Bursten textbook, *Chemistry: The Central Science*, where you can learn more about those topics. You may want to use this chart throughout the year to review what you've learned. It is also an excellent place to begin your pre-exam review of subjects.

AP CHEMISTRY TOPICS	CORRELATION TO *CHEMISTRY: THE CENTRAL SCIENCE* (NINTH EDITION)
STRUCTURE OF MATTER	
Atomic Theory and Atomic Structure	**Chapter 2: Atoms, Molecules, and Ions** ■ The Atomic Theory of Matter ■ The Discovery of Atomic Structure ■ The Modern View of Atomic Structure ■ Atomic Weights **Chapter 6: Electronic Structure of Atoms** ■ The Wave Nature of Light ■ Quantized Energy and Photons ■ Line Spectra and the Bohr Model ■ Quantum Mechanics and Atomic Orbitals ■ Representations of Orbitals ■ Many-Electron Atoms ■ Electron Configurations ■ Electron Configurations and the Periodic Table **Chapter 7: Periodic Properties of the Elements** ■ Effective Nuclear Charge ■ Sizes of Atoms and Ions ■ Ionization Energy ■ Electron Affinities ■ Metals, Nonmetals, and Metalloids
Chemical Bonding	**Chapter 8: Basic Concepts of Chemical Bonding** ■ Chemical Bonds, Lewis Symbols, and the Octet Rule ■ Ionic Bonding ■ Covalent Bonding ■ Bond Polarity and Electronegativity ■ Drawing Lewis Structures ■ Resonance Structures ■ Strengths of Covalent Bonds

Solutions	**Chapter 13: Properties of Solutions**
	▪ Saturated Solutions and Solubility
	▪ Factors Affecting Solubility
	▪ Ways of Expressing Concentration
	▪ Colligative Properties

REACTIONS

Reaction Types	**Chapter 4: Aqueous Reactions and Solution Stoichiometry**
	▪ Precipitation Reactions
	▪ Acid-Base Reactions
	▪ Oxidation-Reduction Reactions
	Chapter 16: Acid-Base Equilibria
	▪ Acids and Bases: A Brief Review
	▪ Brønsted-Lowry Acids and Bases
	▪ Lewis Acids and Bases
	Chapter 20: Electrochemistry
	▪ Oxidation-Reduction Reactions
	▪ Balancing Oxidation-Reduction Equations
	▪ Voltaic Cells
	▪ Cell EMF
	▪ Spontaneity of Redox Reactions
	▪ Effect of Concentration on Cell EMF
Stoichiometry	**Chapter 3: Stoichiometry: Calculations with Chemical Formulas and Equations**
	▪ Chemical Equations
	▪ Formula Weights
	▪ The Mole
	▪ Empirical Formulas from Analyses
	▪ Limiting Reactants
	Chapter 4: Aqueous Reactions and Solution Stoichiometry
	▪ General Properties of Aqueous Solutions
	▪ Precipitation Reactions
	▪ Concentrations of Solutions
	▪ Solution Stoichiometry and Chemical Analysis
	Chapter 20: Electrochemistry
	▪ Balancing Oxidation-Reduction Equations
Equilibrium	**Chapter 4: Aqueous Reactions and Solution Stoichiometry**
	▪ General Properties of Aqueous Solutions
	▪ Precipitation Reactions
	Chapter 13: Properties of Solutions
	▪ Saturated Solutions and Solubility
	▪ Ways of Expressing Concentration
	Chapter 14: Chemical Kinetics
	▪ Temperature and Rate

Chapter 15: Chemical Equilibrium

- The Equilibrium Constant
- Heterogeneous Equilibria
- Calculating Equilibrium Constants
- Applications of Equilibrium Constants
- Le Châtelier's Principle

Chapter 16: Acid-Base Equilibria

- The Autoionization of Water
- The pH Scale
- Strong Acids and Bases
- Weak Acids
- Weak Bases
- Relationship Between K_a and K_b
- Lewis Acids and Bases

Chapter 17: Additional Aspects of Aqueous Equilibria

- Buffered Solutions
- Solubility Equilibria
- Factors that Affect Solubility
- Precipitation and Separation of Ions

Chapter 19

- Spontaneous Processes

Kinetics

Chapter 14: Chemical Kinetics

- Factors that Affect Reaction Rates
- Reaction Rates
- Concentration and Rate
- The Change of Concentration with Time
- Temperature and Rate
- Reaction Mechanisms
- Catalysis

Thermodynamics

Chapter 5: Thermochemistry

- The First Law of Thermodynamics
- Enthalpy
- Enthalpies of Reaction
- Calorimetry
- Hess's Law
- Enthalpies of Formation

Chapter 19: Chemical Thermodynamics

- Entropy and the Second Law of Thermodynamics
- The Molecular Interpretation of Entropy
- Entropy Changes in Chemical Reactions
- Gibbs Free Energy
- Free Energy and Temperature
- Free Energy and the Equilibrium Constant

Chapter 20: Electrochemistry

- Spontaneity of Redox Reactions

DESCRIPTIVE CHEMISTRY	**Chapter 7: Periodic Properties of the Elements**
	■ Sizes of Atoms and Ions
	■ Metals, Nonmetals, and Metalloids
	■ Group Trends for the Active Metals
	■ Group Trends for Selected Nonmetals
	Chapter 13: Properties of Solutions
	■ The Solution Process
	Chapter 20: Electrochemistry
	■ Oxidation-Reduction Reactions
	Chapter 22: Chemistry of the Nonmetals
	■ General Concepts: Periodic Trends and Chemical Reactions
	■ Group 8A: The Noble Gases
	■ Group 7A: The Halogens
	■ Oxygen
	■ The Other Group 6A Elements: S, Se, Te, and Po
	■ Nitrogen
	■ The Other Group 5A Elements: P, As, Sb, and Bi
	■ Carbon
	■ The Other Group 4A Elements: Si, Ge, Sn, and Pb
	Chapter 23: Metals and Metallurgy
	■ Metallic Bonding
	■ Transition Metals
	Chapter 24: Chemistry of Coordination Compounds
	■ Metal Complexes
	■ Ligands with More than One Donor Atom
	■ Isomerism
	Chapter 25: The Chemistry of Life: Organic and Biological Chemistry
	■ Some General Characteristics of Organic Molecules
	■ Introduction to Hydrocarbons
	■ Functional Groups: Alcohols and Ethers
LABORATORY	*See the College Board's website for a complete list of twenty-two suggested laboratories.*

Topical Review with Sample Questions and Answers and Explanations

Part II is keyed to *Chemistry, The Central Science* by Brown, Lemay, and Bursten. It gives an overview of important information in bulleted form and provides sample multiple-choice and free-response questions, along with answers and explanations. Refer to the Summary and end of chapter exercises in your textbook before attempting the practice questions. Be sure to review the answers (correct and incorrect) thoroughly to prepare yourself for the range of test items you will encounter on the AP Chemistry Examination.

CHAPTER 1

Introduction: Matter and Measurement

Much of the study of chemistry is descriptive, or **qualitative,** and does not require mathematics for understanding concepts and communicating them. However, some aspects of chemistry are **quantitative,** and they involve measurements and calculations.

Uncertainty in Measurement

▪ **Exact numbers** have values that are known exactly. Most exact numbers are defined, or they are counting numbers.
▪ **Inexact numbers** are those that have some uncertainty. Numbers determined by measurement are inexact numbers because of the limitations of measuring tools and of human error in reading results.

Precision and Accuracy

▪ **Precision** measures how closely individual measurements agree.
▪ **Accuracy** refers to how closely measurements agree with a correct value.

Significant Figures

▪ All the digits of measured quantities are called **significant figures.** The last digit, although significant, is uncertain.
▪ All non-zero digits are significant.
▪ Zeros that are part of the measured value are significant. If the zero is used only to locate the decimal point, it is not significant.
▪ If the number ends in one or more zeros, and no decimal point is written, the zeros might or might not be significant. The use of **exponential notation** eliminates the question of whether a zero that ends a number with no decimal point is significant or not.
▪ Exact numbers are assumed to have an infinite number of significant figures.

Significant Figures in Calculations

▪ When multiplying or dividing, the answer contains the same number of significant figures as the measurement with the fewest number of significant figures.
▪ When adding or subtracting, the answer can have no more decimal places than the measurement with the fewest number of decimal places.
▪ When rounding off a number, look at all the digits to be dropped. If the digit farthest to the left is 5 or greater, increase the preceding number by 1. If it is 4 or less, don't change the preceding number.

■ When performing multi-step calculations, do not round off after each step. Round off the final answer to the correct number of significant figures.

For Additional Review

Examine several measurement devices around your classroom. Based on the calibrations on each device, determine the most accurate measurements you could make using each device. Make a measurement using each device, and indicate which figures are significant, which are certain, and which are uncertain.

Multiple-Choice Questions

1. The correct volume of a container is 0.349 L. If a student has measured the volume of the container three times, which of the following sets of measurements is most accurate?
   (A) 0.348 L, 0.350 L, 0.348 L
   (B) 0.345 L, 0.345 L, 0.346 L
   (C) 0.344 L, 0.346 L, 0.350 L
   (D) 0.330 L, 0.332 L, 0.334 L
   (E) 0.350 L, 0.351 L, 0.352 L

2. Which of the following sets of data is most precise?
   (A) 0.348 L, 0.350 L, 0.348 L
   (B) 0.345 L, 0.345 L, 0.346 L
   (C) 0.344 L, 0.346 L, 0.350 L
   (D) 0.330 L, 0.332 L, 0.334 L
   (E) 0.350 L, 0.351 L, 0.352 L

3. How many significant figures are in the number 0.00230 mL?
   (A) Two
   (B) Three
   (C) Four
   (D) Five
   (E) Six

4. Which of the following measurements contains three significant figures?
   (A) 1.700×10^{-3} g
   (B) 2.30×10^3 g
   (C) 2.6×10^5 g
   (D) 4.210×10^4 g
   (E) 9.000×10^5 g

5. One kilometer equals 1000 m. In this case, how many significant figures are in the number 1000?
   (A) One
   (B) Two
   (C) Three
   (D) Four
   (E) An infinite number

6. How many significant figures will be in the answer to the problem shown below?
   $$0.0034 \text{ g} \times \frac{2.34 \text{ g}}{20,500}$$
   (A) One
   (B) Two
   (C) Three
   (D) Four
   (E) Five

7. What is the value of 0.00430 cm $\times$ $58,903$ cm to the correct number of significant figures?
   (A) 250 cm^2
   (B) 253 cm^2
   (C) 253.3 cm^2
   (D) 253.28 cm^2
   (E) 253.2829 cm^2

8. How many digits will be to the right of the decimal point in the sum of 0.432 cm and 0.0543 cm?
   (A) Two
   (B) Three
   (C) Four
   (D) Five
   (E) An infinite number

9. A piece of wood 25.0 cm long is cut from a board that is 2.5 m long. What is the resulting length of the board to the correct number of significant figures?
(A) 2 m
(B) 2.2 m
(C) 2.3 m
(D) 2.25 m
(E) 22.5 cm

10. What is the value of $(2115 - 2101) \times (5.11 \times 7.72)$ to the proper number of significant figures?
(A) 552
(B) 552.29
(C) 552.3
(D) 5.5×10^2
(E) 6×10^2

Free-Response Question

A rectangular prism has a length of 6.4 cm, a width of 4.28 cm, and a height of 7.94 cm.

(a) What will be the volume of the prism to the correct number of significant figures?
(b) An identical prism is placed so that its length is added to that of the original prism. Will the volume of these combined prisms have the same number of significant figures as the volume of the original prism? Explain your answer.

ANSWERS AND EXPLANATIONS

Multiple-Choice Questions

▌ **1. (A) is correct.** Accuracy measures how close measurements are to an accepted value. The three measurements in the first set of data are closest to the correct value.

▌ **2. (B) is correct.** Precision shows how close measurements are to each other. Although the data in the second set might not be closest to an accepted value, they are closest to each other, so they are most precise.

▌ **3. (B) is correct.** Because the zeros immediately before and after the decimal point in this number are used to locate the decimal point only, they are not significant. Because the zero at the end of the number follows nonzero digits as well as the decimal point, it is significant. Thus, the 2, 3, and final 0 are significant.

▌ **4. (B) is correct.** Zeros that follow other digits and a decimal point are significant. Thus, all the zeros, other than the one in the power of 10, are significant in these numbers.

▌ **5. (E) is correct.** By definition, 1 km = 1000 m. Because the numbers are defined and not measured, they are exact numbers. Exact numbers can be assumed to have an infinite number of significant figures.

▌ **6. (B) is correct.** In multiplication and division, the answer has the same number of significant figures as the number in the problem with the fewest number of significant figures. The number 0.0034 has only two significant figures, and each of the other two numbers has three. Thus, the answer has two significant figures.

■ 7. **(B) is correct.** The number 0.00430 cm has three significant figures, and 58,903 has five. Thus, the answer also has three significant figures.

■ 8. **(B) is correct.** The number 0.432 cm has three digits to the right of the decimal point, and 0.0543 has four. Thus, the sum has three places to the right of the decimal point.

■ 9. **(C) is correct.** When 25.0 cm is converted to 0.250 m, the number of places to the right of the decimal is three. The measurement 2.5 m has one place to the right of the decimal point. So the answer has one place to the right of the decimal also. When the difference of 2.25 m is rounded off, it becomes 2.3 because the uncertain digit is a 5.

■ 10. **(D) is correct.** The difference of 2115 and 2101 is 14, which has two significant figures. Each of the other two factors has three significant figures. Thus, the product must have two significant figures.

Free-Response Question

(a) The smallest number of significant figures in the measurements is two for 6.4 cm. The volume is the product of these numbers, rounded to two significant figures, or 220 cm^3. The answer could be written also as 2.2×10^2 cm^3.

(b) The sum of 6.4 cm and 6.4 cm is 12.8 cm. All dimensions now have three significant figures, so the volume of the combined prisms would have three significant figures also.

This response correctly uses the significant figure rules for multiplication in parts a and b. The response correctly rounds off the results to two significant figures in part a and three significant figures in part b. In addition, the response correctly uses the significant figure rules for addition in part b.

CHAPTER 2

Atoms, Molecules, and Ions

In chemistry, we seek to understand and explain the properties of materials in the submicroscopic world—the world of atoms and molecules. Atoms, like letters in an alphabet, join together in different combinations to form the materials in the world around us. The way that the atoms of each element combine with other atoms is based on the structure of the atom.

The Atomic Theory of Matter

▌ Ancient Greek philosophers speculated that the world is made up of tiny indivisible particles called *atomos*.

▌ In the early 1800s, John Dalton postulated the first modern atomic theory based on the experimental work and observations of many scientists.

▌ According to Dalton's atomic theory, **atoms** are the basic building blocks of matter. They are the smallest particles of an element that have the chemical identity of that element.

The Discovery of Atomic Structure

▌ In the mid-1800s, British scientist J.J. Thomson experimented with streams of negatively charged particles called **cathode rays,** which can be bent in a magnetic or electrical field. The amount of bending depends directly on the charge and inversely on the mass of the particle. Because the charge/mass ratio of these particles was always the same, Thomson proposed that the rays were composed of a fundamental particle found in all atoms. This particle is known as an **electron.**

▌ In 1910, scientists led by the British scientist Ernest Rutherford directed a beam of alpha particles toward a piece of gold foil. Most of the particles passed through the foil with little, if any, deflection. But some were deflected enough that Rutherford theorized that most of the atom's mass and all of its positive charge reside in a small, extremely dense region, which he called the **nucleus.** Later experiments led to the discovery of both positive particles (**protons**) and neutral particles (**neutrons**) in the nucleus.

▌ Modern atomic theory proposes that atoms are composed of **subatomic particles**—the protons and the neutrons in the nucleus and the electrons surrounding the nucleus. Because the atom has no overall charge, the number of protons equals the number of electrons in an atom.

The Modern View of Atomic Structure

∎ The number of protons in the nucleus of an atom is called the **atomic number** of the element. The atomic number is the same for each atom of a particular element. The atomic numbers for all elements are listed in the **periodic table.**

∎ Atoms of an element always have the same number of protons, but the number of neutrons can vary from atom to atom. Atoms of the same element that differ in the number of neutrons are called **isotopes.** An atom of a specific isotope is a **nuclide.** One way to represent an isotope is $_X^Y A$, where Y is the mass number, X is the atomic number, and A is the symbol for the element. Isotopes can also be represented by the symbol of the element and the mass number, such as C-14 for the isotope of carbon that has eight neutrons.

∎ The total number of protons and neutrons in the nucleus is the **mass number** of the atom. Different isotopes of the same elements have different mass numbers.

Atomic Mass

∎ The mass of an atom is expressed using the **atomic mass unit** (amu). The weighted average of the masses of the atoms of an element is the **atomic mass** of the element. Atomic mass is sometimes referred to as atomic weight. The atomic mass of each element is listed in the periodic table.

∎ The **mass spectrometer** is a tool used by chemists for identifying the mass of individual atoms and the relative abundance of different isotopes. Atoms or molecules are bombarded with high-energy electrons to remove electrons from the atoms and to form positive ions; these positive ions are then bent in a strong magnetic field. The amount of bending depends on the charge and the mass of the particle. More bending occurs with greater charge and with less mass.

For Additional Review

Research to find the six main elements required by living organisms. For each of these elements, list important isotopes, the most common mass number, and the atomic mass.

Multiple-Choice Questions

1. Which of the following statements correctly describes the responses of protons, neutrons, and electrons in a magnetic or electrical field?
   (A) Both protons and neutrons are deflected, whereas electrons show no response.
   (B) Both electrons and neutrons are deflected in the same direction, whereas protons show no response.
   (C) Both protons and electrons are deflected in the same direction, whereas neutrons show no response.
   (D) Protons and electrons are deflected in opposite directions, whereas neutrons shows no response.
   (E) Only protons are deflected, whereas neutrons and electrons show no response.

2. Which of the following statements is NOT true concerning Rutherford's conclusions about the structure of the atom?
   (A) Some alpha particles were deflected slightly, so the nucleus must have a positive charge.
   (B) A few alpha particles bounced back because they hit a small center of the atom.
   (C) Most of the alpha particles passed through the foil, so most of the atom must be empty space.
   (D) Some of the alpha particles were deflected in opposite directions, so some were repelled by the nucleus and some were attracted to electrons.
   (E) Because the particles that bounced back moved at approximately their original speed, the nucleus of the atom must be very dense.

3. A certain atom of iodine has a mass number of 131. How many protons, neutrons, and electrons does the nuclide have?
   (A) 53 protons, 53 neutrons, 78 electrons
   (B) 78 protons, 53 neutrons, 78 electrons
   (C) 53 protons, 131 neutrons, 53 electrons
   (D) 78 protons, 53 neutrons, 53 electrons
   (E) 53 protons, 78 neutrons, 53 electrons

4. From the information in the periodic table, what is most likely to be the mass number of the most common isotope of silver?
   (A) 47
   (B) 107
   (C) 107.8682
   (D) 108
   (E) 109

5. Why aren't the atomic masses in the periodic table integral numbers?
   (A) Our technology does not allow for exact measurement of such a small quantity.
   (B) Atoms gain and lose electrons easily, and this changes their masses significantly.
   (C) Atomic masses listed in the periodic table are weighted averages of naturally occurring isotopes.
   (D) Atomic masses are measured in real samples that are always contaminated with other elements.
   (E) There is a theoretical uncertainty in the masses of atoms.

6. What is the average atomic mass of neon, if 90% of its atoms have a mass of 19.992 amu and 10% have a mass of 21.991 amu?
   (A) 19.992 amu
   (B) 20.192 amu
   (C) 20.992 amu
   (D) 21.791 amu
   (E) 21.991 amu

7. What would be the representation of an isotope of cobalt that has 27 protons and 33 neutrons?
   (A) $^{27}_{33}Co$
   (B) $^{27}_{60}Co$
   (C) $^{33}_{27}Co$
   (D) $^{60}_{27}Co$
   (E) $^{60}_{33}Co$

8. Which of the following ions would show the greatest bending in a mass spectrometer?
   (A) Cl^+
   (B) Cu^+
   (C) H^+
   (D) Na^+
   (E) Rb^+

9. Which of the following choices correctly represents different isotopes of the same element?

(A) $^{16}_{7}N$ and Nitrogen-7

(B) $^{15}_{30}P$ and Phosphorus-16

(C) $^{60}_{27}Co$ and Cobalt-61

(D) $^{92}_{238}U$ and $^{92}_{236}U$

(E) $^{35}_{17}Cl$ and Chlorine-35

10. The mass of an amu is 1.66054×10^{-24} g. A proton has a mass of 1.0073 amu, and the mass of a neutron is 1.0087 amu. What is the mass of the nucleus of the most common isotope of carbon?

(A) 2.0086×10^{-23} g

(B) 2.0072×10^{-23} g

(C) 2.0100×10^{-23} g

(D) 3.3476×10^{-24} g

(E) 1.0043×10^{-23} g

Free-Response Question

Assume that 51.83% of all silver atoms have a mass of 106.905 amu, and that 48.17% have a mass of 108.905 amu. What is the average atomic mass of silver?

ANSWERS AND EXPLANATIONS

Multiple-Choice Questions

▌ **1. (D) is correct.** Any charged particle will be deflected by a magnetic or an electrical field. Because they have opposite charges, protons and electrons will be deflected in opposite directions. Because they have no charge, neutrons will not be deflected.

▌ **2. (D) is correct.** In the gold foil experiment, most of the alpha particles passed directly through the foil, showing that nothing was close enough to deflect them. However, the particles that were deflected either were repelled by passing close to the strong positive charge of the nucleus or actually hit this dense center of the atom. Although electrons are negatively charged, they are spread throughout the gold and would not deflect the particles because they would attract them from all directions.

▌ **3. (E) is correct.** All iodine atoms have an atomic number of 53, so they have 53 protons and 53 electrons. Mass number is the total number of protons and neutrons, so the nuclide has 131 − 53 (or 78) neutrons.

▌ **4. (D) is correct.** The average atomic mass of silver is 107.8682 amu. This number is the weighted average of the mass of each of its isotopes. Because the average atomic mass is close to 108, this number is most likely the mass number of its most common isotope.

▌ **5. (C) is correct.** Most elements occur in nature as mixtures of isotopes. The atomic masses listed in the periodic table are weighted averages of naturally occurring isotopes. They are determined by calculating from the masses of various isotopes and their relative abundances.

▌ **6. (B) is correct.** The average atomic mass is found by multiplying the percent of atoms having a certain mass by that mass for each isotope. Then all these products are added together. For neon, 0.90×19.992 amu $+ 0.10 \times 21.991$ amu $= 20.192$ amu.

▌**7. (D) is correct.** In these representations of isotopes, the number at the top is the mass number, and the number at the bottom is the atomic number. The mass number of this isotope of cobalt is 27 + 33 (or 60), and the atomic number is 27. Answer *D* shows a mass number of 60 and an atomic number of 27.

▌**8. (C) is correct.** If charge is equal, less massive particles will be bent more than will more massive particles. The lightest atom listed is hydrogen, and all the charges are equal, so the hydrogen atom will show greatest bending.

▌**9. (C) is correct.** Two isotopes of the same element will have the same atomic number and different mass numbers. In the two forms of representation shown, the atomic number is the subscript, and the mass number is the superscript and the hyphenated number. Only answer *C* shows two different mass numbers for the same element and has all numbers in the correct places.

▌**10. (A) is correct.** The answer is correctly calculated by determining the mass of the protons in the atom: 6 protons $\times$ 1.0073 amu/proton $\times$ 1.66054 $\times$ 10^{-24} g/amu = 1.0036 $\times$ 10^{-23} g. Then the mass of the neutrons is calculated: 6 neutrons $\times$ 1.0087 amu/neutron $\times$ 1.66054 $\times$ 10^{-24} g/amu = 1.0050 $\times$ 10^{-23} g. The mass of the nucleus is the sum of these two masses.

Free-Response Question

The average atomic mass is the weighted average of all the isotopes. The mass contributed by the isotope of silver that has a mass of 106.905 amu is 0.5183 $\times$ 106.905 amu, or 55.409 amu. The mass contributed by the other isotope is 0.4817 $\times$ 108.905 amu, or 52.460 amu. The total of these masses gives an average atomic mass of 107.869 amu.

This response correctly converts the percents to decimals and accurately calculates the mass contributed by each element. It then correctly determines the total mass by adding the masses contributed by each element.

CHAPTER 3

Stoichiometry: Calculations with Chemical Formulas and Equations

Stoichiometry is a branch of chemistry based on the **law of conservation of mass,** which states that the total mass of all substances present after a chemical reaction is the same as the total mass before the reaction.

Chemical Equations

▌ **Chemical equations** are a concise way to show what happens in chemical reactions.

▌ In a chemical equation, chemical formulas to the left of the arrow represent substances that are initially present, or **reactants.** Chemical formulas to the right of the arrow represent substances produced by the reaction, or **products.**

▌ Each chemical equation must be **balanced.** That is, it must have an equal number of each type of atom on both sides of the equation.

▌ A **subscript** shows the number of atoms present in the formula of a substance. Changing a subscript changes the identity of a substance, so you should never balance a chemical equation by changing a subscript.

▌ A **coefficient,** which is a number in front of a formula, shows the number of units of that substance. A new coefficient changes the amount—but not the identity—of a substance. Chemical equations are balanced by changing the coefficients of the formulas in the equation.

▌ The coefficients in a balanced chemical equation show the relative numbers of units of reactants and products, and they show the **mole ratio** among the substances, as well.

Formula Weights

▌ The **formula mass** of a substance is the sum of the atomic masses of the atoms in its chemical formula. For molecules, **formula mass** is also the **molecular mass.**

▌ The percent of the compound, by mass, contributed by an element can be calculated. You multiply the number of atoms of that element in the formula by the atomic weight of the element. Divide this product by the formula weight, and then multiply by 100.

▌ The **percentage composition** of a compound is the percentage by mass contributed by each element in the compound.

The Mole

▌ A **mole** (mol) is the amount of matter that contains as many objects as the number of atoms in exactly 12 g of pure ^{12}C.

▌ A mole of anything always contains 6.022×10^{23} objects. This number is called **Avogadro's number.**

▌ The mass in grams of 1 mol of a substance is called its **molar mass.** The molar mass (in g/mol) of any substance is always numerically equal to its formula mass (in amu).

▌ If the number of moles, the mass, or the number of particles of a substance is known, the other two variables can be calculated by using either molar mass or Avogadro's number.

$$\text{Moles} = \frac{\text{Mass}}{\text{Molar mass}}$$

$$\text{Moles} = \frac{\text{Number of particles}}{\text{Avogadro's number}}$$

Note that the mole is the common part of such calculations; if mass or number of particles is to be found from the other quantity, the number of moles must be calculated first.

Empirical Formulas from Analyses

▌ The **empirical formula** for any substance shows the relative number of atoms of each element it contains. The empirical formula can be calculated if the percentage composition of the substance is known, according to the steps shown below.

1. Assume 100 g of the substance is present. Use the percentage composition to find the mass of each element in the sample.
2. For each element, use the molar mass to convert the mass to number of moles.
3. Use the number of moles as subscripts in the formula. To find the simplest ratio, divide each of the subscripts by the smallest one.
4. Round subscripts that are close to a whole number, or multiply all subscripts by a common factor until all subscripts are whole numbers. The resulting formula is the empirical formula for the substance.

▌ The **molecular formula** shows the actual composition of a molecule. The subscripts in a molecular formula are a whole number multiple of the subscripts in the molecule's empirical formula.

▌ A molecular formula can be determined from the empirical formula and the molecular weight of the compound. Divide the molecular mass of the compound by the molecular mass of the empirical formula to find a whole number. Multiply this whole number by the subscripts in the empirical formula to find the molecular formula.

Limiting Reactants

■ When a reactant is completely consumed in a reaction, it is called a **limiting reactant** because it determines, or limits, the amount of product formed. The other reactants are sometimes called **excess reactants** (or excess reagents).

■ If initial amounts of reactants are given, the limiting reactant is determined by first calculating the number of moles of each reactant. Then you can use the mole ratios in the balanced chemical equation to determine which reactant is in shortest supply.

■ The quantity of product that is calculated to form when all of the limiting reactant reacts is called the **theoretical yield.** The amount of product actually obtained in a reaction is called the **actual yield.** The actual yield is nearly always less than the theoretical yield.

For Additional Review

Do research on an industrial process that uses a chemical reaction. Write a balanced chemical equation for the reaction. Assuming you have 500 kg of each reactant, find out which reactant is limiting, and then calculate the theoretical yield of each product.

Multiple-Choice Questions

1. What are the coefficients when the following chemical equation is balanced?

$$Al(NO_3)_3 + Na_2S \rightarrow Al_2S_3 + NaNO_3$$

   (A) 2, 3, 1, 6
   (B) 2, 1, 3, 2
   (C) 1, 1, 1, 1
   (D) 4, 6, 3, 2
   (E) 2, 3, 2, 3

2. A sample of C_3H_8O that contains 200 molecules contains how many carbon atoms?
   (A) 600 atoms
   (B) 200 atoms
   (C) 3.61×10^{26} atoms
   (D) 1.20×10^{26} atoms
   (E) 4.01×10^{25} atoms

3. The formula of nitrobenzene is $C_6H_5NO_2$. What is the molecular weight of this compound?
   (A) 107.11 amu
   (B) 43.03 amu
   (C) 109.10 amu
   (D) 123.12 amu
   (E) 3.06 amu

4. What percentage of Al_2O_3 is aluminum?
   (A) 26.46 %
   (B) 20.93 %
   (C) 52.92 %
   (D) 47.08 %
   (E) 53.21 %

5. A sample of magnesium chloride contains 1.265×10^{24} formula units. How many moles of magnesium chloride are in the sample?
   (A) 1.051 mol
   (B) 2.101 mol
   (C) 4.202 mol
   (D) 6.303 mol
   (E) 1.265×10^{24} mol

6. A 10.31-g sample of a compound contains 6.180 g carbon, 1.386 g hydrogen, and 2.744 g oxygen. What is the empirical formula of the compound?
   (A) C_3H_8O
   (B) C_3H_5O
   (C) $C_6H_{16}O_2$
   (D) $C_3H_9O_3$
   (E) $C_3H_6O_3$

7. A compound has a molar mass of 174 g/mol and an empirical formula of CHO. What is the molecular formula of the compound?
   (A) CHO
   (B) $C_2H_2O_2$
   (C) $C_4H_4O_4$
   (D) $C_6H_6O_6$
   (E) $C_{12}H_{12}O_{12}$

8. A 25.0-g sample of hydrogen gas is burned in 175 g of oxygen gas. What is the limiting reactant in this reaction?
   (A) Hydrogen
   (B) Oxygen
   (C) Water
   (D) Both reactants will be used up.
   (E) The limiting reactant depends on the pressure and temperature.

9. Under appropriate conditions, nitrogen and hydrogen undergo a combination reaction to yield ammonia.

   $$N_2(g) + 3H_2(g) \rightarrow 2NH_3(g)$$

   A 7.1-g sample of N_2 requires what mass of H_2 for complete reaction?
   (A) 0.51 g
   (B) 0.76 g
   (C) 1.2 g
   (D) 1.5 g
   (E) 17.2 g

10. The following chemical equation shows how oxygen reacts with iron to produce iron(III) oxide.

   $$4Fe + 3O_2 \rightarrow 2Fe_2O_3$$

   If you react a 4.25-g sample of oxygen with excess iron, how many formula units of iron(III) oxide are produced?
   (A) 5.34×10^{22}
   (B) 1.07×10^{23}
   (C) 2.67×10^{23}
   (D) 5.34×10^{23}
   (E) 5.34×10^{24}

Free-Response Question

Ascorbic acid (vitamin C) contains 40.92% C, 4.58% H, and 54.50% O by mass. What is the empirical formula of ascorbic acid?

ANSWERS AND EXPLANATIONS

Multiple-Choice Questions

▌ **1. (A) is correct.** Change coefficients for each reactant and product until there are equal numbers of each type of atom on both sides of the equation. Because the nitrate ion stays the same after the reaction, it can be balanced as an ion—not as individual nitrogen and oxygen atoms. Answer *A* provides two aluminum atoms, six nitrate ions, six sodium atoms, and three sulfur atoms on both sides of the equation.

2. (A) is correct. As shown by the subscript 3, one molecule of C_3H_8O contains three carbon atoms. There are 3 C atoms/molecule $\times$ 200 molecules, or 600 C atoms in the 200 molecules.

3. (D) is correct. The molecular weight of the compound is the total weight of six carbon atoms, five hydrogen atoms, one nitrogen atom, and two oxygen atoms. Thus, the molecular weight is 12.01 amu/C atom $\times$ 6 C atoms + 1.01 amu/H atom $\times$ 5 H atoms + 14.01 amu/N atom $\times$ 1 N atom + 16.00 amu/O atom $\times$ 2 O atoms, or 123.12 amu.

4. (C) is correct. The mass of aluminum in one unit of Al_2O_3 is 26.98 amu/Al atom $\times$ 2 Al atoms, or 53.96 amu. The formula mass of Al_2O_3 is 26.98 amu/Al atom $\times$ 2 Al atoms + 16.00 amu/O atom $\times$ 3 O atoms, or 101.96 amu. The percent of the compound that is Al is 53.96 amu/101.96 amu $\times$ 100, or 52.92%.

5. (B) is correct. Although three atoms are present in one unit of magnesium chloride, the number of formula units given and the number of moles asked for refer to the compound, not to the number of atoms. Thus, there are 1.265×10^{24} formula units/(6.022×10^{23} formula units/mol), or 2.101 mol magnesium chloride.

6. (A) is correct. The number of moles of each element in the compound is found by dividing the mass of each element by its molar mass. These numbers are then used as subscripts in the formula, $C_{0.5146}H_{1.372}O_{0.1715}$. To find the simplest whole-number ratio, divide each of these subscripts by the smallest one, 0.1715, resulting in the formula $C_{3.001}H_{8.000}O_{1.000}$. Round off the 3.001 to 3, and the formula is C_3H_8O.

7. (D) is correct. The molar mass of the empirical formula is 12.01 g/mol + 1.01 g/mol + 16.00 g/mol, or 29.02 g/mol. Dividing 174.12 g/mol by 29.02 g/mol shows that the molecular formula has six times the mass of the empirical formula. Multiplying all subscripts by six results in a formula of $C_6H_6O_6$.

8. (B) is correct. The balanced chemical equation for this reaction is $2H_2 + O_2 \rightarrow 2H_2O$. Thus, 2 mol of hydrogen are needed for every mole of oxygen used. One approach to this problem is to find the number of available moles of each reactant. The 25-g sample of hydrogen gas contains 25.0 g H_2/2.02 g/mol, or 12.4 mol H_2. This amount of hydrogen would react with half as much (or 6.2 mol) oxygen. The sample of oxygen contains 175 g O_2/32.00 g/mol, or 5.47 mol O_2. Because not enough oxygen is available to react completely with the available hydrogen, oxygen is the limiting reactant.

9. (D) is correct. The coefficients in a chemical equation provide mole, not mass, ratios. Therefore, 7.1 g N_2 must be changed to moles, the equivalent number of moles of hydrogen must be found, and that number of moles must be converted to grams of hydrogen. Dividing mass by the molar mass of 28.02 g/mol shows that there is 0.25 mol N_2. Three moles of hydrogen react for every mole of nitrogen, so 0.75 mol H_2 react. The mass of this amount of hydrogen is 0.75 mol H_2 $\times$ 2.02 g/mol, or 1.5 g H_2.

■ **10. (A) is correct.** Mass cannot be directly converted into formula units, so moles must be calculated. The 4.25-g sample of O_2 equals 4.25 g O_2/32.00 g/mol, or 0.133 mol O_2. The moles of oxygen and iron(III) oxide are in a 3 : 2 ratio, so the reaction produces 0.133 mol O_2 × 2 mol Fe_2O_3/3 mol O_2, or 0.0887 mol Fe_2O_3. This amount equals 0.0887 mol × 6.022 × 10^{23} formula units/mol, or 5.34 × 10^{22} formula units.

Free-Response Question

Assume that you have 100 g of ascorbic acid, so you will have 40.92 g C, 4.58 g H, and 54.50 g O. Calculate the number of moles of each sample.

Moles C = (40.92 g C)(1 mol C/12.01 g C) = 3.407 mol C
Moles H = (4.58 g H) (1 mol H/1.008 g H) = 4.54 mol H
Moles O = (54.50 g O)(1 mol O/16.00 g O) = 3.406 mol O

Determine the simplest whole-number ratio of moles by dividing each number of moles by the smallest number of moles, 3.406.

C: 3.407/3.406 = 1.000   H: 4.54/3/406 = 1.33
O: 3.406/3.406 = 1.000

Because the ratio for H is not close to a whole number, multiply the ratios by 3 to obtain whole numbers.

C : H : O = 3(1 : 1.33 : 1) + 3 : 4 : 3

This whole-number mole ratio gives you the subscripts for the empirical formula. Thus, the empirical formula is $C_3H_4O_3$.

This response correctly uses percents and molar masses to calculate the relative number of moles of each element present. The response also determines the ratio of these moles, simplifies the ratios to small whole numbers, and applies these numbers correctly as subscripts in the correct empirical formula.

CHAPTER 4

Aqueous Reactions and Solution Stoichiometry

Water covers almost two thirds of our planet and possesses many unusual properties essential to support life. One important property is its ability to dissolve a wide variety of substances. Solutions in which water is the dissolving medium are called **aqueous solutions.**

General Properties of Aqueous Solutions

▌ A **solution** is a homogeneous mixture of two or more substances. The substance present in greater quantity is the **solvent.** Any substance dissolved in the solvent is a **solute.**

▌ An aqueous solution that contains ions can conduct electricity. A substance whose water solution contains ions is called an **electrolyte.** A substance that doesn't form ions in aqueous solution is a **nonelectrolyte,** and solutions of nonelectrolytes do not conduct electricity. Most molecular compounds are nonelectrolytes.

▌ **Strong electrolytes** are those solutes that exist in solution completely or nearly completely as ions. **Weak electrolytes** are those solutes that exist in solution mostly in the form of molecules, with few ions present in solution.

▌ Chemists use a formula with a double arrow to represent the ionization of weak electrolytes

$$HC_2H_3O_2 \rightleftarrows H^+ + C_2H_3O_2^-$$

and a single arrow to represent the formation of ions by strong electrolytes.

$$HCl \rightarrow H^+ + Cl^-$$

A double arrow indicates that the solution is in **dynamic equilibrium,** which means that two opposite processes occur simultaneously at the same rate in opposite directions.

Precipitation Reactions

▌ A **precipitate** is formed when pairs of oppositely charged ions in solution attract each other so strongly that they form an insoluble ionic solid. A reaction that results in the formation of an insoluble product is known as a **precipitation reaction.**

SOLUBILITY GUIDELINES FOR COMMON IONIC COMPOUNDS IN WATER		
Soluble Ionic Compounds		**Important Exceptions**
Compounds containing	NO_3^-	None
	$C_2H_3O_2^-$	None
	Cl^-	Compounds of Ag^+, Hg_2^{2+}, and Pb^{2+}
	Br^-	Compounds of Ag^+, Hg_2^{2+}, and Pb^{2+}
	I^-	Compounds of Ag^+, Hg_2^{2+}, and Pb^{2+}
	SO_4^{2-}	Compounds of Sr^{2+}, Ba^{2+}, Hg_2^{2+}, and Pb^{2+}
Insoluble Ionic Compounds		**Important Exceptions**
Compounds containing	S^{2-}	Compounds of NH_4^+, the alkali metal cations, and Ca^{2+}, Sr^{2+}, and Ba^{2+}
	CO_3^{2-}	Compounds of NH_4^+ and the alkali metal cations
	PO_4^{3-}	Compounds of NH_4^+ and the alkali metal cations
	OH^-	Compounds of the alkali metal cations, and Ca^{2+}, Sr^{2+}, and Ba^{2+}

▌ The **solubility** of a substance is the amount of that substance that dissolves in a given quantity of solvent. In addition to the solubility rules in the table above, note that compounds containing alkali metal ions (group 1A of the periodic table) or the ammonium ion (NH_4^+) are soluble in water.

▌ To predict whether a precipitate forms when aqueous solutions of two electrolytes are mixed, note the ions present in the reactant, consider the possible combinations of the cations and anions, and determine whether any of these combinations is insoluble.

▌ Precipitation reactions are examples of **exchange reactions**—reactions where positive and negative ions seem to exchange partners (AX + BY → AY + BX). Another name for exchange reactions is **metathesis** reactions.

▌ A chemical equation that lists the complete chemical formulas for all reactants and products is called a **molecular equation**. A **complete ionic equation** shows all dissolved electrolytes as their component ions. A **net ionic equation** shows just the ions and molecules directly involved in the reaction and does not show those ions that go through the reaction unchanged.

▌ Charge is conserved in reactions, so the sum of the charges of the ions must be the same on both sides of a balanced ionic equation.

Acid-Base Reactions

▌ **Acids** increase the concentration of $H^+(aq)$ ions when they are added to solutions. Because H^+ is simply a proton, acids are proton donors.

▌ **Bases** produce hydroxide ions (OH^-) when they dissolve in water. Bases are proton acceptors.

▌ Acids and bases may be strong or weak electrolytes. Strong acids completely ionize and strong bases completely dissociate in solution. Weak acids and bases form relatively few ions in solution. The reactivity of an acid or base depends on both the strength of the acid or base and the nature of the other species that make up the compound.

■ The following table lists common strong acids and bases.

COMMON STRONG ACIDS AND BASES	
Strong Acids	**Strong Bases**
Hydrochloric, HCl	Group 1A metal hydroxides (LiOH, NaOH, KOH, RbOH, CsOH)
Hydrobromic, HBr	Heavy group 2A metal hydroxides [$Ca(OH)_2$, $Sr(OH)_2$, $Ba(OH)$]
Hydroiodic, HI	
Chloric, $HClO_3$	
Perchloric, $HClO_4$	
Nitric, HNO_3	
Sulfuric, H_2SO_4	

■ When an acidic solution and a basic solution are mixed, a **neutralization reaction** occurs.

■ One product of a neutralization reaction is water, which is formed when H^+ ions and OH^- ions combine. The other product of a neutralization reaction is a **salt**. A salt is any ionic compound whose cation comes from a base and whose anion comes from an acid.

Oxidation-Reduction Reactions

■ Loss of electrons by a substance is called **oxidation.** Gain of electrons by a substance is called **reduction.** In **oxidation-reduction** (or **redox**) reactions, electrons are transferred between substances. Thus, the oxidation of one substance is always accompanied by the reduction of another.

■ **Oxidation numbers** are a way to keep track of electrons in chemical reactions. Oxidation numbers are assigned according to the following rules.

1. The oxidation number for an atom in its elemental form is always zero.
2. For any monoatomic ion, the oxidation number equals the charge on the ion. The alkali metals always have an oxidation number of $+1$. The alkaline earth metals are always $+2$. Halogen ions are -1, and aluminum group metals are always $+3$. Hydrogen is usually $+1$, and oxygen is usually -2.
3. Nonmetals usually have negative oxidation numbers, although they can sometimes be positive.
4. The sum of the oxidation numbers of all atoms in a neutral compound is zero. The sum of the oxidation numbers in a polyatomic ion equals the charge of the ion.

■ The reaction of a metal with either an acid or salt is an example of a **displacement reaction.** Displacement reactions follow this general pattern: $A + BX \rightarrow AX + B$. The products of these displacement reactions are always an element (H_2 or a metal) and a salt.

■ A list of metals in order of how easily they oxidize is called an **activity series.** Alkali metals and alkaline earth metals, which are the most easily oxidized metals, are called **active metals.** The most stable metals are called **noble metals.** Any element on the list can be oxidized by the ions of the elements below it.

Activity Series of Metals in Aqueous Solution		
Metal	**Oxidation Reaction**	
Lithium	$Li(s) \longrightarrow Li^+(aq) + e^-$	
Potassium	$K(s) \longrightarrow K^+(aq) + e^-$	
Barium	$Ba(s) \longrightarrow Ba^{2+}(aq) + 2e^-$	
Calcium	$Ca(s) \longrightarrow Ca^{2+}(aq) + 2e^-$	
Sodium	$Na(s) \longrightarrow Na^+(aq) + e^-$	
Magnesium	$Mg(s) \longrightarrow Mg^{2+}(aq) + 2e^-$	
Aluminum	$Al(s) \longrightarrow Al^{3+}(aq) + 3e^-$	
Manganese	$Mn(s) \longrightarrow Mn^{2+}(aq) + 2e^-$	
Zinc	$Zn(s) \longrightarrow Zn^{2+}(aq) + 2e^-$	
Chromium	$Cr(s) \longrightarrow Cr^{3+}(aq) + 3e^-$	
Iron	$Fe(s) \longrightarrow Fe^{2+}(aq) + 2e^-$	
Cobalt	$Co(s) \longrightarrow Co^{2+}(aq) + 2e^-$	
Nickel	$Ni(s) \longrightarrow Ni^{2+}(aq) + 2e^-$	
Tin	$Sn(s) \longrightarrow Sn^{2+}(aq) + 2e^-$	
Lead	$Pb(s) \longrightarrow Pb^{2+}(aq) + 2e^-$	
Hydrogen	$H_2(g) \longrightarrow 2H^+(aq) + 2e^-$	
Copper	$Cu(s) \longrightarrow Cu^{2+}(aq) + 2e^-$	
Silver	$Ag(s) \longrightarrow Ag^+(aq) + e^-$	
Mercury	$Hg(l) \longrightarrow Hg^{2+}(aq) + 2e^-$	
Platinum	$Pt(s) \longrightarrow Pt^{2+}(aq) + 2e^-$	
Gold	$Au(s) \longrightarrow Au^{3+}(aq) + 3e^-$	

Ease of oxidation increases

Concentrations of Solutions

▌ **Concentration** is a measure of the amount of solute dissolved in a given quantity of solvent or solution. The amount of solute is directly proportional to the concentration.

▌ **Molarity** (*M*) expresses the concentration of a solution as the number of moles of solute in a liter of solution. If two quantities in the following equation are known, the third quantity can be calculated.

$$\text{Molarity} = \frac{\text{moles solute}}{\text{volume of solution in liters}}$$

▌ This same equation can be used to find concentration or volume in dilution problems. The number of moles stays the same so the product of molarity and volume before the dilution equals the product of molarity and volume after the dilution.

Solution Stoichiometry and Chemical Analysis

▌ **Titration** is a method used to determine the concentration of a particular solute in a solution. Titration can be used for this purpose if the solute will undergo an acid-base, redox, or precipitation reaction with another reactant in another solution.

■ The other solution in a titration is a reagent solution of known concentration, called a **standard solution.** The standard solution is added until there is some visual indication that the reaction is complete. **Indicators,** which are dyes that change color at the endpoint, are used in acid-base titrations to show when the reaction is complete.

■ The point in the titration at which equivalent quantities of the two reactants are brought together is known as the **equivalence point** of the titration.

■ The equation that relates molarity, number of moles, and volume can be used to calculate the concentration of the unknown solution. Consider the chemical reaction involved, and determine how many moles of the standard solution will react with 1 mol of the substance in the unknown solution. Using this information, the molarity of the standard solution, and the volumes used of the standard and unknown solutions, you can find the concentration of the unknown solution.

For Additional Review

The stomach secretes acid (HCl) to help digest foods, yet at times the acid can attack underlying tissues. Antacids are sometimes used to address the problem of excess stomach acid. Check labels on antacids to determine what substances are used to reduce stomach acidity, and explain the reactions that these substances undergo with stomach acid.

Multiple-Choice Questions

1. Which of the following compounds are weak electrolytes?
   I. HCl
   II. $HC_2H_3O_2$
   III. NH_3
   IV. KCl
   (A) I and IV
   (B) I, II, III, and IV
   (C) II and IV
   (D) II and III
   (E) I, II, and IV

2. Which of the following pairs of substances will NOT react with each other?
   (A) Lithium and lead(II) chloride
   (B) Nickel and copper(II) nitrate
   (C) Copper and silver nitrate
   (D) Zinc and hydrobromic acid
   (E) Gold and nitric acid

3. Which of the following chemical equations represents a precipitation reaction if it occurs in aqueous solution?
   (A) $HCl + NaOH \rightarrow NaCl + H_2O$
   (B) $Ba(OH)_2 + 2HNO_3$
        $\rightarrow Ba(NO_3)_2 + 2H_2O$
   (C) $(NH_4)_2CO_3 + CaI_2 \rightarrow 2NH_4I + CaCO_3$
   (D) $K_3PO_4 + 3LiBr \rightarrow 3KBr + Li_3PO_4$
   (E) $CaSO_4 + Mg(C_2H_3O_2)_2$
        $\rightarrow Ca(C_2H_3O_2)_2 + MgSO_4$

4. Sodium does not occur in nature as sodium metal because sodium
   (A) is easily reduced to Na^-
   (B) is easily oxidized to Na^+
   (C) does not readily react with water
   (D) is easily replaced by silver in its ores
   (E) metal has an oxidation number of zero

5. In which of the following compounds does phosphorus have a +5 oxidation number?
   (A) H_3PO_4
   (B) Na_3PO_3
   (C) K_3P
   (D) P_2O_3
   (E) H_3PO_2

6. Which of the following chemical equations is the net ionic equation for the reaction between hydrochloric acid and barium hydroxide in aqueous solution?
   (A) $HCl + Ba(OH)_2 \rightarrow BaCl_2 + H_2O$
   (B) $2HCl + Ba(OH)_2 \rightarrow BaCl_2 + 2H_2O$
   (C) $2H^+ + 2Cl^- + Ba^{2+} + 2OH^-$
      $\rightarrow Ba^{2+} + 2Cl^- + 2H_2O$
   (D) $2Cl^- + Ba^{2+} \rightarrow Ba^{2+} + 2Cl^-$
   (E) $2H^+ + 2OH^- \rightarrow 2H_2O$

7. How many moles of K^+ are present in 343 mL of a 1.27 M solution of K_3PO_4?
   (A) 0.436 mol
   (B) 1.31 mol
   (C) 0.145 mol
   (D) 3.70 mol
   (E) 11.1 mol

8. What is the molarity of an aqueous methanol solution produced when 0.200 L of a 2.00 M solution is diluted to 0.800 L?
   (A) 0.800 M
   (B) 0.200 M
   (C) 0.500 M
   (D) 0.400 M
   (E) 8.00 M

9. In a titration of 35.00 mL of 0.737 M H_2SO_4, what volume of a 0.827 M KOH solution is required for neutralization?
   (A) 35.0 mL
   (B) 1.21 mL
   (C) 25.8 mL
   (D) 62.4 mL
   (E) 39.3 mL

10. A 17.5-mL sample of an acetic acid (CH_3COOH) solution required 29.6 mL of 0.250 M NaOH for neutralization. The concentration of acetic acid was
   (A) 0.150 M
   (B) 0.423 M
   (C) 1300 M
   (D) 6.80 M
   (E) 0.211 M

Free-Response Question

Write the net ionic equation for the precipitation reaction that occurs when aqueous solutions of calcium chloride and sodium carbonate are mixed.

ANSWERS AND EXPLANATIONS

Multiple-Choice Questions

▌ 1. (D) is correct. Weak electrolytes produce few ions in aqueous solution. Because weak acids and bases produce few ions, they are weak electrolytes. $HC_2H_3O_2$ is a weak acid, and NH_3 is a weak base, so they are weak electrolytes. HCl is a strong acid, and KCl is a soluble ionic compound, so they are strong electrolytes.

▌ 2. (E) is correct. A free element in the activity series will replace any ion below it in the series. For all answers except E, the metal listed is higher in the activity series than the positive ion in the compound, and a reaction will occur.

3. (C) is correct. According to the table of solubilities, all products in the answers are soluble except $CaCO_3$. Thus, this compound is the only one that forms a precipitate.

4. (B) is correct. Because it is an alkali metal, sodium easily loses an electron to form a Na^+ ion. Losing an electron is oxidation, so answer *B* is correct.

5. (A) is correct. The oxidation number of oxygen is -2, and the oxidation number of hydrogen and alkali metals is $+1$. The overall charge on a compound is zero. Using this information, answer *A* is the only compound that gives an overall charge of zero to the compound if phosphorus has an oxidation number of $+5$.

6. (E) is correct. Because Ba^{2+} and Cl^- are ions in both the reactants and the products, they are not included in the net ionic equation. The species that remain are shown in answer *E*.

7. (B) is correct. Because the number of moles equals the product of the molarity and the volume, $0.343 \text{ L} \times 1.27 \text{ mol } K_3PO_4/\text{L}$, or $0.436 \text{ mol } K_3PO_4$, is in the sample. Because each mole of K_3PO_4 contains 3 mol of K^+, the sample contains $0.436 \text{ mol } K_3PO_4 \times 3 \text{ mol } K^+/\text{mol } K_3PO_4$, or $1.31 \text{ mol } K^+$.

8. (C) is correct. Because the number of moles of methanol remains the same before and after the dilution, the product of molarity and volume before the dilution equals the product of molarity and volume after the dilution: $0.200 \text{ L} \times 2.00 \text{ mol/L} = 0.800 \text{ L} \times \text{molarity}$, so molarity $= 0.200 \text{ L} \times 2.00 \text{ mol/L}/0.800 \text{ L}$, and the diluted solution is $0.50 \; M$.

9. (D) is correct. Because the number of moles of H^+ and OH^- must be the same, $35.00 \text{ mL } H_2SO_4 \times 0.737 \text{ mol/L} \times 2 \text{ mol } H^+/\text{mol } H_2SO_4 = V \times 0.827 \text{ mol/L} \times 1 \text{ mol } OH^-/\text{mol KOH}$. Solving for volume, 62.4 mL of KOH are required.

10. (D) is correct. The acid and the base react on a 1:1 mole ratio. Thus, $0.0296 \text{ L} \times 0.250 \text{ mol/L} = 0.0175 \text{ L} \times M$. The molarity equals $0.0296 \text{ L} \times 0.250 \text{ mol/L}/0.0175 \text{ L}$, or $0.423 \; M$.

Free-Response Question

According to solubility guidelines, $CaCO_3$ is insoluble and NaCl is soluble. The balanced molecular equation is

$$CaCl_2(aq) + Na_2CO_3(aq) \rightarrow CaCO_3(s) + 2NaCl(aq)$$

In a complete ionic equation, only dissolved strong electrolytes, such as soluble ionic compounds, are written as separate ions. $CaCO_3$ is an ionic compound, but it is not soluble. The formula of any insoluble compound is not written as its component ions. Thus, the complete ionic equation is

$$Ca^{2+}(aq) + 2Cl^-(aq) + 2Na^+(aq) + CO_3^{2-}(aq)$$
$$\rightarrow CaCO_3(s) + 2Na^+(aq) + 2Cl^-(aq)$$

The ions Cl^- and Na^+ are on both sides of the complete ionic equation. Removing them from both sides of the complete ionic equation gives the following net ionic equation:

$$Ca^{2+}(aq) + CO_3^{2-}(aq) \rightarrow CaCO_3(s)$$

This response correctly determines what reactants and products will ionize in solution. The response also includes the three steps to writing a net ionic equation: writing a balanced molecular equation, then writing a complete ionic equation, and then writing a net ionic equation. It correctly identifies spectator ions and removes them from the complete ionic equation, resulting in the net ionic equation.

CHAPTER 5

Thermochemistry

Chemical reactions involve a change in energy. The study of energy and its transformations is known as **thermodynamics.** The relationship between chemical reactions and energy changes involving heat is **thermochemistry.**

The First Law of Thermodynamics

▐ The **first law of thermodynamics** states that energy can be changed from one form to another, but energy can be neither created nor destroyed.

▐ For the study of thermodynamics, a specific amount of matter is defined as the **system.** Everything outside the system is the **surroundings.**

▐ The **internal energy** of the system is the sum of all the kinetic and potential energy of all the components of the system. Internal energy is an example of a **state function,** which is a system that is defined by specifying its condition or its state (in terms of temperature, pressure, location, and so on). The value of a state function depends only on its present condition.

▐ One specific example of a state function is change in its internal energy, ΔE. When a system undergoes any chemical or physical change, the accompanying ΔE is given by the heat added or liberated from the system (q) plus the work (w) done on or by the system. Thus, $\Delta E = q + w$. The sign conventions that follow show how the relationships among heat, work, and energy change are expressed.

SIGN CONVENTIONS USED AND THE RELATIONSHIP AMONG q, w, AND ΔE	
Sign Convention for q:	**Sign of $\Delta E = q + w$**
$q > 0$: Heat is transferred from the surroundings to the system	$q > 0$ and $w > 0$: $\Delta E > 0$
$q < 0$: Heat is transferred from the system to the surroundings	$q > 0$ and $w < 0$: The sign of ΔE depends on the magnitudes of q and w
Sign Convention for w:	$q < 0$ and $w > 0$: The sign of ΔE depends on the magnitudes of q and w
$w > 0$: Work is done by the surroundings on the system	$q < 0$ and $w < 0$: $\Delta E < 0$
$w < 0$: Work is done by the system on the surroundings	

Enthalpy; and Enthalpies of Reaction

▌ **Enthalpy** is also a state function. Enthalpy accounts for heat flow in chemical changes occurring at constant pressure when no forms of work are performed (other than work from pressure-volume changes). Enthalpy (H) equals the internal energy plus the product of the pressure and the volume of the system: $H = E + PV$.

▌ The enthalpy change that accompanies a chemical reaction is called the **enthalpy of reaction,** or the **heat of reaction.** Balanced chemical equations that show enthalpy change, such as the following equation, are called **thermochemical equations.**

$$2H_2(g) + O_2(g) \rightarrow 2H_2O(g) \qquad \Delta H = -483.6 \text{ kJ}$$

▌ When ΔH is positive, the system absorbs heat, and the process is **endothermic.** When ΔH is negative, the system gives off heat, and the process is **exothermic.**

▌ The following guidelines are helpful when using thermochemical equations and diagrams.

1. Enthalpy is an extensive property. The magnitude of the change in enthalpy (ΔH) is directly proportional to the amount of reactant consumed in the process.
2. The enthalpy change for a reaction is equal in magnitude, but opposite in sign, to ΔH for the reverse reaction.
3. The enthalpy change for a reaction depends on the state of the reactants and products.

Calorimetry

▌ The value of ΔH can be determined experimentally by measuring the heat flow accompanying a reaction at constant pressure. This measurement of heat flow is **calorimetry.** An instrument that measures heat flow is a **calorimeter.**

▌ The **heat capacity** of an object is the amount of heat required to raise its temperature by 1 K (1°C). The heat capacity of one mole of a substance is its **molar heat capacity.** The heat capacity of one gram of a substance is its **specific heat.**

▌ One of the most important types of reactions studied using calorimetry is **combustion,** in which a compound reacts completely with excess oxygen. Combustion reactions are studied using a **bomb calorimeter,** in which a cup holding the sample is placed inside a bigger container that is full of water. When the material in the cup burns, the temperature change of the water is measured.

Hess's Law

▌ **Hess's law** states that if a reaction is carried out in a series of steps, ΔH for the reaction will equal the sum of the enthalpy changes for the individual steps.

▌ Hess's law is applied also to any thermochemical equations that can be added to produce a final chemical equation for a chemical reaction.

■ Examine the series of equations and determine how they can be reversed or multiplied by a constant to end up with the overall chemical equation when they are added together.

■ For example, consider the chemical reaction in which hydrogen peroxide breaks down into water and oxygen.

(a) $2H_2O_2(l) \rightarrow 2H_2O(g) + O_2(g)$

The equation in which water is formed from hydrogen and oxygen

(b) $2H_2(g) + O_2(g) \rightarrow 2H_2O(l)$ $\Delta H = -572$ kJ

and the equation in which hydrogen peroxide is formed from its elements

(c) $H_2(g) + O_2(g) \rightarrow H_2O_2(l)$ $\Delta H = -188$ kJ

can be used to determine the final equation and ΔH. Because hydrogen peroxide is a reactant, you must reverse equation "c." Remember to reverse the sign of ΔH. Because two moles of H_2O_2 are needed in the final equation, multiply through the reversed equation and ΔH by 2.

(d) $2H_2O_2(l) \rightarrow 2H_2(g) + 2O_2(g)$ $\Delta H = 376$ kJ

Add equations "b" and "d," and the result is equation "a," with a value of -196 kJ for ΔH.

Enthalpies of Formation

■ An important process used for tabulating thermochemical data is the formation of a compound from its constituent elements. The enthalpy change related to this process is called the **enthalpy of formation.** It is labeled ΔH_f, where the subscript f indicates that the substance has been formed from its elements.

■ The standard state of a substance is its pure form at atmospheric pressure (1 atm) and a stated temperature, which is usually 298 K. The **standard enthalpy** of a reaction is the enthalpy change when all reactants and products are in their standard states. Standard enthalpy is written $\Delta H°$, with the superscript standing for standard-state conditions. The standard enthalpy of formation of a compound is the change in enthalpy for the reaction that forms 1 mol of the compound from its elements, with all substances in their standard states. Thus, the standard enthalpy of formation of any element in its normal, standard state is zero.

For Additional Review

To understand how the body's heating and cooling mechanisms operate, one can view the human body as a thermodynamic system. Review the three ways heat is transferred from the body to its surroundings, as well as the effects of that transfer on the body.

Multiple-Choice Questions

1. An amount of heat equal to 3500 J is added to a system. In addition, 1500 J of work is done by the system on the surroundings. What is the change in internal energy of the system?
   - (A) 1500 J
   - (B) 2000 J
   - (C) 3500 J
   - (D) 5000 J
   - (E) −5000 J

2. $\Delta H°$ for the reaction below is −482 kJ. Calculate the heat released when 12.0 g of $CO(g)$ reacts completely, according to the following chemical equation:

   $$2CO(g) + O_2(g) \rightarrow 2CO_2(g)$$

   - (A) 2.89×10^3 kJ
   - (B) 206 kJ
   - (C) 103 kJ
   - (D) 65.7 kJ
   - (E) −482 kJ

3. For a specific process, $\Delta H = -432$ J. This process is
   - (A) endothermic
   - (B) exothermic
   - (C) positive
   - (D) negative
   - (E) zero

4. ΔE is always positive
   - (A) when a system absorbs heat and does work
   - (B) when a system gives off heat and does work
   - (C) when a system absorbs heat and has work done on it
   - (D) when a system gives off heat and has work done on it
   - (E) in none of the circumstances listed above

5. Under what condition(s) is the enthalpy change of a process equal to the amount of heat transferred into or out of the system? Hint: $P\Delta V = -w$.
   - I. Temperature is constant.
   - II. Pressure is constant.
   - III. Volume is constant.
   - (A) I only
   - (B) II only
   - (C) III only
   - (D) I and II
   - (E) II and III

6. What is the specific heat of iron if 13.5 J is required to raise the temperature of a 10-g sample 3 K?
   - (A) 0.45 J/g-K
   - (B) 2.22 J/g-K
   - (C) 4.05 J/g-K
   - (D) 45 J/g-K
   - (E) 405 J/g-K

7. The specific heat of methane, CH_4, is 2.20 J/g-K. What is the molar heat capacity of methane?
   - (A) 0.137 J/g-K
   - (B) 2.20 J/g-K
   - (C) 7.30 J/g-K
   - (D) 16.05 J/g-K
   - (E) 35.31 J/g-K

8. Given that:

   $$2S(s) + 3O_2(g) \rightarrow 2SO_3(g) \quad \Delta H = -790 \text{ kJ}$$
   $$S(s) + O_2(g) \rightarrow SO_2(g) \quad \Delta H = -297 \text{ kJ}$$

   What is the enthalpy of the reaction in which sulfur dioxide is oxidized to sulfur trioxide?

   $$2SO_2(s) + O_2(g) \rightarrow 2SO_3(g)$$

   - (A) 196 kJ
   - (B) −196 kJ
   - (C) 1087 kJ
   - (D) −1384 kJ
   - (E) −543 kJ

9. For what species in the following chemical reaction is ΔH_f° zero?

$$2Co(s) + H_2(g) + 8PF_3(g) \rightarrow 2HCo(PF_3)_4(l)$$

(A) $Co(s)$
(B) $H_2(g)$
(C) PF_3
(D) $HCo(PF_3)_4(l)$
(E) Both $Co(s)$ and $H_2(g)$

10. For which one of the following reactions is the value of ΔH_{rxn}° equal to ΔH_f° for the product?
(A) $H_2(g) + \frac{1}{2}O_2(g) \rightarrow H_2O(l)$
(B) $H_2(g) + O_2(g) \rightarrow H_2O_2(l)$
(C) $2C(s, graphite) + 2H_2(g) \rightarrow C_2H_4(g)$
(D) $\frac{1}{2}N_2(g) + O_2(g) \rightarrow NO_2(g)$
(E) All of the above

Free-Response Question

How much heat is released when 4.50 g of methane is burned in a constant-pressure system?

$$CH_4(g) + 2O_2(g) \rightarrow CO_2(g) + 2H_2O(l) \qquad \Delta H = -890 \text{ kJ}$$

ANSWERS AND EXPLANATIONS

Multiple-Choice Questions

1. (B) is correct. The change in internal energy of a system is calculated using the equation $\Delta E = q + w$. Because 3500 J is added to a system, q is 3500 J. Because 1500 J of work is done by the system, w is -1500 J. Thus, $\Delta E = 3500$ J $+ (-1500$ J$) = 2000$ J.

2. (B) is correct. The value of ΔH° is based on 1 mol of product being produced. For every 1 mol of product, 1 mol of CO is used. Because only 12.0 g/28.01 g/mol, or 0.428 mol, of CO is used, only 0.428 mol of CO_2 is produced. Therefore, 0.428 mol $\times$ 482 kJ/mol, or 206 kJ, is released. The negative sign in the problem is there because energy is released, not absorbed, so it is not involved in these calculations.

3. (B) is correct. A negative ΔH indicates an exothermic process. Although the value of ΔH is negative, the process itself is not considered to be negative.

4. (C) is correct. Change in internal energy is calculated by $\Delta E = q + w$. For ΔE to be positive, either q and w are both positive, or, if q and w have opposite signs, the number with the positive sign is larger. The only certain way for ΔE to be greater than zero is for both q and w to be positive. If the system absorbs heat, q is positive. If the system has work done on it, w is positive.

5. (B) is correct. Enthalpy can be calculated by $H = E + PV$. If pressure is constant, $\Delta H = \Delta E + P\Delta V$. The value of ΔE can be calculated by $w + q$, and $P\Delta V = -w$. Therefore, $\Delta H = w + q - w$, or q, if pressure is constant.

6. (A) is correct. The specific heat is the amount of heat needed to raise 1 g of a substance 1 K. Thus, specific heat is calculated by dividing the amount of heat absorbed by the mass and the temperature change, 13.5 J/(10 g $\times$ 3 K), or 0.45 J/g-K.

7. (E) is correct. The mass used for specific heat is 1 g, but the mass used for molar heat capacity is the mass of one mole. One mole of methane has a mass of 16.05 g, so the molar heat capacity equals 16.05 × 2.20 J/g-K, or 35.31 J/g-K.

8. (B) is correct. Hess's law states that if a reaction is carried out in a series of steps, ΔH for the reaction will equal the sum of the enthalpy changes for the individual steps. Use the first equation, and add to it twice the reverse of the second equation so that the substances common to both sides of the equation can be removed. Note that the sign of ΔH is changed because the equation is reversed.

$$2S(s) + 3O_2(g) \rightarrow 2SO_3(g) \qquad \Delta H = -790 \text{ kJ}$$
$$\underline{2SO_2(g) \rightarrow 2S(s) + 2O_2(g) \quad \Delta H = 594 \text{ kJ}}$$
$$2SO_2(s) + O_2(g) \rightarrow 2SO_3(g) \qquad \Delta H = -196 \text{ kJ}$$

9. (E) is correct. ΔH_f° is zero for free elements. Both $Co(s)$ and $H_2(g)$ are free elements. All other substances in the equation are compounds.

10. (E) is correct. ΔH_{rxn}° is equal to ΔH_f° for reactions where compounds are formed from the elements that make them up. All of the chemical equations meet that requirement.

Free-Response Question

The amount of energy released when 1 mol CH_4 is burned at constant pressure is -890 kJ. However, only 4.5 g methane is burned. A proportion using this mass, molar mass, and the energy released from one mole can be used to calculate the energy released from this mass of methane:

$$\frac{4.50 \text{ g CH}_4}{16.05 \text{ g CH}_4} = \frac{E}{-890 \text{ kJ}}$$

$$E = \frac{4.50 \text{ g CH}_4 \times (-890 \text{ kJ})}{16.05 \text{ g CH}_4} = -250 \text{ kJ.}$$

This response correctly recognizes the relationship between actual mass and molar mass and the effect of this relationship on determining the amount of energy released. Using this relationship, a proportion is correctly set up and solved for the actual amount of energy released.

CHAPTER 6

Electronic Structure of Atoms

When atoms react, it is the electrons that interact. The number, arrangement, and energies of electrons in an atom collectively are called an atom's **electronic structure.**

The Wave Nature of Light

▌ **Electromagnetic radiation** carries energy through space and is also called **radiant energy.** All types of electromagnetic radiation, including visible light, move through a vacuum at the speed of light, 3.00×10^8 m/s, which is represented by the constant c. An analysis of visible light has contributed greatly to understanding electronic structure.

▌ All light has wavelike characteristics, caused by oscillations in electronic and magnetic forces. The distance between peaks or troughs is **wavelength,** λ (lambda). The number of complete wavelengths, or cycles per second, is **frequency,** ν (nu). There is an inverse relationship between wavelength and frequency, $\nu\lambda = c$.

▌ The **electromagnetic spectrum** arranges various kinds of electromagnetic radiation in order of increasing wavelength, from gamma rays through radio frequencies. Visible light makes up the part of the electromagnetic spectrum that has a frequency range of 400 to 700 nm.

Quantized Energy

▌ Current knowledge of electronic structure is based on **quantum theory,** which states that energy can be released or absorbed by electrons only in discrete units of electromagnetic radiation.

▌ The smallest unit of this energy is a **quantum.** The energy (E) of a single quantum equals **Planck's constant** (h, or 6.63×10^{-34} J-s) times frequency (ν), $E = h\nu$. Planck's constant is named after Max Planck, who first proposed the quantum theory.

Line Spectra and the Bohr Model

▌ Most radiation sources emit radiation of several different wavelengths. When a range of radiation is separated into its different wavelengths, a pattern of lines called a **spectrum** is produced.

▌ A spectrum containing radiation of only specific wavelengths is a **line spectrum.** The line spectrum of each element is unique and can be used for identification.

- Niels Bohr proposed a model of the atom that explains the line spectrum for hydrogen. He assumed that electrons move in circular orbits around the nucleus. Bohr based his model on three postulates:

  1. Only orbits of certain radii are permitted for electrons in an atom.
  2. An electron in a permitted orbit has specific energy and is in an "allowed" energy state. An electron in this state will not radiate energy or spiral into the nucleus.
  3. Energy is emitted or absorbed by an electron only as it falls or rises between allowed energy levels. This energy is emitted or absorbed as a tiny packet of energy known as a **photon**, whose energy can be calculated by using $E = h\nu$.

- In Bohr's model, the energy of the electron depends on the value of a number (n), which is one of several **quantum numbers** that describe the behavior and the location of electrons in an atom. The allowed energy levels are given values for n, starting with the energy level closest to the nucleus ($n = 1$). The energy of the atom increases as n increases.

- When an electron is in the lowest energy level that it can occupy, it is in its **ground state.** If it is in a higher energy level, it is said to be in an **excited state.** Energy must be absorbed when an electron moves from a lower to a higher energy level, and this same amount of energy is emitted when an electron drops back from a higher to a lower state.

- Although Bohr's model adequately describes the electron in a hydrogen atom, it does not completely explain electrons in other atoms.

Quantum Mechanics and Atomic Orbitals

- The **current theory of atomic structure** includes a model that precisely describes the energy of an electron while also describing its location in terms of probabilities. Regions where there is a high probability of finding an electron are said to be regions of high **electron density.**

- The wave functions that describe the densities for electrons are called **orbitals.** Each orbital describes a specific distribution of electron density in space, as determined by probability. Each orbital has a characteristic energy and shape.

- The quantum mechanical model uses three quantum numbers, n, l, and m_l, to describe an orbital.

  1. The **principal quantum number,** n, can have positive integral values starting with 1. As n increases, the orbital becomes larger, and the electron spends more time farther from the nucleus. An increase in n also means that the electron has a higher energy.
  2. The second quantum number, l, is also called the **azimuthal quantum number.** It can have integral values from 0 to $n - 1$ for each value of n. This quantum number defines the shape of the orbital. The value of l for a particular orbital is generally designated by the letter s, p, d, or f, corresponding to l values of 0, 1, 2, or 3, respectively.

3. The **magnetic quantum number,** m_l, can have integral values between l and $-l$, including zero. This quantum number describes the orientation of the orbital in space.

▌ The collection of orbitals with the same value of n is called an **electron shell.** The set of orbitals that have the same n and l values is called the **subshell.** The relationship among values of n, l, and m_l can be summarized in the following table.

	RELATIONSHIP AMONG VALUES OF n, l, AND m_l THROUGH $n = 4$				
n	Possible Values of l	Subshell Designation	Possible Values of m_l	Number of Orbitals in Subshell	Total Number of Orbitals in Shell
1	0	$1s$	0	1	1
2	0	$2s$	0	1	
	1	$2p$	1, 0, −1	3	4
3	0	$3s$	0	1	
	1	$3p$	1, 0, −1	3	
	2	$3d$	2, 1, 0, −1, −2	5	9
4	0	$4s$	0	1	
	1	$4p$	1, 0, −1	3	
	2	$4d$	2, 1, 0, −1, −2	5	
	3	$4f$	3, 2, 1, 0, −1, −2, −3	7	16

Representations of Orbitals

▌ Intermediate regions in orbitals, where the probability of finding an electron drops to zero, are called **nodes.** The number of nodes increases with the increasing value for the principal quantum number, n. Also, as n increases, the size of the orbital increases.

▌ All **s orbitals** are spherical, but the distance of the electron from the nucleus increases as n increases.

▌ The distribution of electron density for a **p orbital** is not spherical. Instead, the electron density is concentrated in two regions, one on either side of the nucleus, separated by a node at the nucleus. This dumbbell-shaped orbital has two lobes. The p orbitals also increase in size as n increases. Each shell, beginning with $n = 2$, has three p orbitals.

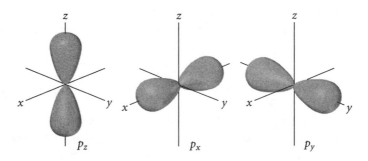

When *n* is 3 or greater, electrons can form **d orbitals.** There are five 3*d* orbitals, five 4*d* orbitals, and so forth. The different *d* orbitals have different shapes and orientations in space. Four of the *d*-orbital contours have a "four-leaf clover" shape, and each lies primarily in a plane. The fifth *d* orbital has the same energy but looks different, with two lobes along the *x* axis and a doughnut shape around the middle.

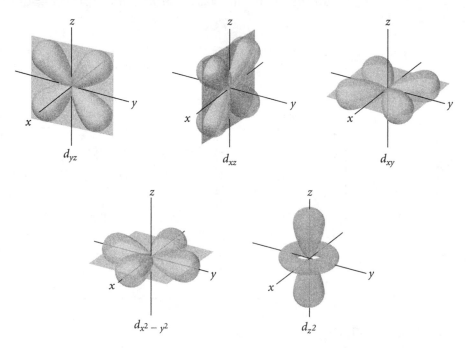

When *n* is 4 or greater, there are seven equivalent **f orbitals** that have complicated shapes.

Many-Electron Atoms

The shapes of orbitals in atoms with many electrons do not differ from those of hydrogen atoms. However, their energy levels do vary because of electron-to-electron repulsions. Different subshells hold different energies.

In a many-electron atom, for a given value of *n*, the energy of an orbital increases with the increasing value of *l*.

All orbitals of any given subshell have the same amount of energy. Orbitals with the same energy are called **degenerate orbitals.**

All electrons have a property called **electron spin.** Electrons spin on their own axes, like tiny planets. The **spin magnetic quantum number** is designated by m_s, where the subscript stands for "spin." The spinning charge generates a magnetic field whose direction depends on the direction of electron spin. There are two possible values for m_s, $+1/2$ and $-1/2$, depending on spin direction.

Physicist Wolfgang Pauli discovered the principle that governs the arrangements of electrons in many-electron atoms. The **Pauli exclusion principle** states that no two electrons in an atom can have the same set of four quantum numbers *n*, *l*, m_l, and m_s. For a given orbital, the values of *n*, *l*, and m_l are fixed. Any orbital can hold a maximum of two electrons, and they must have opposite spins.

Electron Configurations; and Electron Configurations and the Periodic Table

▎ The way in which electrons are distributed in various orbitals is an atom's **electron configuration.**

▎ The most stable electron configuration is one in which the electrons are in the ground state. Orbitals are filled in order of increasing energy, with no more than two electrons per orbital.

▎ To represent electron configuration, write the symbol for the occupied sub-shell and add a superscript to indicate the number of electrons in that subshell. Electron configurations can also be represented by orbital diagrams, as shown in the following figure.

		ELECTRON CONFIGURATIONS OF SEVERAL LIGHTER ELEMENTS					
Element	Total Electrons	Orbital Diagram					Electron Configuration
		$1s$	$2s$	$2p$		$3s$	
Li	3	↑↓	↑				$1s^2 2s^1$
Be	4	↑↓	↑↓				$1s^2 2s^2$
B	5	↑↓	↑↓	↑			$1s^2 2s^2 2p^1$
C	6	↑↓	↑↓	↑ ↑			$1s^2 2s^2 2p^2$
N	7	↑↓	↑↓	↑ ↑ ↑			$1s^2 2s^2 2p^3$
Ne	10	↑↓	↑↓	↑↓ ↑↓ ↑↓			$1s^2 2s^2 2p^6$
Na	11	↑↓	↑↓	↑↓ ↑↓ ↑↓		↑	$1s^2 2s^2 2p^6 3s^1$

▎ **Hund's rule** states that for degenerate orbitals, the lowest energy is attained when the number of electrons with the same spin is maximized. Consequently electrons will occupy orbitals singly to the maximum extent possible. Electrons repel one another, so by occupying different orbitals, the electrons stay as far as possible from each other.

▎ The **condensed electron configuration** of an element is written showing the electron configuration of the nearest noble-gas element of lower atomic number, with its symbol in brackets. Electrons represented by the symbol for a noble gas are referred to as **core electrons.** The electrons given after the noble-gas core are referred to as the outer-shell electrons, or **valence electrons.**

ELECTRON CONFIGURATIONS OF THE GROUP 2A AND 3A ELEMENTS	
Group 2A	
Be	$[\text{He}]2s^2$
Mg	$[\text{Ne}]3s^2$
Ca	$[\text{Ar}]4s^2$
Sr	$[\text{Kr}]5s^2$
Ba	$[\text{Xe}]6s^2$
Ra	$[\text{Rn}]7s^2$
Group 3A	
B	$[\text{He}]2s^22p^1$
Al	$[\text{Ne}]3s^23p^1$
Ga	$[\text{Ar}]3d^{10}4s^24p^1$
In	$[\text{Kr}]4d^{10}5s^25p^1$
Tl	$[\text{Xe}]4f^{14}5d^{10}6s^26p^1$

▍ The electron configurations of elements are related to their locations in the periodic table. The periodic table is structured so that elements with the same pattern of valence electrons are arranged in columns. The following diagram shows groupings of elements according to the type of orbital being filled.

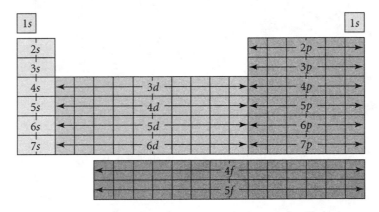

▍ As shells become larger and contain more subshells, they begin to overlap. This pattern can be seen in the previous figure, where, for example, the $4s$ subshell fills before the $3d$ subshell.

For Additional Review

Different gases emit light of different characteristic colors upon excitation in an electrical discharge. Review the colors emitted, taking special note of those for hydrogen and neon, and list a commercial use for "neon" lights.

Multiple-Choice Questions

1. The energy of a single quantum that has a frequency of $18.21 \times 10^{15} s^{-1}$ is
   (A) 5.44×10^{-18} J
   (B) 1.99×10^{-25} J
   (C) 3.49×10^{-48} J
   (D) 1.21×10^{-17} J
   (E) 6.44×10^{-18} J

2. In order for two samples to be made up of identical elements,
   (A) the spectra must be similar
   (B) the spectra must be identical
   (C) the samples must be heated to excite the electrons
   (D) the lines on one spectrum must have the same average wavelength as the lines on the other spectrum
   (E) they must come from the same location

3. Which of the following atoms is in an excited state?
   (A) $1s^2 2s^2 2p^1$
   (B) $1s^2 2s^2 2p^4$
   (C) $1s^2 2s^2 2p^5 3s^1$
   (D) $1s^2 2s^2 2p^6 3s^2$
   (E) $1s^2 2s^2 2p^6 3s^2 3p^2$

4. Based on the Pauli exclusion principle, what is the maximum number of electrons that could be present in the fourth shell?
   (A) 8 electrons
   (B) 14 electrons
   (C) 18 electrons
   (D) 32 electrons
   (E) 60 electrons

5. All of the orbitals in a given subshell have the same value of the
   (A) principal quantum number only
   (B) azimuthal quantum number only
   (C) magnetic quantum number only
   (D) principal quantum number and azimuthal quantum number
   (E) azimuthal quantum number and magnetic quantum number

6. How many orbitals are in the third shell?
   (A) 1 orbital
   (B) 4 orbitals
   (C) 9 orbitals
   (D) 16 orbitals
   (E) 25 orbitals

7. The $3p$ subshell in the ground state of atomic xenon contains how many electrons?
   (A) 2 electrons
   (B) 6 electrons
   (C) 8 electrons
   (D) 10 electrons
   (E) 36 electrons

8. The electronic configuration of a ground-state Cd atom is
   (A) $[Ar]4s^2 4d^{10}$
   (B) $[Kr]5s^2 4d^{10}$
   (C) $[Kr]5s^1 3d^{11}$
   (D) $[Ar]4s^1 4p^6 4d^5$
   (E) $[Kr]5s^2 4d^9$

9. How many unpaired electrons are present in a ground-state oxygen atom?
   (A) 0 electrons
   (B) 1 electron
   (C) 2 electrons
   (D) 3 electrons
   (E) 16 electrons

10. How many different principal quantum numbers can be found in the ground-state electron configuration of nickel?
    (A) 2 quantum numbers
    (B) 3 quantum numbers
    (C) 4 quantum numbers
    (D) 5 quantum numbers
    (E) 6 quantum numbers

Free-Response Question

> *The highest-energy electron in an unexcited atom has quantum numbers of* n = 3, l = 2, m$_l$ = 1, *and* m$_s$ = +1/2. *The electron is the last electron that can go in the subshell it is in. This electron is in an atom of what element? Explain.*

ANSWERS AND EXPLANATIONS

Multiple-Choice Questions

1. (D) is correct. The energy of a single quantum is given by $E = h\nu$. The value of Planck's constant, h, is 6.63×10^{-34} J-s.
Therefore, $E = 6.63 \times 10^{-34}$ J-s $\times 18.21 \times 10^{15}$ s^{-1} = 1.21×10^{-17} J.

2. (B) is correct. The spectrum of each element reflects the difference in energy levels for the electrons in the atoms of the element. Spectra might have lines in common, but the overall pattern of lines is unique for each element. Spectra must be identical for two samples to be composed of the same element.

3. (C) is correct. For an atom to be in an excited state, at least one electron must be in an energy level that is above its ground state. The ground state is the lowest energy level an electron can occupy. The only configuration that does not show an unexcited atom is answer C. This atom could have six electrons in the $2p$ subshell. The ground state of the electron that is in the $3s$ subshell is in the $2p$ subshell, but the electron has been excited.

4. (D) is correct. For the fourth shell, $n = 4$. Therefore, there are four possible values for l, and s, p, d, and f orbitals exist. For the $4s$ subshell, $m_l = 1$, and $m_s = +1/2$ and $-1/2$. Thus, the $4s$ subshell can contain two electrons. For the $4p$ subshell, $m_l = 3$, and $m_s = +1/2$ and $-1/2$. Thus, the $4p$ subshell can contain six electrons. For the $4d$ subshell, $m_l = 5$, and $m_s = +1/2$ and $-1/2$. Thus, the $4d$ subshell can contain ten electrons. For the $4f$ subshell, $m_l = 7$, and $m_s = +1/2$ and $-1/2$. Thus, the $4f$ subshell can contain fourteen electrons. The total number of electrons in the shell is the sum of these numbers, or thirty-two electrons.

5. (D) is correct. All of the orbitals in a given subshell have the same value of both the principal and azimuthal quantum numbers.

6. (C) is correct. The third shell contains an s orbital, three p orbitals, and five d orbitals. The total number of orbitals in the shell is nine.

7. (B) is correct. Xenon has an atomic number of 54, so it must also have fifty-four electrons. Adding each electron in the lowest-energy subshell it can go results in the configuration of $1s^2 2s^2 2p^6 3s^2 3p^6 4s^2 3d^{10} 4p^6 5s^2 4d^{10} 5p^6$. Even without completing the configuration, it can be seen that the $3p$ sublevel contains six electrons.

8. (B) is correct. A periodic table shows that the noble gas preceding silver is krypton, and the configuration of krypton ends in $4p^6$. Cadmium has an atomic number of 48, and the atomic number of krypton is 36, so silver has $48 - 36$, or twelve more electrons than krypton has. The electron configuration that starts after $4p^6$ and adds 12 more electrons is $[Kr]5s^2 4d^{10}$.

9. (C) is correct. An oxygen atom contains eight electrons. Two of them are in the 1s subshell, and two more are in the 2s subshell. The four remaining electrons are in the 2p subshell. According to Hund's rule, one electron is placed in each of the three 2p orbitals. The fourth electron must pair with one of these three, leaving two unpaired electrons.

10. (C) is correct. The number of principal quantum numbers can be found either by writing the electron configuration of nickel or by looking at the periodic table. The highest principle quantum number in the configuration is 4, so the electrons in a nickel atom are in shells 1 through 4.

Free-Response Question

The highest-energy electron is in shell 3 because $n = 3$ and the d subshell because $l = 2$. Thus, the electron completes the 3d subshell, $3d^{10}$. The element can be identified by writing the electron configuration to $3d^{10}$, counting the electrons, and finding what element has that atomic number. Or it could be found by looking at the periodic table and finding what element completes the 3d subshell. Using either method, the element is zinc. The magnetic and spin quantum numbers are not used to solve this problem because the orientation of the orbital and the direction of spin of the electron are not needed.

This response correctly interprets the quantum numbers as a specific subshell. It then provides a correct method of using this subshell to locate the required element. It also recognizes superfluous information provided in the problem.

CHAPTER 7

Periodic Properties of the Elements

The periodic table is a tool for organizing and recalling chemical information about elements. Elements in the table are arranged according to increasing atomic number. Those elements in the same column contain the same number of electrons in their valence orbitals. Electron configurations can be used to explain the similarities, differences, and trends in the properties of elements.

Effective Nuclear Charge

▌ Properties of atoms depend not only on electron configurations but also on the strength of the attraction between the outer electrons and the nucleus. The **effective nuclear charge** is the net positive charge affecting an electron in a many-electron atom. This charge is not the full nuclear charge because inner electrons shield outer electrons from the full attraction of the nucleus. Electrons in the same shell do not shield one another effectively.

▌ The effective nuclear charge experienced by outer electrons increases from element to element left to right across any row of the periodic table as the number of outer shell electrons increases. This increase occurs because nuclear charge increases left to right across a row of the periodic table but the number of shells does not.

Sizes of Atoms and Ions

▌ **Atomic radius** is an estimate of the size of an atom.

▌ The closest distances separating the nuclei during collisions between two atoms of the same element determine the apparent radius of an atom. This apparent radius is called the **nonbonding radius.**

▌ When two atoms are chemically bonded, their electron clouds overlap somewhat; this overlap does not occur in a nonbonding collision. Thus, the distance separating the nuclei of chemically bonded atoms is less than the nonbonding radius and is known as the **bonding atomic radius.** Scientists have assigned a bonding atomic radius to each element.

▌ In general, atomic radii increase moving down the columns of the periodic table because of an increase in the principle quantum number (*n*) of outer electrons.

▌ Atomic radii tend to decrease moving left to right across each row in the periodic table because the effective nuclear charge increases in elements across the row. A higher nuclear charge draws electrons closer to the nucleus and reduces the atomic radius.

- The size of an ion depends also on its nuclear charge, the number of electrons, and the orbitals in which the outer shell electrons reside.
- **Cations** (positively charged ions) are smaller than their parent atoms because the ionization involves losing valence electrons. **Anions** (negatively charged ions) are larger than their parent atoms because an added electron increases repulsion among valence electrons. Going down a group in the periodic table, ionic size increases for ions of the same charge.

Ionization Energy

- The **ionization energy** of an atom or ion is the minimum energy required to remove an electron from an isolated gaseous atom or ion in the ground state. The ease with which electrons can be removed from an atom is an important indicator of the atom's chemical behavior.
- The first ionization energy, I_1, is the energy needed to remove the first electron from a neutral atom. The second ionization energy, I_2, is the energy needed to remove the second electron, and so forth for successive electron removals. Each ionization energy is greater than the one before it because it is more difficult to remove an electron from a positively charged ion than from a neutral atom.
- With the exception of helium, a noble gas has eight electrons in its outermost shell; this is a very stable electron configuration, ns^2np^6. Thus, every element has a large increase of ionization energy when electrons are removed from its noble gas core, and this explains why only outer electrons are involved in sharing and transferring electrons for chemical bonding.
- There are also **trends in ionization energies** in the periodic table:

  1. Within each row, I_1 generally increases with increasing atomic number. Alkali metals have the lowest ionization energies in each row because they tend to lose electrons. Noble gases have the highest.
  2. Within each group, ionization energy generally decreases with increasing atomic number because the outer electrons of larger atoms are less attracted to the nucleus.
  3. The representative elements show a larger range of values of I_1 than do the transition-metal elements. Generally, the ionization energies of the transition elements increase slowly as one proceeds from left to right in a period. The f-block metals also show a small variation left to right.

Electron Affinities

- When an electron is added to a gaseous atom or ion, the energy change that occurs is called **electron affinity** because it measures the attraction (affinity) of the atom for the added electron.
- In most cases, energy is released when an electron is added, so electron affinity has a negative value. The greater the attraction between an atom and an electron, the more negative is the electron affinity. A negative electron affinity means that an anion is stable.

For some elements, especially noble gases, electron affinity can be positive because an added electron would have to occupy a new, higher-energy sub-shell. The anion is higher in energy than the atom and electron were separately. A positive electron affinity means that an anion will not form readily.

Electron affinity generally becomes increasingly negative moving left to right in each row of the periodic table toward the halogens, which have the most negative electron affinities. Electron affinities do not change greatly within a group on the periodic table.

Electron Affinities

1A	2A		3A	4A	5A	6A	7A	8A
H −73								**He** >0
Li −60	**Be** >0		**B** −27	**C** −122	**N** >0	**O** −141	**F** −328	**Ne** >0
Na −53	**Mg** >0		**Al** −43	**Si** −134	**P** −72	**S** −200	**Cl** −349	**Ar** >0
K −48	**Ca** −2		**Ga** −30	**Ge** −119	**As** −78	**Se** −195	**Br** −325	**Kr** >0
Rb −47	**Sr** −5		**In** −30	**Sn** −107	**Sb** −103	**Te** −190	**I** −295	**Xe** >0

Metals, Nonmetals, and Metalloids

The periodic table groups elements into the categories of metals, nonmetals, and metalloids.

Most elements are metals. They are found on the left side and middle of the periodic table. Nonmetals appear in the upper right portion of the table. The metalloids are found in a narrow, diagonal band between metals and nonmetals.

The **metallic character,** or characteristic properties of metals, generally increases moving down a column of the periodic table and from right to left across rows.

Group Trends for the Active Metals

Alkali metals (group 1A) are soft, metallic solids. They have the metallic properties of luster and conductivity. They also have low densities and low melting points. Although alkali metal ions are colorless, they emit colors when placed in a flame. These metals are extremely reactive. They have a general electron configuration of ns^1, and an alkali metal easily loses one electron to form a cation with a +1 charge.

Alkali metals tend to have increasing atomic radii, reactivity, and density and decreasing ionization energy and melting points moving down the group in the periodic table.

Alkaline earth metals (group 2A) are solids, and they are harder, denser, and less reactive than alkali metals. They melt at higher temperatures, and the heavier alkaline earth metal ions also give off colors when heated in a flame.

They have a general electron configuration of ns^2, and an alkaline earth metal easily loses two electrons to form a cation with a $+2$ charge.

▋ Alkaline earth metals follow the same trends down the group as alkali metals follow.

Group Trends for Selected Nonmetals

▋ Group 6A is the **oxygen group.** Moving down this group, there is an increase in metallic character, density, melting point, and atomic radius, but ionization energy decreases.

▋ Group 7A is the **halogen group.** All of the halogens are nonmetals whose melting and boiling points increase with higher atomic numbers. Halogens have high electron affinities that decrease down the group. They have a general electron configuration of ns^2np^5, and a halogen easily gains one electron to form an anion with a -1 charge.

▋ Group 8A is made up of **noble gases.** These nonmetals increase in boiling point, density, and atomic radius down a group, and they decrease in ionization energy.

For Additional Review

Practice arranging atoms and ions in order of decreasing size: [Mg^{2+}, Ca^{2+}, and Ca] and [S^{2-}, Cl^-, K^+, and Ca^{2+}]. Then show trends by labeled arrows on a blank periodic table.

Multiple-Choice Questions

1. In which set of elements would all members be expected to have similar chemical properties?
   (A) O, S, Se
   (B) N, O, F
   (C) Na, Mg, K
   (D) S, Se, Si
   (E) Ne, Na, Mg

2. For which of the following elements would the effective nuclear charge be greatest for its valence electrons?
   (A) Ca
   (B) Cd
   (C) He
   (D) N
   (E) Pb

3. Which of the following elements has the greatest atomic radius?
   (A) Br
   (B) Cu
   (C) K
   (D) Mn
   (E) V

4. The only noble gas that lacks the ns^2np^6 valence electron configuration is
   (A) helium
   (B) krypton
   (C) neon
   (D) radon
   (E) none of the above, since all noble gases have the ns^2np^6 valence electron configuration

5. Which of the following elements has the largest first ionization energy?
   (A) Li
   (B) K
   (C) Na
   (D) H
   (E) Rb

6. Which of the following elements has the most negative electron affinity?
   (A) Ne
   (B) Li
   (C) Be
   (D) N
   (E) F

7. Of the elements below, which is the most metallic?
   (A) sodium
   (B) barium
   (C) magnesium
   (D) calcium
   (E) cesium

8. Between which two elements is the difference in metallic character the greatest?
   (A) Rb and O
   (B) O and I
   (C) Rb and I
   (D) Li and O
   (E) Li and Rb

9. Considering the general valence electron configuration of ns^2, which of the following statements is true?
   (I) Elements with this electron configuration are expected to form -1 anions.
   (II) Elements with this electron configuration might have positive electron affinities.
   (III) Elements with this electron configuration have higher first ionization energies than the ns^1 elements in the same period.
   (A) I only
   (B) I and II
   (C) I and III
   (D) II and III
   (E) I, II, and III

10. Going down the halogen group,
    (A) melting points increase
    (B) electron affinities become more negative
    (C) ionization energies increase
    (D) ion size decreases
    (E) atomic radius remains the same

Free-Response Question

Compare and contrast the elements antimony (Sb) and iodine (I) in terms of electron affinity, first ionization energy, atomic radius, and metallic character.

ANSWERS AND EXPLANATIONS

Multiple-Choice Questions

1. **(A) is correct.** Elements in the same group have similar chemical properties. Of the sets of elements listed, only the set of O, S, and Se, from group 6A, are in the same group.

■ **2. (C) is correct.** Generally, the smaller the atom, the greater the effective nuclear charge for the valence electrons, because the valence electrons are closer to the nucleus, and they have less shielding from the attraction of the nucleus by core electrons. The smallest atom listed is He. The electrons in helium are close to the nucleus, and they are not shielded by other electrons. Thus, the effective nuclear charge is greatest for the valence electrons of helium.

■ **3. (C) is correct.** All the elements listed are in period 4. Atomic radius decreases left to right across a period because nuclear charge increases but the number of shells does not. Of all the elements listed, K is farthest to the left in the period, so it has the greatest atomic radius.

■ **4. (A) is correct.** All the elements listed are noble gases. Helium cannot have the listed configuration because it has only two electrons, and the configuration contains eight.

■ **5. (D) is correct.** Ionization energy increases left to right across a period and going up a group. All the listed elements are in group 1A. Therefore, the element with the lowest atomic number, which is hydrogen, will have the greatest first ionization energy.

■ **6. (E) is correct.** With the exception of the noble gases, electron affinity becomes more negative from left to right across a period. The electron affinity of the noble gas in the list, Ne, is positive. All the other elements are also in period 2, but fluorine (F) is farthest to the right.

■ **7. (E) is correct.** Metallic character increases going right to left across a period and going down a group. Of all the metals listed, cesium and sodium are farthest to the left. Cesium is below sodium in group 1A.

■ **8. (A) is correct.** Metallic character increases going right to left across a period and going down a group. The diagonal distance on the periodic table separating Rb and O is greatest, so they have the greatest difference in metallic character.

■ **9. (D) is correct.** Elements with this electron configuration are in group 2A. These elements form +2 cations. They may have positive electron affinities. Elements in this group are alkaline earth metals, and they do have higher first ionization energies than elements in the alkali metal group.

■ **10. (A) is correct.** Going down the halogen group, melting points increase, electron affinities become less negative, and ionization energies decrease. Also, ion size and atomic radii both increase. The only correct answer is *A*.

Free-Response Question

The elements Sb and I are both in period 5, but they are in different groups. The element I is to the right of Sb in the period. Thus, I has a more negative electron affinity, a greater first ionization energy, a larger atomic radius, and less metallic character.

This response correctly locates the two elements on the periodic table and relates their locations to each other. It then recognizes the periodic trends for electron affinity, first ionization energy, atomic radius, and metallic character and relates these trends to the relative locations of Sb and I on the periodic table.

CHAPTER 8

Basic Concepts of Chemical Bonding

The properties of compounds, polyatomic ions, and diatomic elements are determined in large part by the chemical bonds that hold their atoms together.

Chemical Bonds, Lewis Symbols, and the Octet Rule

▌ A **chemical bond** attaches atoms or ions to one another. There are three basic types of chemical bonds: ionic, covalent, and metallic. An **ionic bond** is an attractive force between ions of opposite charges. A **covalent bond** results from the sharing of electrons between two atoms. **Metallic bonds** occur when a metal atom is bonded to more than one other metal atom by attraction to their collective electrons.

▌ Chemical bonding occurs among the valence electrons—those electrons in the incomplete outer shell of an atom. A **Lewis symbol** for an element shows the valence electrons as dots around the symbol for the element. Each of the four sides of the atomic symbol represents an orbital, and dots are placed around the symbol in the same manner as the valence s and p orbitals are filled.

LEWIS SYMBOLS					
Element	Electron Configuration	Lewis Symbol	Element	Electron Configuration	Lewis Symbol
Li	[He]$2s^1$	Li·	Na	[Ne]$3s^1$	Na·
Be	[He]$2s^2$	·Be·	Mg	[Ne]$3s^2$	·Mg·
B	[He]$2s^2 2p^1$	·Ḃ·	Al	[Ne]$3s^2 3p^1$	·Ȧl·
C	[He]$2s^2 2p^2$	·Ċ·	Si	[Ne]$3s^2 3p^2$	·Ṡi·
N	[He]$2s^2 2p^3$	·N̈:	P	[Ne]$3s^2 3p^3$	·P̈:
O	[He]$2s^2 2p^4$	:Ö:	S	[Ne]$3s^2 3p^4$	:S̈:
F	[He]$2s^2 2p^5$	·F̈:	Cl	[Ne]$3s^2 3p^5$	·C̈l:
Ne	[He]$2s^2 2p^6$	:N̈e:	Ar	[Ne]$3s^2 3p^6$	:Ȧr:

▌ The number of valence electrons of any representative element is the same as its group number on the periodic table.

▌ Eight valence electrons is a stable electron configuration. The **octet rule** states that atoms tend to gain, lose, or share electrons until they are surrounded by eight valence electrons (an **octet**). Completing an octet gives the atom the same number of valence electrons as are in a noble gas. An octet of electrons consists of full s and p subshells of an atom.

Ionic Bonding

■ Ions form when electrons are transferred from an atom of low ionization energy to an atom with a high affinity for electrons. An **ionic bond** results from the attraction of these oppositely charged ions. Typical ionic compounds consist of positively charged ions of a metal and negatively charged ions of a nonmetal.

■ Lewis symbols and electron configurations can be used to determine what elements will form ions.

■ In general, atoms with three or fewer valence electrons (groups 1A through 3A) will lose these electrons and form positive ions. The magnitude of the charge on the ion equals the number of electrons the atom loses. Because of the irregularities in the electron configurations of the transition metals, most transition metals will form more than one positive ion. For example, copper forms Cu^+ and Cu^{2+}.

■ Atoms of groups 5A through 7A need only a few more valence electrons to give them an octet. These atoms will gain three, two, or one electron, respectively, and will form negative ions. The magnitude of the charge of these ions is equal to the number of electrons gained.

■ The attraction between ions of unlike charge makes ionic compounds stable. This attraction draws ions together, releasing energy and causing the ions to form a solid lattice.

■ **Lattice energy** is the energy required to completely separate a mole of a solid ionic compound into its gaseous ions. Lattice energy is a measure of stability. Lattice energy, and thus stability, increases as the charges on the ions increase and as their radii decrease. The magnitude of the lattice energy of an ionic compound depends primarily on the ionic charges because ionic radii do not vary over a wide range.

■ Lattice energies are high in ionic compounds. This strong attraction tends to make ionic compounds hard and brittle, with high melting points.

Covalent Bonding

■ When two reacting atoms do not have much difference in electron affinity, their electron clouds overlap, and they share electrons to achieve a full valence shell. The bond formed by two atoms sharing electrons is called a **covalent bond.** A hydrogen molecule is the simplest example of a covalent bond. The atoms in H_2 are held together principally because the two nuclei are electrostatically attracted to the concentration of negative charge between them. The shared pair of electrons in any covalent bond acts as a kind of "glue" to bind atoms together.

■ A single covalent bond is sometimes called a **single bond.** When two electron pairs are shared, a **double bond** forms. A **triple bond** corresponds to the sharing of three pairs of electrons.

■ Covalent bonds can be represented by **Lewis structures,** which use Lewis symbols for the elements in the compound. In Lewis structures, each electron pair shared between atoms is represented as a line between their chemical symbols. Unshared electron pairs are shown as dots.

Bond Polarity and Electronegativity

▮ When electrons are shared equally between two atoms, the bond formed is a **nonpolar covalent bond.** In a **polar covalent bond,** one of the atoms attracts shared electrons more strongly than the other atom does.

▮ **Electronegativity** is the ability of an atom in a molecule to attract electrons to itself. The greater an atom's electronegativity, the greater the attraction of the atom for shared electrons.

▮ Values for electronegativity are not measured amounts; they are relative numbers assigned to atoms based on ionization energy, electron affinity, and other properties.

▮ Fluorine is the most electronegative element (4.0); the least electronegative element is cesium (0.7). On the periodic table, there is an increase in electronegativity moving from left to right across a period. Within any group, electronegativity tends to decrease as atomic number increases.

▮ The greater the difference in electronegativity between two covalently bonded atoms, the more polar is their bond.

▮ A molecule can be polar. When a molecule, such as HF, has centers of positive and negative charge that do not coincide, the molecule is a **polar molecule.** Not all molecules that contain polar bonds are polar. When the partial charges resulting from polar bonds are balanced in the molecule, as they are in CO_2, the molecules are nonpolar, even though the molecules contain polar bonds.

▮ A polar molecule with a slightly positive charge at one end and a slightly negative charge at the other is a **dipole.** The magnitude of a dipole is called its **dipole moment.** The dipole moment will increase in size as the magnitude of charge that is separated or the distance between charges increases; $\mu = Qr$, where μ is the dipole moment, Q is electrical charge, and r is distance.

▮ When writing formulas, the less electronegative element is written first. When naming compounds, the less electronegative element is named first.

Drawing Lewis Structures; and Resonance Structures

▮ Lewis symbols for individual atoms can be used to draw Lewis structures for molecules and polyatomic ions. These structures are helpful for understanding the bonding and the properties of these entities. Use the following procedure for drawing these Lewis structures.

1. Use the periodic table to determine the number of valence electrons in each atom that is in the molecule or polyatomic ion. Add these valence electrons to obtain a total number of available electrons. For an anion, add an electron for each negative charge. For a cation, subtract an electron for each positive charge.

2. Write the symbols for the atoms to show how the atoms are attached to each other. Usually the central atom is written first. Represent each single

bond by a dash between the symbols. Each of these single bonds uses two of the available electrons.

3. If the atoms bonded to the central atom can contain an octet, add dots around the symbols to complete the octets. Subtract the number of dots used from the remaining available electrons.
4. Place any leftover electrons on the central atom.
5. If there are not enough electrons to give the central atom an octet, use one or more of the unshared pairs of electrons bonded to the central atom to form multiple bonds.

▌ Exceptions to using the octet rule to draw these Lewis structures occur when molecules or ions have an odd number of electrons or when the central atom has more or less than an octet.

▌ **Resonance structures** are all the individual Lewis structures that are equally good descriptions of a single molecule or polyatomic ion. All the structures are illustrated, with a double-headed arrow between them that indicates that the molecule or ion is described by an average of the structures.

Strengths of Covalent Bonds

▌ The strength of a covalent bond is measured by its **bond enthalpy,** which is the enthalpy change when a particular bond is broken in a mole of a gaseous substance. The greater the bond enthalpy, the stronger the bond.

▌ A molecule with high bond enthalpy is less likely to be involved in a chemical reaction than a molecule with low bond enthalpy.

▌ The **bond length** between two bonded atoms is the distance between the nuclei of the atoms involved in the bond. As the number of bonds between atoms increases, bond length decreases, and bond enthalpy increases.

For Additional Review

Use Lewis structures to draw resonance structures for the nitrite ion (NO_2^-) and sulfur dioxide (SO_2).

Multiple-Choice Questions

1. How many valence electrons does an atom have if it is located in period 4 and group 6A of the periodic table?
   (A) 4 valence electrons
   (B) 6 valence electrons
   (C) 8 valence electrons
   (D) 10 valence electrons
   (E) 34 valence electrons

2. How many dots would be used to write the Lewis symbol for bromine?
   (A) 1 dot
   (B) 2 dots
   (C) 3 dots
   (D) 7 dots
   (E) 8 dots

3. Which of the following pairs of atoms is most likely to form an ionic bond?
   (A) P and O
   (B) As and Cl
   (C) He and Si
   (D) Ca and Br
   (E) I and F

4. Which of the following pairs of elements will form the most polar bond? The number by each symbol is the electronegativity for that element.
   (A) P (2.1) and O (3.5)
   (B) H (2.1) and C (2.5)
   (C) S (2.5) and F (4.0)
   (D) Si (1.8) and Cl (3.0)
   (E) Two I atoms (2.5)

5. The octet rule is NOT violated by the central atom in
   (A) SF_4
   (B) KrF_2
   (C) CF_4
   (D) XeF_4
   (E) ICl_4^-

6. Given its location on the periodic table, which of the following elements has the greatest electronegativity?
   (A) O
   (B) Na
   (C) Cs
   (D) Cu
   (E) Br

7. A Lewis structure is drawn for a molecule that contains one arsenic atom and three bromine atoms. How many valence electrons are available from these atoms?
   (A) 12 valence electrons
   (B) 19 valence electrons
   (C) 21 valence electrons
   (D) 26 valence electrons
   (E) 36 valence electrons

8. The Lewis structure of N_2H_2 shows
   (A) a nitrogen-nitrogen triple bond
   (B) a nitrogen-nitrogen single bond
   (C) that each nitrogen atom has one nonbonding electron pair
   (D) that each nitrogen atom has two nonbonding electron pairs
   (E) that each hydrogen atom has one nonbonding electron pair

9. As the number of covalent bonds between two atoms increases, the distance between the atoms
   (A) increases, and the strength of the bond between them increases
   (B) decreases, and the strength of the bond between them decreases
   (C) increases, and the strength of the bond between them decreases
   (D) decreases, and the strength of the bond between them increases
   (E) Both the distance and strength are unpredictable.

10. Of the possible bonds between carbon atoms,
    (A) a triple bond is longer than a single bond
    (B) a double bond is stronger than a triple bond
    (C) a single bond is stronger than a triple bond
    (D) a double bond is longer than a triple bond
    (E) a single bond is stronger than a double bond

Free-Response Question

Answer both of the following questions, and explain your answers.

(a) Which bond is more polar, B—Cl or C—Cl?

(b) Consider a bond between phosphorus and chlorine. Which atom has the partial negative charge?

ANSWERS AND EXPLANATIONS

Multiple-Choice Questions

1. (B) is correct. All atoms in group 6A have six valence electrons. The period it is in makes no difference.

2. (D) is correct. The number of dots in the Lewis symbol equals the number of valence electrons in the atom. Bromine is in group 7A, so an atom of bromine contains seven electrons. Thus, the Lewis symbol for bromine would contain seven dots.

3. (D) is correct. An ionic bond is most likely to form between a metal and a nonmetal. Calcium is the only choice that is a metal, and the other element in the pair, bromine, is a nonmetal.

4. (C) is correct. The greater the difference in electronegativity, the greater the polarity of the bond. The greatest difference in electronegativity of the pairs of elements listed is 1.5, for sulfur and fluorine.

5. (C) is correct. Drawing Lewis structures for SF_4, KrF_2, XeF_4, and ICl_4^- shows that the central atom in each molecule has more than an octet. The compound CF_4 is the only compound shown that obeys the octet rule.

6. (A) is correct. Electronegativity increases from left to right across a period and going up a group. Thus, the closer the element is to the upper right-hand corner of the periodic table, the greater the electronegativity. Oxygen is closest to this corner.

7. (D) is correct. Arsenic is in group 5A, so an arsenic atom has five available valence electrons. Bromine is in group 7A, so each bromine atom contains seven available valence electrons. Because the molecule contains one arsenic atom and three bromine atoms, it contains 1×5 electrons $+ 3 \times 7$ electrons, or 26 available valence electrons.

8. (C) is correct. Two nitrogen atoms and two hydrogen atoms have a total of twelve available valence electrons. In drawing the Lewis structure for this compound, single bonds connecting the two nitrogen atoms together and connecting a hydrogen atom to each of the nitrogen atoms uses only six of the available valence electrons. The other six electrons must be used to provide three dots for each of the nitrogen atoms, each of which now contains seven valence electrons. To provide an octet for the nitrogen atoms, the unpaired electrons on the nitrogen atoms must be shared by both nitrogen atoms, which are now connected by a double bond. Each nitrogen atom also contains an unbonded pair of electrons.

9. (D) is correct. Single bonds are longer and weaker than double bonds, and double bonds are longer and weaker than triple bonds. Thus, as the number of bonds increases, bond length decreases, and bond strength increases.

10. (D) is correct. Increasing the number of bonds increases the strength of the bonds and decreases the bond length. The only answer that meets these requirements is *D*.

Free-Response Question

Solution

(a) Electronegativity increases from left to right across a period, and boron is to the left of carbon in the same period. Thus, the electronegativity of carbon is greater than that of boron. Because the electronegativity difference between boron and chlorine is greater than that of carbon and chlorine, the B−Cl bond is more polar.

(b) Because it is farther to the right in the same period on the periodic table, chlorine is more electronegative than phosphorus. Thus, chlorine will have a stronger attraction for the shared electrons, and chlorine will have the partial negative charge in the molecule.

This response correctly recognizes the trend of electronegativity within a period. It correctly applies this trend to determining the polarity of a bond and to determining the poles of a polar molecule.

CHAPTER 9

Molecular Geometry and Bonding Theories

The shape and size of a molecule, in addition to the strength and polarity of its bonds, determine the properties of a molecular substance.

Molecular Shapes

▌ **Molecular geometry** is the arrangements of atoms in a molecule in space.

▌ **Bond angle** determines the overall shape of a molecule, but **bond length** also affects the shape and size of a molecule.

▌ For molecules with a central atom, the formula representing shape is AB_n, where A is the central bonded atom and n is number of atoms of element B that are bonded to the central atom.

▌ Molecular shapes are based on **five fundamental geometries.** These shapes are shown in the following figure.

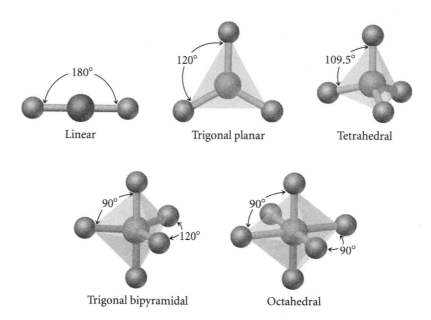

▌ When corner atoms are removed from these fundamental geometries, additional molecular shapes result, as is seen in the following figure.

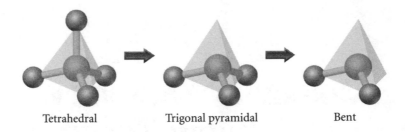

Tetrahedral → Trigonal pyramidal → Bent

The VSEPR Model

▌ Both bonding and nonbonding pairs of atoms create **electron domains** around themselves. Electron domains are regions where elections can be found. The arrangement of electron domains around a central atom of a molecule or ion is its **electron-domain geometry.**

▌ VSEPR stands for <u>V</u>alence-<u>S</u>hell <u>E</u>lectron-<u>P</u>air <u>R</u>epulsion. Because electron domains are negatively charged, they repel one another. According to the **VSEPR model,** the best arrangement of a given number of electron domains is the one that minimizes the repulsions among them.

▌ To predict the shapes of molecules with the VSEPR model, use the following steps.

1. Draw the Lewis structure of the molecule or ion, and count the total number of electron domains around the central atom. Each nonbonding electron pair and each single or multiple bond counts as an electron domain.

2. Determine the electron-domain geometry by arranging the total number of electron domains so that the repulsions among them are minimized, as shown in the table on the next page.

3. Use the arrangement of the bonded atoms to determine the molecular geometry. Examples of the molecular geometry for molecules with two to four electron domains around the central atom are shown in the table on the next page.

Electron-Domain Geometries and Molecular Shapes for Molecules with Two, Three, and Four Electron Domains Around the Central Atom

Number of Electron Domains	Electron-Domain Geometry	Bonding Domains	Nonbonding Domains	Molecular Geometry	Example
2	Linear	2	0	Linear	$\ddot{O}=C=\ddot{O}$
3	Trigonal planar	3	0	Trigonal planar	$F-B(-F)-F$
		2	1	Bent	$[O-N-O]^-$
4	Tetrahedral	4	0	Tetrahedral	CH_4
		3	1	Trigonal pyramidal	NH_3
		2	2	Bent	H_2O

- When determining molecular geometry, consider that nonbonding electron pairs have slightly greater repulsions than bonding pairs and that multiple bonds exert greater repulsions than single bonds.
- When molecules involve a central atom that has more than an octet, the molecules have a variety of shapes based on the trigonal bipyramid, which has five electron domains, and the octahedron, which has six electron domains.

Molecular Shape and Molecular Polarity

▌ For a molecule with more than two atoms, the **dipole moment** (the amount of charge separation) depends on both the polarities of the individual bonds and the geometry of the molecule. For each bond in the molecule, the **bond dipole** is the dipole moment due only to the two atoms in that bond.

▌ Bond dipoles and dipole moments are **vector quantities.** That is, they have both magnitude and direction.

▌ The overall dipole moment for a polyatomic molecule is the sum of its bond dipoles.

▌ In certain molecular shapes, even though the individual parts have charges, the bond dipole is zero because the electron domains are directly opposite each other, and the charges cancel one another out. Thus, the entire molecule is nonpolar, even though it might contain polar bonds. However, in bent molecules, charges aren't directly opposite each other. The charges do not cancel one another out, and a polar molecule is the result.

Covalent Bonding and Orbital Overlap; and Hybrid Orbitals

▌ **Valence-bond theory** is an extension of Lewis's work on electron-pair bonds. It states that covalent bonds form when atomic orbitals of two atoms overlap. The electrons in the area of overlap are attracted to two nuclei, so the greater the overlap, the stronger the bond.

▌ In polyatomic molecules, more orbitals overlap. The s and p (and sometimes the d) orbitals mix to form **hybrid orbitals,** each of which is equivalent to the other hybrid orbitals but differs in shape from the unhybridized orbitals. Hybrid orbitals can include nonbonding pairs of electrons. The number of hybrid orbitals formed is equal to the number of atomic orbitals that were mixed.

▌ Hybrid orbitals are designated by the orbitals that mix to form them. For example, an sp^2 hybrid is formed from one s orbital and two p orbitals.

▌ Different forms of hybrid orbitals result in different electron domain geometries, as shown below.

> linear $= sp$
> trigonal planar $= sp^2$
> tetrahedal $= sp^3$
> trigonal bipyramidal $= sp^3d$
> octahedral $= sp^3d^2$

Multiple Bonds

▌ A **sigma bond** (σ) forms when two s orbitals overlap. In a sigma bond, the electron density is concentrated symmetrically about the line connecting the nuclei. A line joining the two nuclei would pass through the middle of the overlap region. Single bonds are almost always sigma bonds.

▌ Electrons in sigma bonds are always localized in the area between two atoms, and they don't figure significantly in the bonding of any other atoms.

- In **pi bonds (π),** there is a side-to-side overlap of *p* orbitals. In this covalent bond, the overlap regions lie above and below the internuclear axis. Because the area of overlap in pi bonds is less than that in sigma bonds, pi bonds tend to be weaker than sigma bonds.

- Double bonds are usually one pi bond and one sigma bond. Triple bonds are one sigma bond and two pi bonds.

- When electrons are spread over a number of atoms in a molecule rather than localized between two specific atoms, the electrons are **delocalized.** For example, delocalized electrons are present in a benzene molecule. The three pi bonds in the benzene ring appear to resonate between two structures, with pi bonds alternating locations. In reality, the electrons in the pi bonds are delocalized and are spread out around the entire ring. Delocalization of electrons produces a stable molecule.

Molecular Orbitals

- Molecular orbital theory describes the electrons in molecules that use **molecular orbitals.** A molecular orbital, like an atomic orbital, has a definite energy and holds two electrons of opposite spin. However, these orbitals involve a whole molecule, not an individual atom. When two atomic orbitals overlap, two molecular orbitals form. One of these molecular orbitals is a bonding molecular orbital, and the other one is an antibonding molecular orbital.

- A **bonding molecular orbital** is a molecular orbital in which the electron density is concentrated between the two nuclei. The energy of bonding molecular orbitals is less than the energy of the separate atomic orbitals that form it.

- An **antibonding molecular orbital** is higher in energy than a bonding molecular orbital; therefore, it is less stable. These molecular orbitals concentrate electron density on opposite sides of the nuclei.

- The stability of a bond in molecular orbital theory depends on its **bond order.** Bond order equals half of the difference of the number of bonding electrons and the number of antibonding electrons.

Bond order = 1/2(number of bonding electrons − number of antibonding electrons)

- A bond order of one represents a single bond, a bond order of two is a double bond, and a bond order of three is a triple bond. A bond order of zero means that no bond exists.

Second-Row Diatomic Molecules

- The molecular properties of diatomic molecules from period 2 help to explain their electron configurations.

- Molecules that are attracted by a magnetic field are said to be **paramagnetic.** Molecules with unpaired electrons are paramagnetic. Molecules that have no unpaired electrons are weakly repelled by a magnetic field and are said to be **diamagnetic.**

- Electron configurations can also be related to the bond enthalpies and the bond distances of the molecules. For example, the short bond length and high bond enthalpy of nitrogen indicates a multiple bond.
- If the electronegativities of two bonded atoms of different elements are similar, the molecules will behave much like a diatomic molecule consisting of atoms of the same element.

For Additional Review

Investigate the types of bonds and the molecular shapes in saturated and unsaturated hydrocarbons.

Multiple-Choice Questions

1. The molecular geometry of the SF_2 molecule is
   (A) linear
   (B) bent
   (C) trigonal planar
   (D) tetrahedral
   (E) octahedral

2. The central iodine atom in IF_5 has in its valence shell
   (A) one unbonded electron pair and five bonded electron pairs
   (B) no unbonded electron pairs and five bonded electron pairs
   (C) five unbonded electron pairs and one bonded electron pair
   (D) four unbonded electron pairs and one bonded electron pair
   (E) one unbonded electron pair and four bonded electron pairs

3. The hybridization of the central atom in the XeF_4 molecule is
   (A) sp
   (B) sp^2
   (C) sp^3
   (D) sp^3d
   (E) sp^3d^2

4. In the overall process of hybrid orbital formation, the purpose of promoting one or more electrons is to
   (A) increase the number of atomic orbitals
   (B) increase the number of unpaired electrons
   (C) increase the number of hybrid orbitals
   (D) make sure that every atomic orbital is occupied prior to hybridization
   (E) make sure that all of the electrons in atomic orbitals are unpaired prior to hybridization

5. A typical triple bond consists of
   (A) three sigma bonds
   (B) three pi bonds
   (C) one sigma bond and two pi bonds
   (D) two sigma bonds and one pi bond
   (E) three ionic bonds

6. The hybridization of the terminal carbons in $H_2C{=}C{=}CH_2$ is
   (A) sp
   (B) sp^2
   (C) sp^3
   (D) sp^3d
   (E) sp^3d^2

7. According to molecular orbital theory, over-lap of two *s* atomic orbitals produces
   (A) one bonding molecular orbital and one hybrid orbital
   (B) two bonding molecular orbitals
   (C) two bonding molecular orbitals and two antibonding molecular orbitals
   (D) two bonding molecular orbitals and one antibonding molecular orbital
   (E) one bonding molecular orbital and one antibonding molecular orbital

8. The bond order of a homonuclear diatomic molecule can be decreased by
   (A) removing electrons from a bonding molecular orbital or adding electrons to an antibonding molecular orbital
   (B) adding electrons to a bonding molecular orbital or removing electrons from an antibonding molecular orbital
   (C) adding electrons to a molecular orbital
   (D) removing electrons from a molecular orbital
   (E) none of the above, because the bond order of a homonuclear diatomic molecule cannot be decreased by any means

9. Both a water molecule and a carbon dioxide molecule contain two atoms of the same element bonded to a central atom. Why is the water molecule bent and the carbon dioxide molecule linear?
   (A) All molecules that contain hydrogen are bent.
   (B) The oxygen atom in water contains two pairs of unbonded electrons that repel other electrons.
   (C) All molecules containing double bonds are linear.
   (D) The oxygen in water forms *sp* hybrid orbitals.
   (E) An electron domain formed by unbonded electrons is smaller than other electron domains.

10. Assume a second-row diatomic molecule, X_2, has a bond order of 2, a bond enthalpy of 620 kJ/mol, and a bond length of 1.31 Å. Element X is in the same period as element Z. If Z_2 has a bond order of 3, which of the following choices could describe the bond enthalpy and the bond length of Z_2?
    (A) 750 kJ/mol, 1.10 Å
    (B) 750 kJ/mol, 1.50 Å
    (C) 530 kJ/mol, 1.10 Å
    (D) 530 kJ/mol, 1.50 Å
    (E) There are no trends in bond length and bond enthalpy.

Free-Response Question

A molecule of ammonia, NH_3, and a molecule of methane, CH_4, each have four electron domains. Explain why the bond angles are different for these two molecules.

ANSWERS AND EXPLANATIONS

Multiple-Choice Questions

1. (B) is correct. The structure of SF_2 is determined by the arrangement of electrons around its central atom. Sulfur is an atom from group 6A, so initially it has six electrons. Two of these six electrons form bonds with fluorine atoms. The other four electrons form two pairs of unbonded electrons in the molecule.

Because these unbonded pairs of electrons repel each other as well as the bonded electrons, the molecule is bent.

▌ **2. (A) is correct.** The central iodine atom originally had seven valence electrons. After reacting with fluorine, single bonds exist between the iodine atom and five fluorine atoms, leaving the iodine atom with two of its initial electrons that are not bonded. Thus, the central iodine atom contains one unbonded pair of electrons and five bonded pairs of electrons that it shares with the fluorine atoms.

▌ **3. (E) is correct.** Because it is a noble gas, a xenon atom contains two valence electrons in an s orbital and six more electrons, two in each of three p orbitals, for a total of eight valence electrons. In the molecule, each fluorine atom shares one of its electrons with the xenon atom, so there are a total of twelve electrons around the xenon atom. These twelve electrons must fill six orbitals—one s, three p, and two d. Thus, the hybridization of the atom is sp^3d^2.

▌ **4. (B) is correct.** Paired electrons do not form chemical bonds with other atoms. When electrons are promoted, the electrons that were paired in an orbital become two unpaired electrons in two different orbitals, each of which is capable of bonding with another atom. The number of hybrid or atomic orbitals and the total number of electrons don't matter; the orbitals merely must contain the necessary number of unpaired electrons.

▌ **5. (C) is correct.** The first bond formed between two atoms will be a sigma bond that is formed by the overlapping of two s orbitals or of some combination of s orbitals, ends of p orbitals, or ends of hybrid orbitals. After the sigma bond forms, any other bond will be a pi bond, which is formed by the side-to-side overlap of p orbitals. Thus, in a triple bond, a sigma bond forms first, and the other two bonds must be pi bonds.

▌ **6. (B) is correct.** The terminal carbon atoms in this molecule have one single bond with each of two hydrogen atoms and a double bond with another carbon atom. Almost all single bonds that form are sigma bonds. A double bond contains one sigma bond and one pi bond. Sigma bonds can form from hybrid orbitals, but the pi bond is formed from side-by-side overlapping of p orbitals. Therefore, three of the four valence electrons of carbon form hybrid orbitals, leaving the other p valence electron to form the pi bond. After one electron is promoted from an s orbital to a p orbital, one of the three electrons that form hybrid orbitals is from the s orbital, and two are from p orbitals. Thus, sp^2 hybridization occurs.

▌ **7. (E) is correct.** Whenever two atomic orbitals overlap, two molecular orbitals form. One molecular orbital will be a bonding molecular orbital that results in electron density between the nuclei. The other molecular orbital will be an antibonding molecular orbital that results in electron density on opposite sides of the nuclei.

▌ **8. (A) is correct.** Bond order is calculated by taking half of the difference of the number of bonding electrons and the number of antibonding electrons; bond order = ½(number of bonding electrons − number of antibonding electrons). Using this equation, bond order can be made smaller in one of two ways; either decrease the number of bonding electrons or increase the number of antibonding electrons. Either change will make the difference in the number of bonding electrons and antibonding electrons smaller. Thus, bond order also decreases.

▍**9. (B) is correct.** The carbon atom in carbon dioxide is double bonded to two oxygen atoms. No electrons on the carbon atom are unbonded. In water, two of the six electrons from the oxygen atom are bonded to the two hydrogen atoms. The remaining four electrons are present as two unbonded pairs. These unbonded electrons repel each other and the bonded electrons, making the molecule bent.

▍**10. (A) is correct.** When bond order increases, an additional bond is added. A double bond (bond order = 2) is longer than a triple bond (bond order = 3). Because a triple bond is stronger than a double bond, it takes more energy to break a triple bond. Thus, the bond enthalpy is greater for a triple bond. The only answer in which bond length decreases and bond enthalpy increases is *A*.

Free-Response Question

Both molecules have four electron domains, so the basic arrangement of electron domains is the same. However, the central carbon atom in methane has a hydrogen atom bonded to each of its available electrons, so each electron domain in methane is identical, and all the angles between electron domains are equal. On the other hand, the central nitrogen atom in ammonia is bonded to only three hydrogen atoms. A pair of unbonded electrons on the nitrogen atom forms the fourth electron domain. Because an electron domain for a pair of unbonded electrons is larger than an electron domain for bonded electrons, the repulsion between unbonded and bonded electron domains in ammonia will be greater than the repulsion between the electron domains in methane. Thus, the bond angles in ammonia will be less than those in methane.

This response correctly refers to and describes electron domains of unbonded electrons and those of bonded electrons, and it contrasts them accurately. For each molecule listed, it describes what types of electron domains it contains and correctly applies this information to the determination of bond angles in the molecules.

CHAPTER 10

Gases

When studying the properties of different states of matter, the properties of gases are probably the most easily understood. Although different gases might have chemical properties that are quite varied, gases behave quite similarly as far as their physical properties are concerned.

Characteristics of Gases

- The components of the atmosphere are examples of substances that are gases under ordinary temperature and pressure. When substances that are liquids and solids under ordinary conditions exist in the gaseous state, they are called **vapors.**
- Gases are nonmetallic elements or compounds that are composed of non-metallic elements with simple molecular formulas and low molar masses. Because the individual molecules in gases are far apart, they expand to fill their containers and are also easily compressed.
- Gases form **homogeneous mixtures** with each other.

Pressure

- **Pressure** is a measured property of a gas that shows the amount of force that acts on a given area. Gases exert force on any surface with which they come in contact.

$$P = \frac{F}{A}$$

- The SI unit for pressure is the **pascal** (Pa). Pressure can also be measured in bars, torrs, mm Hg, or atmospheres (atm).

The Gas Laws

- The variables used to describe a gas are volume (V), pressure (P), temperature (T) and quantity, usually in moles (n). Equations that express the relationships among these quantities are **gas laws.**
- **Boyle's law** states that the volume of a fixed quantity of gas maintained at constant temperature is inversely proportional to the pressure: $PV = $ **constant.**
- **Charles's law** states that the volume of a fixed amount of gas maintained at constant pressure is directly proportional to its absolute temperature: $V = $ **constant** $\times T.$
- **Avogadro's hypothesis** states that equal volumes of gases at the same temperature and pressure contain the same number of molecules.

- **Avogadro's law,** or the law of combining volumes, states that the volume of a gas maintained at constant temperature and pressure is directly proportional to the number of moles of the gas: $V = \textbf{constant} \times \textbf{\textit{n}}.$

The Ideal-Gas Equation

- By relating the gas laws and putting in a proportionality constant (R), one can form the **ideal-gas equation: $PV = nRT.$** An **ideal gas** is a hypothetical gas whose pressure, volume, and temperature behavior is described completely by the ideal-gas equation.
- The ideal-gas equation can be used to solve problems related to gases in chemical reactions.
- The gas law equations can be derived from the ideal-gas equation by recognizing what varies and what is constant. For example, Charles's law assumes pressure and temperature change, and it assumes that volume and amount of gas are constant. Because R is a constant also, the term nR/P is a constant. Therefore, $V/T =$ constant. If the volume or temperature changes for a certain sample of gas at constant pressure, the proportion $V_1/T_1 = V_2/T_2$ can be used to determine any of the four variables if the other three variables are known. Similar equations can be derived from the ideal-gas equation for the other gas laws.
- The value of R depends on the units of P, V, n, and T that are used. The most commonly used values for R are 0.0821 L-atm/mol-K and 8.314 J/mol-K.
- **Standard temperature and pressure (STP)** are 273 K (0°C) and 1 atm. Many properties of gases are tabulated for these conditions.
- **Molar volume** is the volume occupied by 1 mol of an ideal gas at STP. The molar volume of any ideal gas is 22.41 L.

Further Applications of the Ideal-Gas Equation

- The ideal-gas equation can be used to calculate density. Density is expressed as mass per unit volume, $D = m/V.$

  1. The ideal-gas equation can be arranged to obtain moles per unit volume as $n/V = P/RT.$
  2. Because n is in units of moles, multiplying n by the molar mass, M, in g/mol provides the mass of the gas. Because the left side of the equation was multiplied by M, the right side must be multiplied by M also; $nM/V = PM/RT$, so $m/V = PM/RT.$
  3. The left side of the equation is now m/V, which is density. Thus, the equation can be written as $d = \textbf{PM/RT}.$

- This equation can be rearranged to solve for molar mass: $M = \textbf{dRT/P}.$
- Stoichiometric relationships can be used to find information about chemical reactions that involve gases. Because gases are affected by pressure and temperature, conditions of temperature and pressure for the reaction must be stated.

1. If mass or volume of a gas is provided, the number of moles at STP can be determined by dividing by molar mass or molar volume. If the conditions given are other than STP, first change the given information to what it would be at STP.

2. Once the number of moles of one gas is determined, the mole ratios in a balanced chemical equation can be used to determine the corresponding number of moles of another substance in the reaction.

3. From this number of moles, mass or volume of a gas can be determined by multiplying by molar mass or molar volume. If necessary, change the volume at STP to what it would be under the given conditions.

Gas Mixtures and Partial Pressures

▌ **Dalton's law of partial pressures** is based on the fact that when two gases are mixed together, the gas particles of each gas tend to act independently of each other.

▌ Dalton's law states that for a mixture of gases, the total pressure is equal to the sum of the pressures that all the components of the mixture would exert if they were alone and not part of the mixture. For each gas, this pressure is the **partial pressure,** and it equals the mole fraction of the gas times the total pressure; $P_1 = X_1 P_t$. The mole fraction, X, is the ratio of moles of one component to the total moles of the mixture, $\dfrac{n_1}{n_t}$.

▌ When calculating a quantity of gas that has been collected over water, the partial pressure of water vapor in the gas mixture must be subtracted from the total pressure.

▌ As with other pressures, partial pressure depends on the temperature.

Kinetic-Molecular Theory

▌ The **kinetic-molecular theory** explains the properties of gases and gas mixtures.

1. Gases consist of large numbers of particles in continuous, random motion.
2. The volume of an individual gas particle is not considered to be a factor in describing the behavior of the gas.
3. Attractive and repulsive forces between gas molecules are negligible, so they are not considered in explanations or calculations regarding gases.
4. Energy can be transferred between molecules during collisions, but the average kinetic energy of the molecules does not change with time, as long as the temperature of the gas remains constant.
5. The average kinetic energy of the molecules is proportional to Kelvin temperature. At any given temperature, the molecules of all gases have the same average kinetic energy.

▌ The kinetic-molecular theory can be used to explain the gas laws. Two examples follow, and similar explanations can be derived for the other gas laws.

- For Boyle's law, if temperature remains constant and volume is increased, the gas particles move at the same speed, but they have farther to go before undergoing a collision. Fewer collisions mean lower pressure.
- For Charles's law, as temperature increases, the speed of the particles increases. If pressure is to remain constant, the number of collisions must remain constant. Because the particles are moving faster, volume must increase so that the particles have farther to move before they undergo collisions, keeping the number of collisions constant.

Molecular Effusion and Diffusion

- Molecular speed affects **effusion** (the escape of gas through a tiny hole in a container) and **diffusion** (the spread of a gas through space or another substance). **Graham's law** states that the effusion rate of a gas is inversely proportional to the square root of its molar mass; $\frac{r_1}{r_2} = \sqrt{\frac{M_2}{M_1}}$. The rate of effusion is faster for lightweight molecules than for heavy ones.
- Calculations of diffusion rates can be approximated by Graham's law, but molecule collisions cause variances in the calculations. The average distance traveled by a molecule between collisions is the **mean free path.** The mean free path for air molecules at sea level is about 60 nm (6×10^{-6} cm).

Real Gases: Deviations from Ideal Behavior

- **Real gases** are gases whose behavior deviates from ideal-gas behavior.
- Real gases at low pressure approximate the properties of ideal gases. Real gases at high pressures deviate considerably from ideal behavior.
- As temperature increases, properties of real gases more closely match those of ideal gases. Differences become pronounced when temperature decreases, and they become significant at about the temperature at which the gas changes into a liquid.
- These deviations occur because real gases have molecules with volume and with some attraction to each other. As pressure increases, molecules must crowd together in less space, and attractions and repulsions become stronger. Similarly, high temperatures increase the kinetic energy so that the attraction between gas particles is less.
- The **van der Waals equation** modifies the ideal-gas equation so that it approximates real-gas behavior. This equation uses the term nb to correct for the volume of real gas molecules and the term n^2a/V^2 to correct for molecular attraction.

$$\left(P + \frac{n^2a}{V^2}\right)(V - nb) = nRT$$

For Additional Review

List five compounds that are gases at room temperature. For each gas, provide its name, its formula, and its characteristics.

Multiple-Choice Questions

1. Which of the following statements about gases is NOT true?
   (A) Gases are highly compressible.
   (B) Distances between molecules of gas are very large compared to bond distances within molecules.
   (C) Non-reacting gas mixtures are homogenous.
   (D) Gases expand spontaneously to fill the containers in which they are placed.
   (E) All gases are colorless and odorless at room temperature.

2. A gas sample at constant temperature has a volume of 250 mL at 3.50 atm. What volume will the sample occupy if the pressure is changed to 1.55 atm?
   (A) 111 mL
   (B) 217 mL
   (C) 565 mL
   (D) 1.36 L
   (E) 5.65 L

3. A sealed balloon will break if its volume reaches 4.50 L. At 20°C, the volume of the balloon is 3.79 L. At what temperature will the balloon break if the pressure stays the same?
   (A) 17°C
   (B) 24°C
   (C) 26°C
   (D) 51°C
   (E) 75°C

4. How many moles of a gas occupy 2.67 L at 2.3 atm and 25°C?
   (A) 2.5×10^{-3} mol
   (B) 0.030 mol
   (C) 0.25 mol
   (D) 3.0 mol
   (E) 4.0 mol

5. A 2.35-mol sample of He gas occupies 57.9 L at 300.0 K and 1.00 atm. What is the volume of this sample at 423 K and 2.00 atm?
   (A) 20.5 L
   (B) 40.8 L
   (C) 81.6 L
   (D) 82.1 L
   (E) 163 L

6. For which of the following changes is it unclear whether the volume of a particular sample of an ideal gas will increase or decrease?
   (A) Increase the temperature, and increase the pressure.
   (B) Increase the temperature, and decrease the pressure.
   (C) Increase the temperature, and keep the pressure constant.
   (D) Keep temperature constant, and decrease the pressure.
   (E) Decrease the temperature, and increase the pressure.

7. What is the density of a sample of nitrogen gas, N_2, at 1.50 atm and 17°C?
   (A) 0.566 g/mL
   (B) 1.77 g/mL
   (C) 0.566 g/L
   (D) 1.77 g/L
   (E) 30.1 g/L

8. A 4.22-g sample of CuS was added to excess HCl, and the resulting H_2S was collected over water. What volume of H_2S was collected at 32°C when the atmospheric pressure was 749 torr (1 atm = 760 torr)? The vapor pressure of water at this temperature is 36 torr.
   (A) 850 L
   (B) 0.124 L
   (C) 0.587 L
   (D) 1.18 L
   (E) 1.55×10^{-3} L

9. Which of the following gases would have the highest average molecular speed at 25°C?
   (A) O_2
   (B) N_2
   (C) CO_2
   (D) CH_4
   (E) SF_6

10. In the van der Waals equation, the constants a and b are
    (A) used to correct for the finite volume of gas molecules and the attractive forces between gas molecules
    (B) equal to each other for any real gas
    (C) used to correct for the difference between Celsius and Kelvin
    (D) equal to 1 for ideal gases
    (E) used to correct for the fact that collisions of gas molecules are not really completely elastic

Free-Response Question

A gaseous mixture made from 6.00 g of O_2 and 9.00 g of CH_4 is placed in a 15.0-L vessel at 0°C. What is the partial pressure of each gas, and what is the total pressure in the vessel?

ANSWERS AND EXPLANATIONS

Multiple-Choice Questions

▌ **1. (E) is correct.** A gas has no definite volume, so it can be compressed, or it will expand. Most of a gas is empty space, and gas mixtures are evenly mixed on the molecular level if the gases don't react with each other. However, some gases, such as chlorine, are colored, and some gases, such as hydrogen sulfide, have distinct odors.

▌ **2. (C) is correct.** Because it relates pressure and volume when the amount of gas and the temperature are constant, this problem is an application of Boyle's law. Pressure and volume are inversely related, so $P_1V_1 = P_2V_2$ relates pressure and volume for the same sample of gas at constant temperature. In this case, the initial pressure, initial volume, and final pressure are known; 3.50 atm $\times$ 250 mL = 1.55 atm $\times$ V_2. Dividing both sides of the equation by 1.55 atm shows that the final volume equals 565 mL.

▌ **3. (E) is correct.** Because it relates temperature and volume when the amount of gas and the pressure are constant, this problem is an application of Charles's law. Kelvin temperature and volume are directly related, so $\dfrac{T_1}{V_1} = \dfrac{T_2}{V_2}$ relates Kelvin temperature and volume for the same sample of gas at constant pressure. In this case, initial temperature, initial volume, and final volume are known; $\dfrac{(20 + 273)\,K}{3.79\,L} = \dfrac{T_2}{4.50\,L}$. Multiplying both sides of the equation by 4.50 L shows that the final temperature is 348 K, which equals $(348 - 273)$°C, or 75°C.

▌ **4. (C) is correct.** The equation $PV = nRT$ can be used to find n if pressure, volume, and temperature are known. Substituting the given information into the equation, 2.3 atm $\times$ 2.67 L = n $\times$ 0.0821 L-atm/mol-K $\times$ (25 + 273) K. Dividing both sides of the equation by the values of R and T, the amount of gas is 0.25 mol.

▌ **5. (B) is correct.** From one set of conditions to another, the amount of gas stays the same. In other words, in the equation $PV = nRT$, nR is the same constant for both sets of conditions. Because $\frac{P_1V_1}{T_1}$ equals a constant, and $\frac{P_2V_2}{T_2}$ equals the same constant, $\frac{P_1V_1}{T_1} = \frac{P_2V_2}{T_2}$. Substituting the known values into the equation, $\frac{1.00 \text{ atm} \times 57.9 \text{ L}}{300.0 \text{ K}} = \frac{2.00 \text{ atm} \times V_2}{423 \text{ K}}$. Multiplying both sides of the equation by 423 K and dividing by 2.00 atm shows that the final volume is 40.8 L.

▌ **6. (A) is correct.** Because volume and temperature are directly related, if one variable decreases or increases, the other variable follows the same pattern. Because volume and pressure are inversely related, if one variable decreases or increases, the other variable follows the opposite pattern. In answers B, C, and D, the changing conditions favor increasing volume. The changes in answer E favor decreasing volume. Answer A has one change that favors increasing volume and one change that favors decreasing volume. Without knowing the magnitude of the changes, you cannot predict whether the volume will increase or decrease.

▌ **7. (D) is correct.** The density of a gas under specified conditions can be determined by using the equation $D = PM/RT$. The molar mass of nitrogen gas is 28.02 g/mol. Substituting the known quantities into the equation, $D = 1.50 \text{ atm} \times 28.02 \text{ g/mol}/[0.0821 \text{ L-atm/mol-K} \times (17 + 273) \text{ K}]$. The density of the gas is 1.77 g/L.

▌ **8. (D) is correct.** Because 4.22 g CuS reacts, 4.22 g/95.62 g/mol, or 0.0441 mol CuS reacts. The balanced chemical equation for the reaction is $CuS + 2HCl \rightarrow H_2S + CuCl_2$.
From the equation, CuS and H_2S have a mole ratio of 1 : 1. Therefore, 0.0441 mol H_2S is produced.
The pressure of this gas is (749 torr − 36 torr) $\times$ 1 atm/760 torr, or 0.938 atm. Temperature is (32 + 273) K, or 305 K. Substituting all this information into the equation $PV = nRT$ gives 0.938 atm $\times$ V = 0.0441 mol $\times$ 0.0821 L-atm/mol-K $\times$ 305 K.
Dividing both sides of the equation by 0.938 atm to solve for V shows that V = 1.18 L.

▌ **9. (D) is correct.** Graham's law shows that a gas with a smaller molar mass will effuse faster than a gas with a larger molar mass, and rate of effusion reflects average molecular speed. Thus, the lightest of the listed gases will have the highest speed. The gases listed have molar masses of 32.00 g/mol, 28.02 g/mol, 44.02 g/mol, 16.06 g/mol, and 146.07 g/mol, respectively, so CH_4 has the lowest molar mass and will have the highest average molecular speed. Temperature is immaterial as long as all of the gases remain gases and the temperature is the same for all of them.

▌ **10. (A) is correct.** The complete term that is used to correct for molecular attraction is n^2a/V^2, and a is the only constant used in this term. The complete term that is used to correct for the volume of real gas molecules is nb, and b is the only constant in this term. The constants a and b are not necessarily equal to each other or to 1. They do not adjust temperature or elasticity.

Free-Response Question

The amount of O_2 present is 6.00 g/32.00 g/mol, or 0.188 mol. The amount of CH_4 present is 9.00 g/16.05 g/mol, or 0.561 mol. The total number of moles of gas present is 0.749 mol. Substituting the known information into the equation $PV = nRT$ gives $P \times 15.0$ L = 0.749 mol $\times$ 0.0821 L-atm/mol-K − 273 K. Dividing both sides of the equation by 15.0 L to solve for P results in $P = 1.12$ atm for the total pressure. P_{O_2} equals 1.12 atm $\times$ 0.188 mol/0.749 mol, or 0.281 atm. P_{CH_4} equals 1.12 atm $\times$ 0.561 mol/0.749 mol, or 0.839 atm.

This response correctly calculates the number of moles of each gas present and the total number of moles. It recognizes what equation to use, based on information given and asked for. The total pressure is accurately calculated. Mole fractions are calculated and then used to find partial pressures.

CHAPTER 11

Intermolecular Forces, Liquids, and Solids

One of the major assumptions of the study of ideal gases is that gas particles have no attraction for each other. However, physical properties of liquids and solids depend largely on forces that exist between molecules—**intermolecular forces.**

A Molecular Comparison of Liquids and Solids

▮ In **liquids,** attractive forces are strong enough to hold molecules close together. Thus, every liquid has a definite volume that is independent of the size of its container. However, molecules in a liquid can move past each other, so a liquid takes the shape of its container.

▮ In **solids,** the intermolecular attractive forces are stronger—strong enough not only to hold molecules close together, but also to lock them in place.

▮ Solids and liquids are called **condensed phases** because their particles are fairly close together compared with those of a gas.

Intermolecular Forces

▮ The **strengths of intermolecular forces** of different substances vary over a wide range. Most intermolecular attractions are much weaker than ionic or covalent bonds. Less energy is required to vaporize a liquid or to melt a solid than to break covalent bonds in molecules.

▮ Many properties of liquids, including their boiling points and melting points, reflect the strengths of intermolecular forces. The molecules of a liquid must overcome attractive forces to separate and form a vapor, and the molecules of a solid must overcome attractive forces to slide past each other when the solid melts. The stronger the attractive forces, the higher is the temperature at which the liquid boils or melts.

▮ There are three types of intermolecular attractive forces (also called **van der Waals forces**) between neutral molecules: dipole-dipole forces, London dispersion forces, and hydrogen-bonding forces. A fourth attractive force, the ion-dipole, is important in solutions.

▮ All four forces are **electrostatic** because they involve attractions between positive and negative poles.

▮ Polar molecules are dipoles. An **ion-dipole force** exists between an ion and the oppositely charged end of a polar molecule. Ion-dipole forces exist in solutions of ionic substances in polar liquids, such as a solution of NaCl in water.

- **Dipole-dipole forces** are attractions between positive and negative ends of polar molecules. They are effective only when polar molecules are very close together, and, in general, they are weaker than ion-dipole forces. Molecules with smaller volumes have higher dipole-dipole forces because they are freer to move.
- Because electrons repel one another, the motions of an electron may influence its near neighbors, causing a temporary dipole. The attraction of temporary dipoles for each other is called the **London dispersion force.** As with permanent dipole-dipole forces, this force is significant only when molecules are very close together. London dispersion forces operate among all molecules.
- **Polarizability** is a measure of the ease with which an external electrical field can distort the charge distribution in a molecule. The strength of London dispersion forces tends to increase with increasing molecular size because there are more electrons and because they are farther from the nucleus, increasing polarizability. Molecular shape also affects the strength of the force.
- **Hydrogen bonding** is a special type of intermolecular attraction between a hydrogen atom in a polar bond and an unshared electron pair on a nearby small, highly electronegative ion or atom (usually an F, O, or N atom on another molecule). Hydrogen bonds are stronger than the other attractive forces previously described.

Some Properties of Liquids

- **Viscosity** is the resistance of a liquid to flow. Viscosity depends on the attractive forces between molecules and on whether structural features exist that cause the molecules to become entangled. The stronger the intermolecular forces, the greater the viscosity.
- **Surface tension** is a measure of the inward forces that must be overcome in order to expand the surface area of a liquid. Surface tension is the energy (measured in joules per area) required to increase the surface area of a liquid by a unit amount.
- Intermolecular forces that bind similar molecules to one another are called **cohesive forces.** Intermolecular forces that bind a substance to a surface are called **adhesive forces.**

Phase Changes

- Changes from one state of matter to another are **phase changes.** Every phase change is accompanied by a change in the energy of the system, as summarized in the following figure.

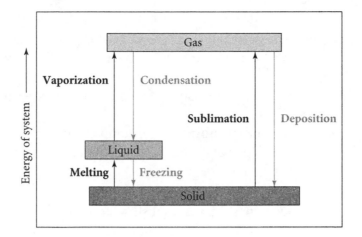

- The increased freedom of motion of the molecules or ions when melting occurs is measured by the **heat of fusion,** or enthalpy of fusion, ΔH_{fus}. The energy required for vaporization is the **heat of vaporization,** or enthalpy of vaporization, ΔH_{vap}.
- The molecules of a solid can also change directly to a gaseous state. The enthalpy change required for this transition is called the **heat of sublimation.**
- A **heating curve** graphs the temperature of the system versus the amount of heat added. Note on the following figure that added heat increases the temperature of a consistent state of matter. When that state changes to another state, any energy change goes into changing the amount of molecular motion, and the temperature does not change during the change of state.

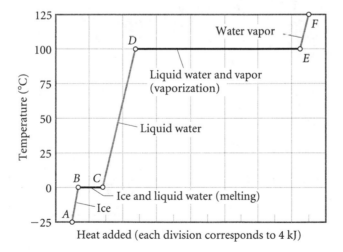

- Pressure applied to a gas can cause it to liquefy. The amount of pressure necessary depends on the temperature. The highest temperature at which a distinct liquid phase can form is referred to as the **critical temperature.** The **critical pressure** is the pressure required to bring about liquefaction at this critical temperature.

Vapor Pressure

▊ The **vapor pressure** of a liquid is the partial pressure exerted by its vapor when the liquid and vapor states are in dynamic equilibrium. In **dynamic equilibrium,** the rates of change from liquid to vapor and back again are equal.

▊ The higher the vapor pressure of a liquid, the more easily it evaporates and the more volatile it is.

▊ The **normal boiling point** is the temperature at which the vapor pressure equals 1 atm. Vapor pressure equals external pressure when boiling occurs.

Phase Diagrams

▊ A **phase diagram** is a graph that shows the conditions needed for equilibrium to exist between the different states of matter. Its axes are temperature and pressure. Phase diagrams show whether a substance is stable at any given temperature and pressure.

▊ The following general phase diagram shows phases and phase changes and how they are affected by temperature and pressure. For example, suppose a manufacturing process requires that the substance for which the phase diagram is drawn boils at 124°C. Go vertically from this temperature on the horizontal axis to line AB, the line that indicates boiling point. Then go horizontally from this point to the pressure on the vertical axis. This pressure is required for the substance to boil at 124°C.

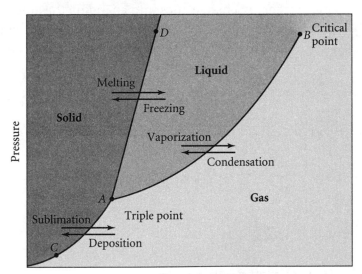

▊ The temperature at the **critical point** is the critical temperature, and the pressure at this point is the critical pressure.

▊ At the **triple point,** all three phases are in equilibrium. Any other point on a curve represents equilibrium between two phases.

Structures of Solids

▌ In a **crystalline solid,** particles are arranged in a repeating pattern. The repeating unit in a crystalline solid is a **unit cell.** The three-dimensional structure of a crystalline solid is its **crystal lattice.**

▌ The simplest unit cells in a lattice are cubic. **Primitive cubic** cells have lattice points at the corners only. **Body-centered cubic** cells also have a lattice point at the center of the unit cell. **Face-centered cubic** cells have lattice points at the center of each face, as well as at each corner.

▌ An **amorphous solid,** such as rubber or glass, is a solid whose particles have no orderly structure. The intermolecular forces in an amorphous solid vary in strength throughout the sample. Amorphous solids do not melt at a specific temperature.

▌ Many solids, including crystalline solids and metals, have a **close-packed structure.** Spherical particles are arranged in the minimal amount of space. This arrangement maximizes attraction between particles.

Bonding in Solids

▌ The physical properties of crystalline solids depend on the arrangement of particles and on the attractive forces between them.

▌ Intermolecular forces hold molecular solids together. Because these forces are weak, molecular solids are soft and have low melting points.

▌ **Covalent-network solids** are held together in large networks or chains by covalent bonds. Because these bonds are much stronger than intermolecular forces, these solids are hard and have high melting points.

▌ Hard and brittle **ionic solids** are held together by ionic bonds.

▌ **Metallic solids** consist entirely of metal cations surrounded by delocalized electrons. Metals vary greatly in the strength of their bonding, based on the number of available electrons.

For Additional Review

Make a flow chart that relates different types of molecules and the types of intermolecular forces they experience.

Multiple-Choice Questions

1. Of the following substances, which has London dispersion forces as the only intermolecular force?
   (A) CH_3OH
   (B) NH_3
   (C) H_2S
   (D) Kr
   (E) HCl

2. Which of the following are particularly polarizable?
   (A) Small molecules
   (B) Large molecules
   (C) Water molecules
   (D) Ionic compounds
   (E) Molecules with low molar masses

3. Large intermolecular forces in a substance are manifested by
   (A) low vapor pressure
   (B) high boiling point
   (C) high heats of fusion and vaporization
   (D) high critical temperatures and pressures
   (E) all of the above

4. Viscosity is
   (A) the "skin" on a liquid caused by intermolecular attraction
   (B) the resistance to flow
   (C) the same as density
   (D) inversely proportional to molar mass
   (E) unaffected by temperature

5. In a recycling plant, aluminum cans are heated to the melting point of aluminum, which is 660.37°C. The temperature is measured again when half of the aluminum is melted. What is the temperature at this point?
   (A) <660.37°C
   (B) 660.37°C
   (C) >660.37°C
   (D) The temperature depends on the pressure.
   (E) The temperature of the liquid is greater than the temperature of the solid.

Use the following diagram to answer questions 6 and 7.

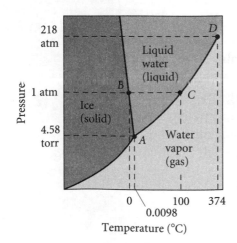

6. In what phase does water exist when the temperature is 50°C and the pressure is 100 atm?
   (A) Solid
   (B) Liquid
   (C) Gas
   (D) Gas and liquid in equilibrium
   (E) Liquid and solid in equilibrium

7. What is the pressure when water is at its triple point?
   (A) 4.58 torr
   (B) 0.0098 atm
   (C) 1 atm
   (D) 100 atm
   (E) 218 atm

8. On a phase diagram, the critical pressure is
   (A) the pressure required to melt a solid
   (B) the pressure below which a substance is a solid at all temperatures
   (C) the pressure above which a substance is a liquid at all temperatures
   (D) the pressure at the triple point
   (E) the pressure required to liquefy a gas at its critical temperature

9. Charcoal is an amorphous form of solid carbon. The structure of charcoal is
   (A) a primitive cubic cell
   (B) a covalent-network solid
   (C) a body-centered cubic cell
   (D) a metallic crystal
   (E) random carbon atoms

10. Which solids are characterized by low melting point, softness, and low electrical conductivity?
    (A) Ionic solids
    (B) Molecular solids
    (C) Metallic solids
    (D) Covalent-network solids
    (E) Both ionic and molecular solids

Free-Response Question

> List the substances $BaCl_2$, H_2, CO, HF, and Ne *in order of increasing boiling points. Justify your choices.*

ANSWERS AND EXPLANATIONS

Multiple-Choice Questions

▌ **1. (D) is correct.** Answers *A, B, C,* and *E* are polar molecules, so they will experience dipole-dipole forces. HCl also experiences hydrogen bonding. All experience London dispersion forces, but only Kr experiences only this force.

▌ **2. (B) is correct.** In general, larger molecules tend to have greater polarizabilities, because they have a greater number of electrons and their electrons are farther from the nuclei. Water molecules are already polar, and ionic compounds do not exist as molecules. Molecules with low molar masses are usually smaller molecules.

▌ **3. (E) is correct.** When a compound has large intermolecular forces between molecules, the molecules are held more tightly than they would be if the forces were weaker. Thus, few vapor particles form because the molecules are held more tightly to the liquid. Because vapor pressure is low, the boiling point must be high because much energy must be added to the liquid to make the vapor pressure equal to external pressure. Similar explanations show that the compounds have high heats of fusion and vaporization and high critical temperatures and pressures.

▌ **4. (B) is correct.** Viscosity is the resistance to flow. The "skin" on a liquid is surface tension. Although viscous liquids might be dense, there is no direct relationship between viscosity and density. Larger molecules, which usually have higher molar mass, are more viscous, so the relationship is direct, not inverse. Because of increased molecular movement, increased temperature decreases viscosity.

▌ **5. (B) is correct.** During a change of state, as is seen on a heating curve, added energy increases the speed of molecules so that they can overcome intermolecular forces. During this change, temperature does not change.

▌ **6. (B) is correct.** Although the axes are not to scale, approximations of the given temperature and pressure result in a point that is in the liquid part of the diagram.

▌ **7. (A) is correct.** The triple point of water is at point A, which is the point at which solid, liquid, and gas are in equilibrium. From the diagram, the pressure at this point is 4.58 torr.

▌ **8. (E) is correct.** The critical pressure is defined as the pressure required to liquefy a gas at its critical temperature. On the diagram for questions 6 and 7, the critical point, which occurs at the critical temperature and the critical pressure, is at point D. Depending on the temperature, melting can occur at many different pressures. Above critical pressure, liquid and gas cannot be distinguished from each other.

9. (E) is correct. The molecules in an amorphous solid have no particular order. They form no crystals at all.

10. (B) is correct. All of these properties are characteristic of compounds that have little attraction between molecules. Ionic, covalent, and metallic bonds are relatively strong forces, so compounds with these forces do not have these characteristics. Among the given answers, only molecular solids have particles that are held together by the much weaker intermolecular forces.

Free-Response Question

The boiling point depends in part on the attractive forces in the liquid. The substances should be ordered according to the relative strengths of the different kinds of forces. The attractive forces are stronger for ionic substances than for molecular ones, so $BaCl_2$ should have the highest boiling point. The intermolecular forces of the remaining substances depend on molecular mass, polarity, and hydrogen bonding. The molecular masses are H_2 (2), CO (28), HF (20), and Ne (20). The boiling point of H_2 should be the lowest because it is nonpolar, has only London dispersion forces, and has the lowest molecular mass. The molecular masses of CO, HF, and Ne are roughly the same. However, HF can hydrogen bond, so it should have the highest boiling point of the three. Next is CO, which is slightly polar, which means it has dipole-dipole forces and has a molecular weight higher than that of Ne. Thus, the predicted order of boiling points is $H_2 < Ne < CO < HF < BaCl_2$.

This response correctly relates attractive forces to boiling point. Each substance is evaluated as to what type of attractive force it contains, and the effect of the attractive force on boiling point is evaluated. The final answer correctly orders the substances according to increasing strength of forces and to increasing boiling point.

Modern Materials

The information presented in Chapter 12 is not tested on the AP Chemistry Examination.

CHAPTER 13

Properties of Solutions

Homogeneous mixtures, in which particles on the molecular level are mixed uniformly throughout, are also called **solutions.** The substances that make up a solution are its **components.** The **solvent** is generally the component present in the greatest amount. The **solutes** are the other components.

The Solution Process

▌ Solutions form when the attractive forces between solute and solvent particles are at least as great as those that exist between the solute particles themselves or between solvent particles themselves.

▌ Ionic and polar covalent compounds will enter solution when polar solvent molecules attract oppositely charged parts of the ionic crystal or the polar molecule. The ionic crystal dissociates, forming ions in solution. Sometimes, polar molecules move intact from the solute, and sometimes they ionize.

▌ An energy change occurs during the solution process, and formation of a solution can be either endothermic or exothermic, as shown in the following figure.

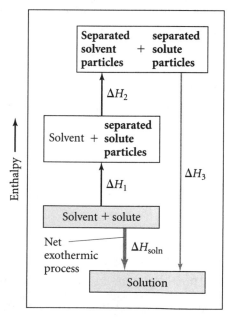

Exothermic ($\Delta H_{soln} < 0$)

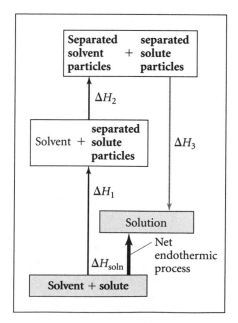

Endothermic ($\Delta H_{soln} > 0$)

▌ Formation of a homogeneous solution increases disorder or randomness, because the molecules of each substance are now mixed and distributed in a larger volume. The amount of disorder in the system is measured by a quantity called **entropy.**

Saturated Solutions and Solubility

▐ As the concentration of solute in solvent increases, a point is reached in which the solvent contains all of a solute it will hold at that temperature. At that point, if the solute is solid, a dynamic equilibrium exists between solution and crystallization. For every solute particle that enters solution, a solute particle deposits on the crystal. A solution in which no overall increase in concentration can occur at that temperature is said to be **saturated.**

▐ The amount of solute needed to form a saturated solution in a given quantity of solvent at a specified temperature is the **solubility** of that solute.

▐ If less solute than is needed to form a saturated solution is present, the solution is **unsaturated.** When a solution contains a greater amount of solute than it normally could hold at that temperature, the solution is **supersaturated.**

Factors Affecting Solubility

▐ The extent to which one substance dissolves in another depends on the nature of the solute and the solvent. Stronger attractions between solute and solvent molecules result in greater solubility.

▐ When the solute is liquid, favorable dipole-dipole attractions between solvent and solute mean that polar liquids tend to dissolve readily in polar solutions; that is, the liquids are **miscible.** Nonpolar liquids are **immiscible** because they tend to be insoluble in polar liquids.

▐ A change in pressure doesn't noticeably affect the solubilities of solid and liquid solutes. However, the solubility of a gas in any solvent is increased in proportion to an increase in pressure over the solvent.

▐ The relationship between the pressure and the solubility of a gas is expressed by a simple equation known as **Henry's law:** $S_g = kP_g$. S_g is the solubility of gas in solution phase. P_g stands for the partial pressure, and k is a proportional constant.

▐ The solubility of most solid solutes in water increases as the temperature of the solution increases. However, the opposite is true for gaseous solutes.

Ways of Expressing Concentration

▐ A solution with relatively small concentration of solute is a **dilute** solution; one with a large concentration is a **concentrated** solution.

▐ There are several mathematical representations of concentration that are based on mass.

  1. **Mass percent** = (mass of solute/total mass of solution) $\times$ 100
  2. **Parts per million (ppm)** = (mass of solute/total mass of solution) $\times 10^6$
  3. **Parts per billion (ppb)** = (mass of solute/total mass of solution) $\times 10^9$

▐ Concentration expressions are often based on the number of moles of one or more components of the solution.

  1. **Mole fraction** (X_{solute}) of component = moles of component/total moles of all components
  2. **Molarity** (M) = moles of solute/liters of solution
  3. **Molality** (m) = moles of solute/kilograms of solvent

■ Units of concentration can be changed from one to another by using concepts such as molar mass and density.

Colligative Properties

■ The physical properties of a solvent change when nonvolatile solutes are added to form a solution. Properties of a solution that depend on the collective concentration of the solution are **colligative properties.** Changes in freezing and boiling points and vapor and osmotic pressures are colligative properties.

■ Adding a nonvolatile solute to a solvent always lowers the vapor pressure. The amount that the pressure of the solvent is lowered is proportional to the concentration of the solute. **Raoult's law** states that, for an ideal solution, the partial pressure a solvent exerts above a solution (P_A) equals the product of the mole fraction of that solvent in the solution (X_A) times the vapor pressure of pure solvent (P_A°), or $P_A = X_A P_A^\circ$.

■ Boiling occurs when vapor pressure equals external pressure. If adding a nonvolatile solute lowers vapor pressure, the temperature of the solvent must be greater to reach the vapor pressure required for boiling. Thus, the boiling point of such a solution is greater than the boiling point of the pure solvent.

■ The amount that the boiling point is elevated depends on the amount of solute added. The number of moles of particles added per moles of solvent can be used with a **molal boiling-point-elevation** constant to determine the amount the boiling point is raised. Note that one mole of solute added does not necessarily mean that one mole of particles is added. For example, CH_3OH remains a molecule in solution, so one mole of the compound produces one mole of particles. However, one mole of $BaCl_2$ produces three moles of ions. Adding one mole of $BaCl_2$ raises the boiling point of a solution three times as much as adding one mole of CH_3OH to the same amount of solvent.

■ The effect on freezing point of adding a nonvolatile solute to a solvent is similar to the effect on boiling point, except that freezing point is lowered instead of elevated. In a similar manner, the number of moles of particles, along with the **molal freezing-point-depression** constant, can be used to determine the freezing point of a solution compared to that of the pure solvent. The following table lists normal boiling and freezing points for some common solvents and also the molal boiling-point-elevation and freezing-point-depression constants.

MOLAL BOILING-POINT-ELEVATION AND FREEZING-POINT-DEPRESSION CONSTANTS				
Solvent	Normal Boiling Point (°C)	K_b (°C/m)	Normal Freezing Point (°C)	K_f (°C/m)
Water, H_2O	100.0	0.51	0.0	1.86
Benzene, C_6H_6	80.1	2.53	5.5	5.12
Ethanol, C_2H_5OH	78.4	1.22	−114.6	1.99
Carbon tetrachloride, CCl_4	76.8	5.02	−22.3	29.8
Chloroform, $CHCl_3$	61.2	3.63	−63.5	4.68

■ In the process of **osmosis**, some portions of a solution move through tiny pores in a membrane. Often the solvent can pass through the membrane, but the solute cannot. In this case, the membrane is **semipermeable**, and the net movement of solvent is always toward the solution of higher concentration. The amount of pressure required to stop osmosis is the **osmotic pressure** of the solution. Osmotic pressure is a colligative property because it depends on the concentration of solute in the solvent.

For Additional Review

Diagram the calculations of molality and molarity when given the mass of the solute, the mass of the solvent, and the density of the solution.

Multiple-Choice Questions

1. Assume the solubility of solute A at 25°C is 2.54 g/100 mL H_2O. If a water solution contains 53.5 g solute A in 2.00 L water, what type of solution is it?
   (A) Unsaturated
   (B) Saturated
   (C) Supersaturated
   (D) Colligative
   (E) It is not possible to have such a solution.

2. In liquids, pressure has an appreciable effect on the solubility of
   (A) gases only
   (B) solids only
   (C) liquids only
   (D) salts only
   (E) solids and liquids

3. A saturated solution of a solid solute at 25°C is warmed to 40°C. What is the most likely type of solution present now?
   (A) Unsaturated
   (B) Saturated
   (C) Supersaturated
   (D) Miscible
   (E) Immiscible

4. What is the molarity of HCl in a solution prepared by dissolving 5.5 g of HCl in 200 g of C_2H_6O? The density of the solution is 0.79 g/mL.
   (A) 61 M
   (B) 0.93 M
   (C) 0.58 M
   (D) $6.0 \times 10^{-4} M$
   (E) 1.72 M

5. A 23.9-g sample of silver nitrate is dissolved in 342 g of water. What is the mass percent of silver nitrate in the solution?
   (A) 1.43%
   (B) 6.53%
   (C) 6.99%
   (D) 7.51%
   (E) 14.3%

6. A 124-g sample of KCl is dissolved in 255 g of water. What is the mole fraction of KCl in the solution?
   (A) 0.104
   (B) 0.117
   (C) 0.132
   (D) 0.327
   (E) 0.486

7. Which of the following compounds produces the greatest number of particles when one mole dissolves in water?
(A) NaCl
(B) NH_4NO_3
(C) NH_4Cl
(D) Na_2SO_4
(E) Sucrose

8. As the concentration of a solute in a solution increases, what is the effect on the freezing point and the vapor pressure of the solution?
(A) The freezing point increases, and the vapor pressure increases.
(B) The freezing point increases, and the vapor pressure decreases.
(C) The freezing point decreases, and the vapor pressure increases.
(D) The freezing point decreases, and the vapor pressure decreases.
(E) The freezing point decreases, and the vapor pressure is unaffected.

9. Which of the following liquids will have the lowest freezing point?
(A) Pure H_2O
(B) Aqueous glucose (0.050 m)
(C) Aqueous CoI_2 (0.030 m)
(D) Aqueous FeI_3 (0.030 m)
(E) Aqueous NaI (0.030 m)

10. What is the boiling point of a 2.41 m solution of $CaCl_2$ dissolved in water?
(A) 96.3°C
(B) 101.2°C
(C) 101.5°C
(D) 102.4°C
(E) 103.7°C

Free-Response Question

Predict whether each of the following substances is more likely to dissolve in carbon tetrachloride (CCl_4) or in water. Justify each answer.

(a) C_7H_{16}
(b) Na_2SO_4
(c) HCl
(d) I_2

ANSWERS AND EXPLANATIONS

Multiple-Choice Questions

▌ 1. (C) is correct. Based on the solubility of the solute, 2.54 g of solute dissolved in 100 mL of water would be a saturated solution. Using a proportion to determine the corresponding amount of solute in 2.00 L of water shows that 50.8 g of solute dissolved in the water would also be a saturated solution. The amount of 53.5 g in the problem is greater than 50.8 g, so the solution must be supersaturated.

▌ 2. (A) is correct. Pressure has no noticeable effect on the solubility of a liquid or a solid. It does have effect on the solubility of a gas.

3. (A) is correct. Although there are a few exceptions, solubility of a solid solute generally increases when temperature increases. Because the solution can hold more dissolved solute at the warmer temperature, it is now unsaturated.

4. (C) is correct. Molarity is moles of solute per liter of solution. The number of moles of HCl can be calculated by dividing 5.5 g HCl by its molar mass, 36.46 g/mol. There is 0.15 mol HCl in the solution. The volume of the solution can be found by dividing the mass of the solution by the density; 205.5 g/0.79 g/mL = 260 mL = 0.26 L. The molarity is 0.15 mol/0.26 L, or 0.58 M.

5. (B) is correct. Mass percent is the mass of the solute divided by the total mass of the solution, times 100. The mass of solute is 23.9 g, and the mass of the solution is 23.9 g + 342 g, or 366 g. The mass percent is 23.9 g/366 g × 100, or 6.53%.

6. (A) is correct. Mole fraction is the number of moles of the component divided by the total moles of all components. The molar mass of KCl is 74.55 g/mol, so the number of moles of KCl in solution is 124 g/74.55 g/mol, or 1.66 mol. The molar mass of water is 18.02 g/mol, so the number of moles of water present is 342 g/18.02 g/mol, or 14.2 mol. The total number of moles present is 1.66 mol + 14.2 mol, or 15.9 mol. Thus, the mole fraction is 1.66 mol/15.9 mol, or 0.104.

7. (D) is correct. Sucrose is molecular, so one mole of it produces one mole of particles. Answers A, B, C, and D are all ionic, so they will produce a number of moles of ions equal to the number of ions present in each formula unit. Answers A, B, and C each contain two ions. Answer D contains two sodium ions and one sulfate ion for a total of three ions. Thus, sodium sulfate produces the most ions in solution.

8. (B) is correct. As concentration increases, fewer solvent particles are on the surface of the liquid, so vapor pressure decreases. Freezing point, however, increases.

9. (D) is correct. The amount the freezing point is lowered depends on the number of solute particles in solution. Pure water will not have its freezing point lowered because it contains no solute particles. Glucose is molecular, so 0.050 mol of it produces 0.050 mol of particles. Every formula unit of CoI_2 produces three ions, so there are 0.090 mol of particles in this solution. FeI_3 produces four ions per formula unit, so 0.12 mol of particles are present. A formula unit of NaI contains two ions, so that solution contains 0.060 mol of particles. The number of moles of solute particles produced in the FeI_3 solution is greatest.

10. (E) is correct. One mole of $CaCl_2$ produces three moles of particles in solution. The boiling-point-elevation constant for water is 0.51°C/m. Therefore, the boiling point elevation for the solution is 2.41 m × 3 × 0.51°C/m, or 3.7°C. When elevated this amount, the boiling point of the water is 103.7°C.

Free-Response Question

Of the two solvents, one is nonpolar (CCl_4), and one is polar (H_2O). Ionic and polar solutes dissolve in polar solvents, and nonpolar solutes dissolve in nonpolar solvents. C_7H_{16} is a hydrocarbon, so it is molecular and nonpolar. Na_2SO_4, a compound containing a metal and nonmetals, is ionic. HCl, a diatomic molecule containing two nonmetals that differ in electronegativity, is polar. I_2, a diatomic molecule with atoms of equal electronegativity, is nonpolar. It is likely that CCl_4 would be the better solvent for C_7H_{16} and I_2, and Na_2SO_4 and HCl would dissolve better in water.

This response recognizes that solvents dissolve solutes that are similar in bonding type to the solvent. It recognizes the nature of two solvents and several solutes and correctly determines which solvent is more likely to dissolve which solute.

CHAPTER 14

Chemical Kinetics

Chemistry is the study of matter and its changes. **Chemical kinetics** is the area of chemistry that studies the changes that involve speeds (or rates) of reactions.

Factors that Affect Reaction Rates

▌ Because chemical reactions involve forming and breaking chemical bonds, the speed of the reaction is determined by the nature of the reactants. However, four factors can change the rates at which reactions occur.

▌ The **physical state** of the reactants determines how much contact reactants have with each other. Increasing contact area by changing state or increasing surface area increases the rate of reaction.

▌ Increasing the **concentration** of one or more reactants increases the rate of reaction because the frequency of molecular collisions increases.

▌ Increasing **temperature** increases reaction rate because it increases the speed of the particles.

▌ Adding a **catalyst** (a substance that affects reaction rates without itself being used up) can increase rate of reaction.

Reaction Rates

▌ **Reaction rate** is the change in concentration of reactants or products over a unit of time, usually expressed in molarity per second (M/s). Rates can be written to represent appearance of products or disappearance of reactants.

▌ For most reactions, the rate slows down as the reaction continues because the concentration of reactants decreases.

▌ **Beer's law** states that, when a spectrometer is used to monitor a chemical reaction, the amount of light absorbed is directly proportional to the concentration of the absorbing substance. Consequently, spectroscopy can be used to monitor the course of reactions.

Concentration and Rate

▌ The **rate law** is an equation that relates concentrations of reactants to reaction rate. A rate law for the general reaction $aA + bB \rightarrow cC + dD$ is mathematically expressed by

$$\text{Rate} = k[A]^m[B]^n,$$

where the constant k is the **rate constant,** and exponents are the **reaction orders.** Brackets indicate the concentration of the species that are in them.

- The magnitude of k changes with temperature and therefore expresses how temperature affects rate.
- If the reaction order is one for a reactant, the rate is **first order** for that reactant in that equation. If the reaction order is two, the rate is **second order** for that reactant.
- The **overall reaction order** is the sum of the orders with respect to each reactant in the rate law. The overall reaction order also is classified as first order, second order, and so on.
- Reaction orders must be determined experimentally. The reaction orders m and n are typically small whole numbers (usually 0, 1, or 2). Occasionally, however, reaction orders can be fractions or even negative numbers.
- The units of a rate law depend on the reaction orders of the reaction.

The Change of Concentration with Time

- Rate laws can be converted into equations that state what the concentrations of the reactants or products are at any time during the course of a reaction.
- A **first-order reaction** has a rate that depends on the concentration of a single reactant raised to the first power; rate $= k[A]$. The equation is written: $\ln[A]_t = -kt + \ln[A]_0$, where ln is the natural logarithm. $[A]_t$ is the concentration of reactant A at time t; k is the rate constant, and $[A]_0$ is the beginning concentration of A.
- A **second-order reaction** is one whose overall reaction order is 2. The rate depends on one reactant concentration raised to the second power or on the concentrations of two different reactants, each raised to the first power. This relationship for one reactant is expressed by the equation: $1/[A]_t = kt + 1/[A]_0$.
- The **half-life** of a reaction is the time it takes for a reactant's concentration to drop to one half of its original value. The half-life of a first-order reaction depends on the rate constant, not on the original concentration $t_{1/2} = 0.693/k$. The half-life of second-order reactions depends on both rate constant and initial concentration: $t_{1/2} = 1/(k[A]_0)$.

Temperature and Rate

- The **collision model** is a theory based on the idea that particles must collide to interact. It explains why the rates of most chemical reactions increase as the temperature or concentrations rise. The greater the number of collisions occurring per second, the greater is the reaction rate.
- In most reactions, molecules must be oriented in a certain way during collisions for a reaction to occur.
- Also, molecules must have at least a certain amount of energy to react. The minimum energy required to initiate a chemical reaction is called the **activation energy**, E_a.
- In most reactions, the increase in rate with increasing temperature is nonlinear. Most reaction-rate data obeys an equation based on three factors: (1) the fraction of molecules possessing an energy of E_a or greater; (2) the number of

collisions occurring per second; and (3) the fraction of collisions that have the appropriate orientation.

▌ These three factors are incorporated into the **Arrhenius equation:** $k = Ae^{-Ea/RT}$. In this equation, k is the rate constant, E_a is the activation energy, R is the gas constant (8.314 J/mol-K) and T is the absolute temperature. The frequency factor, A, is constant as temperature is varied. Thus, reaction rates decrease as E_a increases.

Reaction Mechanisms

▌ The series of individual steps by which a reaction occurs is called the **reaction mechanism.**

▌ Processes in reactions that occur in a single step are **elementary steps.** Each one has a specific rate law that depends on the number of molecules (**molecularity**) involved as reactants. Elementary steps can be **unimolecular, bimolecular,** or **termolecular,** depending on whether one, two, or three reactant molecules are interacting.

▌ The net change in a balanced chemical equation often occurs by a **multi-step mechanism,** which consists of elementary steps. The elementary steps in a multi-step mechanism must always add to give the chemical equation of the overall process.

▌ If you know that a reaction is an elementary step, then you know its rate law. The rate law for each kind of elementary step follows directly from the molecularity of that step, as shown in the following table.

ELEMENTARY STEPS AND THEIR RATE LAWS		
Molecularity	**Elementary Step**	**Rate Law**
*Uni*molecular	A → products	Rate = $k[A]$
*Bi*molecular	A + A → products	Rate = $k[A]^2$
*Bi*molecular	A + B → products	Rate = $k[A][B]$
*Ter*molecular	A + A + A → products	Rate = $k[A]^3$
*Ter*molecular	A + A + B → products	Rate = $k[A]^2[B]$
*Ter*molecular	A + B + C → products	Rate = $k[A][B][C]$

▌ Elementary steps can have different rates. The overall rate of a reaction cannot exceed the rate of the slowest step, which is called the **rate-determining step** (or rate-limiting step).

Catalysis

▌ Any substance that changes the speed of a chemical reaction but undergoes no permanent chemical change itself is a **catalyst.** Catalysts usually work by lowering the overall activation energy in a reaction.

▌ A catalyst that is present in the same phases as the reacting molecules is a **homogeneous catalyst.**

▌ A **heterogeneous catalyst** is in a different phase from the reactants; usually it is a solid with gaseous reactants or a solid with reactants in a liquid solution. Finely divided metals are often used as catalysts.

- The initial step in heterogeneous catalysis is usually **adsorption** of reactants. Adsorption is the binding of molecules to a surface. Adsorption occurs when the molecules at the surface of a solid have unfilled valence shells and are therefore highly reactive.
- The position on the catalyst molecule where the reaction takes place is the **active site.**
- Biological catalysts are known as **enzymes.** Reactant molecules in an enzyme reaction are called **substrates.** In the **lock and key model** of enzyme reactions, substrate molecules bind to the active site of the enzyme. Then the reaction proceeds.

For Additional Review

Review the distinct functions of a catalytic converter that involve both oxidation and reduction. How is this example of catalysis used commercially?

Multiple-Choice Questions

1. Which of the following statements describes the effect of an increase in temperature on a chemical reaction?
   (A) The frequency of molecular collisions increases because more reactant molecules are present.
   (B) An added substance provides a surface for adsorption of reactants.
   (C) An added substance lowers the overall activation energy for a reaction.
   (D) The frequency of molecular collisions increases because the molecules are moving faster.
   (E) The frequency of molecules that interact increases because their orientation is more favorable.

2. Reactant A becomes product B in a chemical reaction. Initially, 2.00 mol of reactant A is placed in a closed 1.00-L container. After 20 seconds, 1.41 mol of reactant A is in the container, and 0.590 mol of reactant B is in the container. What is the rate of this reaction?
   (A) 0.0295 M/s
   (B) 0.0410 M/s
   (C) 0.0705 M/s
   (D) 0.295 M/s
   (E) 10.0 M/s

3. A reaction was found to be third order in A. Increasing the concentration of A by a factor of 3 will cause the reaction rate to
   (A) remain constant
   (B) increase by a factor of 27
   (C) increase by a factor of 9
   (D) triple
   (E) decrease by a factor of the cube root of 3

4. The kinetics of the reaction A + B → P were studied, and it was determined that the reaction rate increased by a factor of 9 when the concentration of B was tripled. The reaction is what order in B?
   (A) Zero order
   (B) First order
   (C) Second order
   (D) Third order
   (E) None of the above

5. The rate law for a reaction is

   rate = $k[A][B]^2$

   Which of the following statements is NOT true?
   (A) The reaction is first order in A.
   (B) The reaction is second order in B.
   (C) The reaction is second order overall.
   (D) k is the reaction rate constant.
   (E) If B is doubled, the reaction rate will increase by a factor of 4.

6. The initial concentration of reactant in a first-order reaction is 0.27 M. The rate constant for the reaction is 0.75 s^{-1}. What is the concentration of reactant after 1.5 s?
   (A) 3.8 M
   (B) 1.7 M
   (C) 8.7 $\times$ 10^{-2} M
   (D) 2.0 $\times$ 10^{-2} M
   (E) 0.135 M

7. One difference between first- and second-order reactions is that
   (A) the half-life of a first-order reaction does not depend on $[A]_0$, whereas the half-life of a second-order reaction does depend on $[A]_0$
   (B) the rate of a first-order reaction does not depend on reactant concentrations, whereas the rate of a second-order reaction does depend on reactant concentrations
   (C) the rate of a first-order reaction depends on reactant concentrations, whereas the rate of a second-order reaction does not depend on reactant concentrations
   (D) a first-order reaction can be catalyzed, whereas a second-order reaction cannot be catalyzed
   (E) the half-life of a first-order reaction depends on $[A]_0$, whereas the half-life of a second-order reaction does not depend on $[A]_0$

8. Consider the chemical reaction between sodium and chlorine; $2NO + Cl_2 \rightarrow 2NOCl$. What is the rate law for the reaction, assuming it involves a single elementary step?
   (A) Rate = $k[NO][Cl_2]$
   (B) Rate = $k[NO]^2[Cl_2]$
   (C) Rate = $k[NO][Cl_2]^2$
   (D) Rate = $k[2NO][Cl_2]$
   (E) Rate = $k^3[NO][Cl_2]$

9. The following chemical equations are the elementary steps for the reaction between NO and H_2 to form N_2 and H_2O. What determines the rate of the entire reaction?
   I. $2NO \rightarrow N_2O_2$ (very fast)
   II. $N_2O_2 + H_2 \rightarrow N_2O + H_2O$ (slow)
   III. $N_2O + H_2 \rightarrow N_2 + H_2O$ (fast)
   (A) I
   (B) II
   (C) III
   (D) I and III
   (E) I, II, and III

10. The primary source of the specificity of enzymes is
    (A) their polarity, which matches that of their specific substrate
    (B) their delocalized electron cloud
    (C) their bonded transition metal, which is specific to the target substrate
    (D) their locations within the cell
    (E) their shape, which relates to the lock-and-key model

Free-Response Question

For a certain second-order reaction, k = 0.452 $M^{-1}s^{-1}$. If the initial concentration of a reactant is 2.43 M, what is the half-life of the reaction?

ANSWERS AND EXPLANATIONS

Multiple-Choice Questions

▌ **1. (D) is correct.** All of the answers refer to factors that increase the rate of the reaction. However, only answer *D* refers to what happens when temperature is increased. Answer *A* refers to an increase in concentration, answers *B* and *C* reflect the addition of a catalyst, and answer E refers to proper orientation of molecules.

■ 2. **(A) is correct.** Rate of reaction is the change in molarity per time of a reactant or a product. Because the volume is 1.00 L, the change in number of moles reflects the change in molarity. The reactant changes from 2.00 mol to 1.41 mol, for a change of 0.590 mol. Because this change takes 20 s, the rate is 0.590 M/20 s, or 0.295 M/s.

■ 3. **(B) is correct.** Because the reaction is third order in A, the part of the rate law that refers to A is $[A]^3$. If the concentration is tripled, this expression becomes $[3A]^3$, which equals $3^3[A]^3$. Thus, the reaction rate increases by a factor of 3^3, or 27.

■ 4. **(C) is correct.** The part of the rate law that refers to B is $[B]^x$. The concentration is tripled, so this expression becomes $[3B]^x$, which equals $3^x[B]^x$. $3^x = 9$, so $x = 2$, and the reaction is in second order in B.

■ 5. **(C) is correct.** The overall order of a reaction equals the sum of the orders of all the reactants. Because the reaction is in first order in A and second order in B, the reaction is third order overall. All other statements are true.

■ 6. **(C) is correct.** The rate equation for a first order reaction is $\ln[A]_t = -kt + \ln[A]_0$. Substituting the known information gives $\ln[A]_t = -(0.75 \text{ s}^{-1})(1.5 \text{ s}) + \ln(0.27)$. Thus, $-1.13 - 1.31 = -2.44 = \ln[A]_t$. The final concentration must be $e^{-2.44}$, or $8.7 \times 10^{-2} M$.

■ 7. **(A) is correct.** One difference between first- and second-order reactions is that the half-life of a first-order reaction does not depend on the concentration of A at the start of the reaction, whereas the half-life of a second-order reaction does depend on the concentration of A at the start of the reaction.

■ 8. **(B) is correct.** Because the reaction involves a single elementary step, the exponents in the rate law are the coefficients from the balanced chemical equation. The coefficient of NO is 2, and that of Cl_2 is 1. Thus, the rate law is: rate = $k[NO]^2[Cl_2]$.

■ 9. **(C) is correct.** The rate of the overall reaction can be no faster than the rate of the slowest step. Thus, step II determines the rate of the overall reaction.

■ 10. **(C) is correct.** Most enzymes are large protein molecules. Although an enzyme is a large molecule, the reaction is catalyzed at a very specific location called the active site. An explanation for the specificity of enzymes can be pictured as a lock-and-key model. The substrate can be pictured as a specific key fitting a lock.

Free-Response Question

The half-life of a second order reaction is given by $t_{1/2} = 1/k[A]_0$. Substituting the known values into the equation, $t_{1/2} = 1/(0.452\ M^{-1}s^{-1} \times 2.43\ M)$. Thus, the half-life is 0.910 s.

This response correctly identifies the equation to be used to calculate half-life. It accurately substitutes the known information into the equation and then uses this information to calculate the half-life for the reaction.

CHAPTER 15

Chemical Equilibrium

Not all chemical reactions continue to completion. When the concentrations of all reactants and products reach the stage where they remain the same over time, the reaction is in **chemical equilibrium.** Chemical equilibrium occurs when initial reactants form initial products and initial products form initial reactants at equal rates.

The Equilibrium Constant

▌ The **law of mass action** gives the relationship between the concentrations of the reactants and the products of the reaction at equilibrium. In gases, the concentrations are expressed as partial pressures; in solutions, they are expressed as molarity.

▌ Consider the chemical equilibrium represented by $aA + bB \leftrightarrows cC + dD$. According to the law of mass action, the equilibrium condition for species in solution can be expressed using the **equilibrium-constant expression,** $K_{eq} = \dfrac{[C]^c[D]^d}{[A]^a[B]^b}$. For gases, the expression is $K_{eq} = \dfrac{[(P_C)^c(P_D)^d]}{[(P_A)^a(P_B)^b]}$. The constant K_{eq} is the **equilibrium constant,** which is determined by inserting actual partial pressures or molarity into the equilibrium-constant expression.

▌ The value of the equilibrium constant changes with temperature. A high value of K_{eq} shows that the mixture contains more products than reactants; a small value shows that the equilibrium mixture has a higher concentration of reactants.

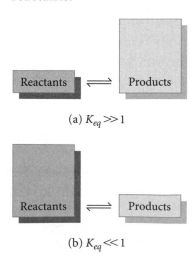

(a) $K_{eq} \gg 1$

(b) $K_{eq} \ll 1$

- The equilibrium-constant expression depends only on the relative concentrations of the reactants, not on the reaction mechanism.
- When working with equilibrium constants, remember the following three points.

    1. The equilibrium-constant expression always has the products as the numerator of the fraction and the reactants as the denominator. Thus, the equilibrium-constant expression for a reaction written in one direction is the reciprocal of the one for the reaction written in the reverse direction.
    2. The equilibrium constant of a reaction that has been multiplied by a number equals the equilibrium constant raised to a power equal to that number.
    3. When a reaction has two or more steps, the equilibrium constant is the product of the equilibrium constants of all the steps.

Heterogeneous Equilibria

- In the previously mentioned equilibria, all substances are in the same phase, and all substances are used in writing the equilibrium-constant expression.
- If the substances that are involved in the equilibrium are in different phases, the equilibrium is **heterogeneous.**
- If a pure solid or a pure liquid is involved in an equilibrium, it is not written in the equilibrium-constant expression. For example, when oxygen and potassium chloride are formed by the decomposition of potassium chlorate in a closed system, $K_{eq} = P_{O_2}$. The solids are not included. When carbonic acid decomposes into water and carbon dioxide, water is not included in the equilibrium-constant expression.

Calculating Equilibrium Constants

- If you know the equilibrium concentration of at least one chemical component in an equilibrium, you can calculate the equilibrium concentrations of the others using the following steps.

    1. Tabulate the known initial and equilibrium concentrations of all components of the equilibrium-constant expression.
    2. For those reactants for which both the initial and equilibrium concentrations are known, calculate the change in concentration that occurs as the system reaches equilibrium.
    3. Use the stoichiometry of the reaction (the coefficients in the balanced chemical equation) to calculate the changes in concentration for all the unknowns in the equilibrium.
    4. From the initial concentrations and the changes in concentration, calculate the equilibrium concentrations. These are used to evaluate the equilibrium constant.

- For an example of this procedure, see Sample Exercise 15.8 on page 589 in *Chemistry: The Central Science.*

Applications of Equilibrium Constants

- The magnitude of K_{eq} indicates the extent to which a reaction will proceed. If K_{eq} is very large, the reaction will tend to proceed far to the right (containing mostly product); if K_{eq} is very small, the equilibrium mixture will contain mainly reactants.

- The equilibrium constant can be used to predict the direction in which a reaction mixture will proceed to achieve equilibrium and to calculate the concentrations of reactants and products when equilibrium has been reached.

- The **reaction quotient** (Q) is a value obtained when concentrations of reactants and products are inserted into the equilibrium expression. If the solution is in equilibrium, Q will equal the equilibrium constant, K_{eq}.

- If $Q > K_{eq}$, substances on the right side of the chemical equation will react to form substances on the left, and the reaction moves from right to left in approaching equilibrium. If $Q < K_{eq}$, the reaction will achieve equilibrium by forming more products, and it moves from left to right.

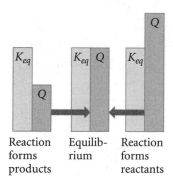

Reaction forms products | Equilib-rium | Reaction forms reactants

- To calculate the amounts of reactants and products at equilibrium, insert initial partial pressures or concentrations, the changes, and the final partial pressures or concentrations into the formula.

Le Châtelier's Principle

- **Le Châtelier's principle,** developed by a French industrial chemist, states that if a system at equilibrium is disturbed by a change in temperature, pressure, or the concentration of one of the components, the system will shift its equilibrium position so as to counteract the effect of the disturbance.

- At constant temperature, **reducing the volume** of a gaseous equilibrium mixture will increase the pressure and the concentration. The system will shift in the direction that reduces the number of moles of gas. **Increasing the volume** causes a shift in the direction that produces more gas molecules.

- When the temperature is increased, the equilibrium shifts in the direction that absorbs heat. The endothermic reaction will be favored until a new equilibrium is reached. If temperature is lowered, the exothermic reaction is favored.

- Catalysts affect the speed of reactions, but they do not affect the value of K_{eq}.

For Additional Review

Research how the Haber process is used to industrially produce ammonia from nitrogen and hydrogen gases. Examine how changes in pressure, temperature, and concentration are used to control the amount of ammonia produced.

Multiple-Choice Questions

1. Which one of the following will change the value of an equilibrium constant?
   (A) Changing temperature
   (B) Adding other substances that do not react with any of the species involved in the equilibrium
   (C) Varying the initial concentrations of reactants
   (D) Varying the initial concentrations of products
   (E) Changing the volume of the reaction vessel

2. The equilibrium-constant expression depends on
   (A) the stoichiometry of the reaction
   (B) the mechanism of the reaction
   (C) both the stoichiometry and the mechanism of the reaction
   (D) the quantities of reactants and products initially present
   (E) the temperature of the reaction

3. At 1000 K, the equilibrium constant for the reaction $2NO(g) + Br_2(g) \leftrightarrows 2NOBr(g)$ is $K_{eq} = 0.013$. Calculate K_{eq} for the reverse reaction.
   (A) 1.6×10^{-4}
   (B) 0.013
   (C) 0.99
   (D) 1.1
   (E) 77

4. Use the equilibrium-constant expression for the following chemical reaction to determine K_{eq} if $[NH_3] = 0.744\ M$, $[N_2] = 0.423\ M$, and $[H_2] = 1.27\ M$.

$$N_2(g) + 3H_2(g) \leftrightarrows 2NH_3(g)$$

   (A) 0.639
   (B) 0.725
   (C) 0.811
   (D) 1.38
   (E) 1.56

5. A few ions exist in liquid water according to the following equation:

$$2H_2O(l) \leftrightarrows H_3O^+(aq) + OH^-(aq)$$

What is the equilibrium-constant expression for this reaction?
   (A) $K_{eq} = [H_3O^+][OH^-]$
   (B) $K_{eq} = [H_3O^+][OH^-]/[H_2O]$
   (C) $K_{eq} = [H_3O^+][OH^-]/[H_2O]^2$
   (D) $K_{eq} = [H_3O^+][OH^-]/[2H_2O]$
   (E) $K_{eq} = [H_3O^+][OH^-][H_2O]$

6. At elevated temperatures, molecular hydrogen and molecular bromine react to form hydrogen bromide. The reaction reaches equilibrium.

$$H_2(g) + Br_2(g) \leftrightarrows 2HBr(g)$$

Samples consisting of 0.682 mol H_2 and 0.440 mol Br_2 are combined in a reaction vessel with a volume of 2.00 L. At equilibrium at 700 K, there is 0.566 mol H_2 present. At equilibrium, how many moles of Br_2 are present in the reaction vessel?
   (A) 0.000 mol
   (B) 0.440 mol
   (C) 0.566 mol
   (D) 0.232 mol
   (E) 0.324 mol

7. How does the reaction quotient of a reaction (Q) differ from the equilibrium constant (K_{eq}) of the same reaction?
   (A) Q does not change with temperature, but K_{eq} does change with temperature.
   (B) K_{eq} does not change with temperature, whereas Q is temperature dependent.
   (C) K_{eq} does not depend on the concentrations or partial pressures of reaction components, but Q does.
   (D) Q does not depend on the concentrations or partial pressures of reaction components, but K_{eq} does.
   (E) Q shows the same concentration relationships, but Q is not necessarily at equilibrium; K_{eq} is always at equilibrium.

8. According to Le Châtelier's principle, what will result in an increase in the number of moles of $SO_3(g)$ in the reaction chamber?

   $$2SO_2(g) + O_2(g) \leftrightarrows 2SO_3(g) + energy$$

   (A) Increasing the pressure
   (B) Increasing the volume of the container
   (C) Increasing the temperature
   (D) Removing some oxygen
   (E) All these factors will increase the amount of $SO_3(g)$.

9. Consider the following reaction at equilibrium:

   $$2NH_3(g) \leftrightarrows N_2(g) + 3H_2(g)$$
   $$\Delta H° = 92.4 \text{ kJ}$$

   According to Le Châtelier's principle, adding $N_2(g)$ to the system will result in
   (A) a decrease in the concentration of $NH_3(g)$
   (B) a decrease in the concentration of $H_2(g)$
   (C) an increase in the value of the equilibrium constant
   (D) a lower partial pressure of $N_2(g)$
   (E) removal of all of the $H_2(g)$

10. The effect of a catalyst on an equilibrium is to
    (A) increase the rate of the forward reaction only
    (B) increase the equilibrium constant so that products are favored
    (C) slow the reverse reaction only
    (D) increase the rate at which equilibrium is achieved without changing the composition of the equilibrium mixture
    (E) shift the equilibrium to the right

Free-Response Question

Given the following information:

$$HF(aq) \leftrightarrows H^+(aq) + F^-(aq) \qquad K_{eq} = 6.8 \times 10^{-4}$$
$$H_2C_2O_4(aq) \leftrightarrows 2H^+(aq) + C_2O_4^{2-}(aq) \qquad K_{eq} = 3.8 \times 10^{-6}$$

determine the value of the equilibrium constant for the following chemical reaction:

$$2HF(aq) + C_2O_4^{2-}(aq) \leftrightarrows 2F^-(aq) + H_2C_2O_4(aq)$$

ANSWERS AND EXPLANATIONS

Multiple-Choice Questions

▌ 1. (A) is correct. For reactants in solution, the equilibrium-constant expression is $K_{eq} = \dfrac{[C]^c[D]^d}{[A]^a[B]^b}$. For gases, the expression is $K_{eq} = \dfrac{[(P_C)^c(P_D)^d]}{[(P_A)^a(P_B)^b]}$.

The constant K_{eq} is the equilibrium constant. Changing temperature will affect concentration and partial pressure, so it affects K_{eq}. Substances that don't enter into the reaction will not be shown in the equilibrium-constant expression. Varying any initial concentrations won't affect K_{eq} because it shows relationships at equilibrium, not at the beginning of the reaction. Changing the volume of the container won't affect solutions at all, and partial pressures will be affected equally.

▌ **2. (A) is correct.** Because products are formed according to the ratios described by a balanced chemical equation, the equilibrium-constant expression is determined by the stoichiometry of the reaction. The mechanism does not affect this expression because the resulting reaction is the same, no matter how many steps it takes. Initial quantities do not affect it because the values in the expression are at equilibrium. Temperature affects the values to be substituted into the expression but not the expression itself.

▌ **3. (E) is correct.** Reversing the reaction means that the substances that were initially reactants are products in the reverse reaction. The substances that were initially products are reactants in the reverse reaction. Thus, the equilibrium-constant expression for the reverse reaction is the reciprocal of the forward reaction; $1/0.013 = 77$.

▌ **4. (A) is correct.** $K_{eq} = \dfrac{[NH_3]^2}{[N_2][H_2]^3}$. Substituting the values given into the expression gives $K_{eq} = \dfrac{(0.744)^2}{[(0.423)(1.27)^3]} = 0.639$.

▌ **5. (A) is correct.** Initially, the equilibrium-constant expression is $K_{eq} = \dfrac{[H_3O^+][OH^-]}{[H_2O]}$. However, solids or pure liquids are not included in the expression. Thus, water is removed from the expression, and the actual expression is $K_{eq} = [H_3O^+][OH^-]$.

▌ **6. (B) is correct.** The amount of H_2 used in the reaction is 0.682 mol − 0.566 mol, or 0.116 mol. The chemical equation for the reaction shows that H_2 and Br_2 react in a 1 : 1 ratio. Thus, 0.116 mol Br_2 react also. The amount of Br_2 remaining is 0.440 mol − 0.116 mol, or 0.324 mol.

▌ **7. (E) is correct.** Q and K_{eq} are both affected by temperature changes. Both depend on concentrations or partial pressures. The difference is that Q does not necessarily occur at equilibrium, but K_{eq} always does.

▌ **8. (A) is correct.** Increasing the pressure favors formation of fewer gas molecules, so it will favor formation of SO_3. All other choices favor a decrease in the amount of SO_3. Increasing the volume decreases pressure, so it will favor formation of reactants because the reactants contain more molecules. Because the reaction is exothermic, adding energy moves the reaction to the left, as does removing oxygen.

▌ **9. (B) is correct.** Adding a product moves the reaction to the left, increasing $[NH_3]$. As long as temperature is constant, K_{eq} remains the same. The partial pressure of N_2 will increase, and not all H_2 will be removed because more is constantly formed from the ammonia. However, because more ammonia is formed, $[H_2]$ decreases.

■ **10. (D) is correct.** A catalyst lowers the activation barrier between the reactants and products. The catalyst thereby increases the rates of both the forward and reverse reactions. As a result, a catalyst increases the rate at which equilibrium is achieved, but it does not change the composition of the equilibrium mixture.

Free-Response Question
Solution

So that the two equations can be added to result in the final equation, the first equation must be multiplied by 2. Because it is multiplied by 2, its equilibrium constant is squared; $(6.8 \times 10^{-4})^2 = 4.6 \times 10^{-7}$.

$$2HF(aq) \rightleftharpoons 2H^+(aq) + 2F^-(aq) \qquad K_{eq} = 4.6 \times 10^{-7}$$

The second equation must be reversed. Thus, its K_{eq} is the reciprocal of the K_{eq} of the forward reaction; $1/(3.8 \times 10^{-6}) = 2.6 \times 10^5$.

$$2H^+(aq) + C_2O_4^{2-}(aq) \rightleftharpoons H_2C_2O_4(aq) \qquad K_{eq} = 2.6 \times 10^5$$

Add the two equations, which results in the net equilibrium equation.

$$2HF(aq) \rightleftharpoons 2H^+(aq) + 2F^-(aq)$$

$$\frac{2H^+(aq) + C_2O_4^{2-}(aq) \rightleftharpoons H_2C_2O_4(aq)}{2HF(aq) + C_2O_4^{2-}(aq) \rightleftharpoons 2F^-(aq) + H_2C_2O_4(aq)}$$

The K_{eq} of the overall equation equals the product of the K_{eq} of the steps.

$$K_{eq} = (4.6 \times 10^{-7})(2.6 \times 10^5) = 0.12$$

This response correctly adjusts the chemical equations that show the steps of the mechanism so that they can be added to give the overall equation. It accurately makes the appropriate changes in the equilibrium constants for the equations for the steps. It then calculates the overall equilibrium constant, using the equilibrium constants of the individual steps.

CHAPTER 16

Acid-Base Equilibria

Acids and bases have properties that are based on the structures and bonding of the compounds. These properties are based also on the chemical equilibria in which acids and bases participate.

Acids and Bases: A Brief Review; and Brønsted-Lowry Acids and Bases

▌ According to the Arrhenius concept of acids and bases, when **acids** are dissolved in water, they increase $[H^+]$. When dissolved in water, **bases** increase $[OH^-]$. This concept of acids and bases is limited because it is restricted to aqueous solutions.

▌ Johannes Brønsted and Thomas Lowry defined acids and bases in terms of their ability to transfer protons. According to their definition, a **Brønsted-Lowry acid** is a substance that can donate a proton to another substance. A **Brønsted-Lowry base** is a substance that can accept a proton. This concept is not limited to changes that occur in an aqueous solution.

▌ According to the Brønsted-Lowry theory, when an acid is added to water, H^+ from the acid forms the hydronium ion $H_3O^+(aq)$ with a water molecule because water acts as a base and accepts the proton.

▌ Water can also act as an acid, such as when ammonia is added to water. Water donates H^+ to ammonia, forming NH_4^+ and OH^-. A substance, such as water, that can act either as an acid or as a base is said to be **amphoteric.**

▌ A **conjugate base** of an acid is what remains when a proton is removed. When a base accepts a proton, the result is the **conjugate acid** of the base. Together, these two species are called a **conjugate acid-base pair.** The stronger the acid, the weaker will be its conjugate base; the stronger a base, the weaker will be its conjugate acid. The following equation shows the formation of a conjugate acid-base pair.

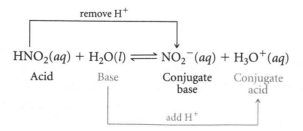

▌ Some acids are better proton donors than others, and some bases are better proton acceptors than others. Acids and bases can be placed into three broad categories based on their behavior in water.

1. **Strong acids** completely transfer their protons to water, leaving no undissociated molecules in solution. Their conjugate bases have little tendency to attract protons in aqueous solution.

2. **Weak acids** only partly dissociate in aqueous solution and, therefore, exist in the solution as a mixture of acid molecules and their constituent ions. The conjugate bases of weak acids are weak bases, but they do show a slight ability to remove protons from water.

3. The substances with negligible acidity are those such as CH_4 that contain hydrogen but do not demonstrate any acidic behavior in water. Their conjugate bases are strong bases, reacting completely and attracting protons from water molecules to form OH^- ions.

		ACID	BASE		
100% ionized in H_2O	Strong	HCl	Cl^-	Negligible	
		H_2SO_4	HSO_4^-		
		HNO_3	NO_3^-		
		$H_3O^+(aq)$	H_2O		
	Weak	HSO_4^-	SO_4^{2-}	Weak	Base strength increases
		H_3PO_4	$H_2PO_4^-$		
		HF	F^-		
Acid strength increases		$HC_2H_3O_2$	$C_2H_3O_2^-$		
		H_2CO_3	HCO_3^-		
		H_2S	HS^-		
		$H_2PO_4^-$	HPO_4^{2-}		
		NH_4^+	NH_3		
		HCO_3^-	CO_3^{2-}		
		HPO_4^{2-}	PO_4^{3-}		
		H_2O	OH^-		
	Negligible	OH^-	O^{2-}	Strong	100% protonated in H_2O
		H_2	H^-		
		CH_4	CH_3^-		

▌ In every acid-base reaction, the equilibrium favors transfer of the proton from the stronger acid to the stronger base. Thus, when a strong acid is placed in water, the reaction goes to the right because water is a stronger base than the anion from the acid. When a weak acid is placed in water, the reaction shifts to the left because the anion from the acid is a stronger base than water.

The Autoionization of Water

■ Water is able to act as either a Brønsted-Lowry acid or a Brønsted-Lowry base. When water acts as both an acid and a base in the same reaction, as shown in the equation below, the process is called the **autoionization of water.**

$$H-\overset{\cdot\cdot}{\underset{|}{O}}: + H-\overset{\cdot\cdot}{\underset{|}{O}}: \rightleftharpoons \left[H-\overset{\cdot\cdot}{\underset{|}{O}}-H\right]^{+} + :\overset{\cdot\cdot}{\underset{\cdot\cdot}{O}}-H^{-}$$

■ Because the autoionization of water is an equilibrium process, an equilibrium-constant expression can be written for it. Note that water is not included in the expression.

$$K_{eq} = [H_3O^+][OH^-]$$

■ This expression is specifically for water, so K_{eq} is replaced by K_w, which is called the **ion-product constant** for water. At 25°C, $K_w = 1.0 \times 10^{-14}$.

■ The ion-product constant for water can be used to calculate $[H_3O^+]$ or $[OH^-]$ if the other value is known, and it applies to any aqueous solution.

The pH Scale

■ Because $[H^+]$ is a small number, it is expressed in **pH,** which is the negative logarithm in base 10 of $[H^+]$; pH $= -\log[H^+]$ or $-\log[H_3O^+]$.

■ As seen from the ion-product constant at 25°C, in a neutral solution, $[H_3O^+] = [OH^-] = 1.0 \times 10^{-7}$. Thus, the pH of a neutral solution is 7.00.

■ Acidic solutions have $[H^+]$ greater than 1.0×10^{-7}, so their pH is lower than seven. Bases have $[H^+]$ less than 1.0×10^{-7}, so their pH is higher than 7.

■ Other useful relationships for making calculations involving acids and bases are:

$$pOH = -\log[OH^-]$$
$$pK_w = -\log K_w = 14$$
$$pK_w = pH + pOH = 14$$

A change in $[H^+]$ by a factor of 10 causes pH to change by 1.

Strong Acids and Bases

■ The seven most common strong acids include six monoprotic acids (HCl, HBr, HI, HNO_3, $HClO_3$, and $HClO_4$) and one diprotic acid (H_2SO_4).

■ Ionic hydroxides of alkali metals and the heavy alkaline earth metals are **strong bases.** The cations of strong bases are negligible in terms of conjugate acidity.

Weak Acids

■ Most acids are weak, only partially ionizing in aqueous solution.

■ The amount of ionization that occurs is represented by K_a, the **acid-dissociation constant.** This value is the equilibrium constant for the reaction and can be written as $K_a = [H^+][A^-]/[HA]$. The larger the value of K_a, the stronger the acid is.

- If you know the concentration of a weak acid and its acid dissociation constant, you can calculate the pH of the solution. For example, $K_a = 6.8 \times 10^{-4}$ for HF. If the concentration of the solution is 0.50 M, $K_a = \dfrac{[H^+][F^-]}{[HF]} = \dfrac{(x)(x)}{0.50 - x} = 6.8 \times 10^{-4}$. Because x is such a small number, [HF] is essentially 0.50, and $K_a = \dfrac{x^2}{0.50} = 6.8 \times 10^{-4}$. Solving for x, $[H^+] = 1.8 \times 10^{-2}$. The pH equals $-\log(1.8 \times 10^{-2})$, or 1.7.
- In a similar procedure, pH can be used to find $[H^+]$. If the concentration of the solution is also known, K_a can be calculated.
- **Polyprotic acids** have more than one ionizable H atom. These substances have more than one acid-dissociation constant, and each one decreases in magnitude as the order increases. It is always easier to remove the first proton from a polyprotic acid than it is to remove the second.
- Because most of the hydrogen ions come from the first dissociation step in a polyprotic acid solution, you can estimate the pH using only the first acid-dissociation constant, K_{a1}.

Weak Bases; and Relationship Between K_a and K_b

- K_b is called the **base-dissociation constant.** The constant K_b always refers to the equilibrium in which a base reacts with H_2O to form the corresponding conjugate acid and OH^-. For example, when ammonia is added to water, and ammonium and hydroxide ions form, $K_b = \dfrac{[NH_4^+][OH^-]}{[NH_3]}$
- The product of the acid-dissociation constant for an acid and the base-dissociation constant for its conjugate base is the ion-product for water. $K_a \times K_b = K_w$.

Lewis Acids and Bases

- For a substance to be a proton acceptor, it must have an unshared pair of electrons for binding the proton.
- A **Lewis acid** is an electron-pair acceptor, and a **Lewis base** is an electron-pair donor. In the Lewis theory, a base can donate its electron pair to something other than H^+. This concept greatly increases the number of species that can be considered acids.

For Additional Review

Make a pH chart, and include some common substances at each pH value.

Multiple-Choice Questions

1. A Brønsted-Lowry base is defined as a substance that
   (A) increases $[H^+]$ when placed in H_2O
   (B) decreases $[H^+]$ when placed in H_2O
   (C) increases $[OH^-]$ when placed in H_2O
   (D) acts as a proton acceptor
   (E) acts as a proton donor

2. Which of the following is a Brønsted-Lowry acid?
   (A) $(CH_3)_3NH^+$
   (B) CH_3COOH
   (C) HF
   (D) HNO_2
   (E) All of the above

3. Which of the following choices can be classified as a weak base?
   I. Ammonia
   II. The fluoride ion
   III. Sodium hydroxide

   (A) I
   (B) II
   (C) III
   (D) I and II
   (E) II and III

4. What is the pH of an aqueous solution at 25°C in which $[H^+]$ is 0.0025 M?
   (A) +3.40
   (B) +2.60
   (C) −2.60
   (D) −3.40
   (E) +2.25

5. For a certain basic solution at 25°C, $[OH^-] = 1.3 \times 10^{-5}$. What is the pH of the solution?
   (A) 4.9
   (B) 7.7
   (C) 9.1
   (D) 14
   (E) 7.7×10^{-10}

6. What is the pOH of a 0.0150 M solution of barium hydroxide?
   (A) 12.2
   (B) 12.5
   (C) 1.52
   (D) 1.82
   (E) 10.4

7. After adding a base to an acid, the pH increased by 2. If the initial $[H^+] = 2.3 \times 10^{-4}$, what is the final $[H^+]$?
   (A) 2.3×10^{-8}
   (B) 2.3×10^{-6}
   (C) 2.3×10^{-2}
   (D) 4.3×10^{-4}
   (E) 4.6×10^{-4}

8. Which of the following choices is the weakest acid?
   (A) HF ($K_a = 6.8 \times 10^{-4}$)
   (B) HClO ($K_a = 3.0 \times 10^{-8}$)
   (C) HNO_2 ($K_a = 4.5 \times 10^{-4}$)
   (D) HCN ($K_a = 4.9 \times 10^{-10}$)
   (E) Acetic acid ($K_a = 1.8 \times 10^{-5}$)

9. The K_a for acetic acid, $HC_2H_3O_2$, is 1.8×10^{-5}. What is the pH of a 0.01 M acetic acid solution?
   (A) 3.4
   (B) 4.2
   (C) 4.7
   (D) 9.3
   (E) 10.6

10. The pH of a solution is 5.7. What is $[H^+]$ for the solution?
    (A) 1.0×10^{-7}
    (B) 5.0×10^5
    (C) 2.0×10^{-6}
    (D) 5.7×10^{-7}
    (E) 5.0×10^{-9}

Free-Response Question

Calculate the concentration of $H^+ (aq)$ in the following two solutions. Assume that the temperature is 25°C. For each solution, state whether it is acidic or basic.

(a) A solution in which $[OH^-]$ is 0.0100 M
(b) A solution in which $[OH^-]$ is 1.8×10^{-9}

ANSWERS AND EXPLANATIONS

Multiple-Choice Questions

▌ **1. (D) is correct.** Brønsted and Lowry defined acids and bases in terms of their ability to transfer protons. According to their definition, an acid is a substance that can donate a proton to another substance. Likewise, a base is a substance that can accept a proton. Answers *B* and *C* occur with many, but not all, Brønsted-Lowry bases.

▌ **2. (E) is correct.** Each answer listed contains a proton that can be donated. These protons are written as the hydrogen atoms in the formulas, with the exception of the hydrogen atoms in the CH_3 groups.

▌ **3. (D) is correct.** In general, strong bases are hydroxides of alkali metals and alkaline earth metals. The only answer listed that is a strong base is sodium hydroxide. The other answers are weak bases.

▌ **4. (B) is correct.** In this solution, $[H^+] = 2.5 \times 10^{-3}$. The pH equals $-\log[H^+]$, so $pH = -\log(2.5 \times 10^{-3}) = 2.60$.

▌ **5. (C) is correct.** $[H^+] = \dfrac{1.0 \times 10^{-14}}{[OH^-]}$; so, for this solution, $[H^+] = \dfrac{1.0 \times 10^{-14}}{1.3 \times 10^{-5}} = 7.7 \times 10^{-10}$. The pH equals $-\log[H^+]$, so $pH = -\log(7.7 \times 10^{-10}) = 9.1$.

▌ **6. (C) is correct.** $[Ba(OH)_2] = 1.5 \times 10^{-2}$. Because each mole of the compound produces two moles of OH^-, $[OH^-] = 3.0 \times 10^{-2}$. The pOH equals $-\log[OH^-]$, so $pOH = -\log(3.0 \times 10^{-2}) = 1.52$.

▌ **7. (B) is correct.** Because pH is a logarithmic function, if pH changes by two units, $[H^+]$ changes by a factor of 100. Because a base is added, and pH increases by 2, $[H^+]$ becomes less by a factor of 100, or 10^2; $[H^+]_f = \dfrac{2.3 \times 10^{-4}}{10^2} = 2.3 \times 10^{-6}$.

▌ **8. (D) is correct.** The weakest acid is the one that will ionize the least. Because $K_a = \dfrac{[H^+][A^-]}{[HA]}$, the lower the value of K_a, the smaller the number of ions formed. Answer *D* has the smallest K_a, so HCN is the weakest acid.

▌ **9. (A) is correct.** $K_a = \dfrac{[H^+][C_2H_3O_2^-]}{[HC_2H_3O_2]}$. Because $[H^+] = [C_2H_3O_2^-]$, substituting known values into the equation for K_a gives $1.8 \times 10^{-5} = \dfrac{x^2}{0.01 - x}$. Because x is such a small number, it can be ignored in $[HC_2H_3O_2]$, assuming that $0.01 - x$ can be considered to be 0.01. Thus, $1.8 \times 10^{-5} = \dfrac{x^2}{0.01}$, and $x^2 = 1.8 \times 10^{-7}$. Solving for x, $[H^+] = 4.2 \times 10^{-4}$. The expression $-\log(4.2 \times 10^{-4})$ equals 3.4, which is the pH.

▌ **10. (C) is correct.** Because the pH is 5.7, $[H^+] = 10^{-5.7} = 2.0 \times 10^{-6}$.

Free-Response Question

(a) At 25°C, $[H^+][OH^-] = 1.0 \times 10^{-14}$

$$[H^+] = \frac{1.00 \times 10^{-14}}{[OH^-]} = \frac{1.0 \times 10^{-14}}{10^{-2}}$$

$$= 1.0 \times 10^{-12} \, M$$

The solution is basic because $[H^+] < [OH^-]$.

(b) In this instance, $[H^+] = \dfrac{1.00 \times 10^{-14}}{[OH^-]} = \dfrac{1.0 \times 10^{-14}}{(1.8 \times 10^{-9})}$

$$= 5.0 \times 10^{-6} \, M$$

The solution is acidic because $[H^+] > [OH^-]$.

This response uses two different expressions of hydroxide ion concentration and the ion-product constant for water to calculate the corresponding hydrogen ion concentration. It then compares the hydrogen ion concentration and the hydroxide ion concentration and correctly determines whether the solution is acidic or basic.

CHAPTER 17

Additional Aspects of Aqueous Equilibria

Because water is the most common and most important solvent on Earth, equilibria that occur in water solutions are of special importance.

The Common-Ion Effect; and Buffered Solutions

▌ When a strong electrolyte is added to a solution of a weak electrolyte with which it has an ion in common, the dissociation effect in the weak electrolyte is less. This phenomenon is called the **common-ion effect.** For example, suppose a $KC_2H_3O_2$ solution is added to the equilibrium $HC_2H_3O_2(aq) \leftrightarrows H^+(aq) + C_2H_3O_2^-(aq)$. The K^+ has no effect on the equilibrium. However, as shown by LeChâtelier's principle, the increase in $[C_2H_3O_2^-]$ shifts the reaction to the left, reducing the amount of acetic acid that dissociates.

▌ Specific examples of the common-ion effect include solutions with weak conjugate acid-base pairs. These solutions undergo only small changes in pH when a strong acid or strong base is added and are called **buffers** or **buffered solutions.**

▌ A buffer resists changes in pH because it contains both an acidic substance to neutralize OH^- ions and a basic one to neutralize H^+ ions. However, both the acid and the base must be weak so that they do not neutralize each other. Buffers usually consist of a weak acid or a weak base and a salt of that acid or base.

▌ An example of a buffer is a solution that contains carbonic acid and the bicarbonate ion. If acid is added to the system, the bicarbonate ions accept protons, creating more carbonic acid. If base is added to the system, it is neutralized by the carbonic acid.

▌ **Buffer capacity** is the amount of acid or base the buffer can neutralize before the pH begins to change to any appreciable degree.

▌ The **Henderson-Hasselbalch equation** represents the relationship among pH, pK_a, and the concentrations of an acid and its conjugate base; $pH = pK_a + \log([base]/[acid])$.

Acid-Base Titrations

▌ In an acid-base titration, a base of known concentration is slowly added to an equivalent amount of acid of unknown concentration, or a known acid is added to an unknown base.

- The point at which the solution has a stoichometrically equal amount of acid and base is its **equivalence point.** Equivalence points are indicated by color changes in acid-base indicators that have been added to the solution.
- A **pH titration curve** is a graph showing the pH versus volume of added titrant. The curve depicts the pH changes that occur when the pH is calculated at various stages of the titration.

Solubility Equilibria

- A heterogeneous equilibrium exists between a solid compound and its ions in a saturated solution. K_{sp} is the **solubility-product constant** for the equilibrium, and it expresses the extent to which the compound dissolves.
- The solubility-product constant is written the same way other equilibrium constants are written. It equals the product of the concentration of the ions involved in the equilibrium, each raised to the power of its coefficient in the equilibrium equation. For example, for $Ag_2CrO_4(s) \leftrightarrows 2Ag^+(aq) + CrO_4^{2-}(aq)$, $K_{sp} = [Ag^+]^2[CrO_4^{2-}]$. Note that even though the solid is not included in the expression, it must be present for the equilibrium to exist.
- Remember that solubility is the amount of a solute that will dissolve to form a saturated solution. Solubility can be used to determine K_{sp}, and K_{sp} can be used to determine solubility according to the following figure.

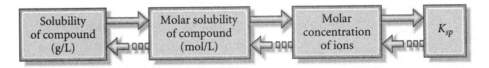

- The following example provides more detail as to how K_{sp} can be used to determine solubility. The K_{sp} for copper(II) carbonate is 2.3×10^{-10}; $K_{sp} = 2.3 \times 10^{-10} = [Cu^{2+}][CO_3^{2-}]$. Because the concentrations of the ions are the same, $x^2 = 2.3 \times 10^{-10}$, and $x = 1.5 \times 10^{-5}$. Thus, $[Cu^{2+}]$ and $[CO_3^{2-}]$ both equal $1.5 \times 10^{-5} M$. Molarity, or mol/L, can be changed to solubility in g/L by multiplying the concentration by the molar mass of the compound; 1.5×10^{-5} mol/L $\times 123.56$ g/mol $= 1.8 \times 10^{-3}$ g/L.
- In a similar fashion, solubility—or another means of determining the concentration of ions in solution—can be used to calculate K_{sp}.

Factors that Affect Solubility

- One factor that can affect the solubility of ionic compounds is the presence of common ions. In general, if a salt is slightly soluble, its solubility is decreased by the presence of a substance that furnishes a common ion.
- The solubility of most ionic compounds is affected by a considerable change in the pH of the solution. The more basic the anion, the more solubility is affected by change in pH.
- When Lewis bases interact with metal ions—particularly those of the transition metals—**complex ions** form, and the solubility of the compound will increase considerably.

Precipitation and Separation of Ions

▌ Equilibrium can be achieved by a solid in a saturated solution, such as when solid AgCl is added to water, and the compound dissolves until the solution becomes saturated. However, Ag^+ and Cl^- can also be added to a solution from salts containing these ions, such as adding silver nitrate and sodium chloride.

▌ If salts provide the ions, a precipitate forms if the solution contains more ions than can remain in solution at that temperature, as reflected by the K_{sp} of the compound. In other words, precipitation occurs when $Q > K_{sp}$, and it continues until $Q = K_{sp}$. Remember that Q is the reaction quotient, which expresses the relationship among actual concentrations.

▌ Ions can be separated from each other based on the solubilities of their salts. For example, $K_{sp} = 6.3 \times 10^{-7}$ for lead(II) sulfate, and $K_{sp} = 1.5 \times 10^{-5}$ for silver sulfate. If Pb^{2+} and Ag^+ ions are present in solution and the sulfate ion is added, $PbSO_4$ will precipitate before Ag_2SO_4 will because its K_{sp} is lower. If just enough sulfate ions are added to precipitate the $PbSO_4$, the lead and silver ions can be separated. Such a process is **selective precipitation.**

For Additional Review

Describe the buffer systems that exist in the human body. Use chemical equations to show what happens to the systems when small amounts of acid or base are added to them.

Multiple-Choice Questions

1. Which of the following choices could form a buffer system?
   (A) NaCl and HCl
   (B) $NaC_2H_3O_2$ and $HC_2H_3O_2$
   (C) NaCN and KCN
   (D) KOH and H_3PO_4
   (E) $Ca(NO_3)_2$ and HNO_3

2. A 50.0-mL sample of an aqueous H_2SO_4 solution is titrated with a 0.375 M NaOH solution. The equivalence point is reached with 62.5 mL of the base. The concentration of H_2SO_4 is
   (A) 0.234 M
   (B) 0.469 M
   (C) 0.150 M
   (D) 0.300 M
   (E) 0.938 M

3. What is the solubility-product constant expression for the equilibrium formed by solid $Cr(OH)_3$ in solution?
   (A) $K_{sp} = [Cr^+][OH^-]$
   (B) $K_{sp} = [Cr^{3+}][OH^-]$
   (C) $K_{sp} = [Cr^{3+}]^3[OH^-]$
   (D) $K_{sp} = [Cr^{3+}][OH^-]^3$
   (E) $K_{sp} = [Cr^+][OH^-]^3/[Cr(OH)_3]$

4. What is the solubility of CuS at 25°C if its $K_{sp} = 6 \times 10^{-37}$?
   (A) 7.4×10^{-17} g/L
   (B) 3.0×10^{-19} g/L
   (C) 7.4×10^{-19} g/L
   (D) 7.7×10^{-19} g/L
   (E) 7.7×10^{-38} g/L

5. What is the solubility at 25°C of $Zn(OH)_2$ if its $K_{sp} = 3.0 \times 10^{-16}$?
   (A) 8.7×10^{-9} g/L
   (B) 4.2×10^{-6} g/L
   (C) 4.2×10^{-4} g/L
   (D) 6.7×10^{-6} g/L
   (E) 6.7×10^{-4} g/L

6. In which of the following choices would you expect AgCl to have the highest solubility?
   (A) Pure water
   (B) $0.020\ M\ BaCl_2$
   (C) $0.015\ M\ NaCl$
   (D) $0.020\ M\ AgNO_3$
   (E) $0.020\ M\ KCl$

7. KCl is added to a solution that contains equivalent amounts of the following three ions. In what order will the ions precipitate out of solution? For $PbCl_2$, $K_{sp} = 1.7 \times 10^{-5}$; for Hg_2Cl_2, $K_{sp} = 1.2 \times 10^{-18}$; and for AgCl, $K_{sp} = 1.8 \times 10^{-10}$.
   I. Pb^{2+}
   II. Hg_2^{2+}
   III. Ag^+
   (A) I, II, III
   (B) I, III, II
   (C) II, III, I
   (D) II, I, III
   (E) III, II, I

8. A solution containing 2.3×10^{-3} mol $CoCl_2$ is added to a solution containing 1.2×10^{-6} mol Na_2CO_3. ($K_{sp} = 1.0 \times 10^{-10}$ for $CoCO_3$.) Which of the following statements is true?
   (A) $CoCO_3$ will precipitate because $Q > K_{sp}$.
   (B) $CoCO_3$ will not precipitate because $Q > K_{sp}$.
   (C) $CoCO_3$ will precipitate because $Q < K_{sp}$.
   (D) $CoCO_3$ will not precipitate because $Q < K_{sp}$.
   (E) $CoCO_3$ will precipitate because $Q = K_{sp}$.

9. Calculate the maximum concentration (in M) of silver ions (Ag^+) in a solution that contains $0.025\ M$ of CO_3^{2-}. The K_{sp} of Ag_2CO_3 is 8.1×10^{-12}.
   (A) $1.8 \times 10^{-5}\ M$
   (B) $1.4 \times 10^{-6}\ M$
   (C) $2.8 \times 10^{-6}\ M$
   (D) $3.2 \times 10^{-10}\ M$
   (E) $8.1 \times 10^{-12}\ M$

10. Which of the following statements is true?
    (A) Some ions, such as $Na^+(aq)$, frequently appear in solutions but never participate in solubility equilibria.
    (B) Adding a common ion does not affect the solubility of a slightly soluble compound.
    (C) The selective precipitation of Ag^+ is promoted by the addition of soluble Cl^-.
    (D) Ions such as K^+ and Na^+ are common ions, so their values in equilibrium constant expressions are always 1.00.
    (E) Common ions precipitate all other ions.

Free-Response Question

Explain how the following equilibrium can act as a buffer system:

$$NH_3(aq) + H_2O(l) \rightleftharpoons NH_4^+(aq) + OH^-(aq)$$

Multiple-Choice Questions

1. **(B) is correct.** A buffer system consists of a weak acid or a weak base and a salt of that acid or base. Acetic acid is a weak acid, and sodium acetate is a salt of that acid. None of the other choices meet these requirements. In answers *A* and *E*, the acids are strong. Answer *C* consists of two salts, and answer *D* is an acid and a base.

2. **(A) is correct.** The equivalence point is reached when the number of moles of H^+ and OH^- are equal. Because 1 mol of OH^- is produced from 1 mol NaOH, the number of moles of OH^- used is 0.375 mol/L $\times$ 0.0625 L, or 0.0234 mol. Because 1 mol H_2SO_4 produces 2 mol H^+, the number of moles of H_2SO_4 needed is 0.0234 mol/2, or 0.0117 mol. The molarity of the H_2SO_4 is 0.0117 mol/0.0500 L, or 0.234 M.

3. **(D) is correct.** The solubility-product constant expression shows the relationships among the concentrations of the species involved in the equilibrium. The subscript of an ion gives the power of the concentration of the ion in the expression. Because the subscript of Cr^{3+} in $Cr(OH)_3$ is 1, the concentration of Cr^{3+} is written $[Cr^{+3}]$. Because the subscript of OH^- in the compound is 3, the concentration of OH^- is written $[OH^-]^3$. The solid compound $Cr(OH)_3$ is not written in the expression.

4. **(A) is correct.** $K_{sp} = 6 \times 10^{-37} = [Cu^{2+}][S^{2-}]$. Because $[Cu^{2+}]$ and $[S^{2-}]$ are in a 1:1 ratio, $x^2 = 6 \times 10^{-37}$, and $x = 7.7 \times 10^{-19}$ M. Multiplying this concentration by the molar mass of CuS gives the solubility; 7.7×10^{-19} mol/L $\times$ 95.62 g/mol = 7.4×10^{-17} g/L.

5. **(C) is correct.** $K_{sp} = 3.0 \times 10^{-16} = [Zn^{2+}][OH^-]^2 = x(2x)^2 = 4x^3$. Thus, $4x^3 = 3.0 \times 10^{-16}$, $x^3 = 7.5 \times 10^{-17}$, and $x = 4.2 \times 10^{-6}$ M. The solubility can be found by multiplying this concentration by the molar mass; 4.2×10^{-6} mol/L $\times$ 99.41 g/mol = 4.2×10^{-4} g/L.

6. **(A) is correct.** The solubility of a solute is decreased when a common ion is added. Each of answers *B* through *E* lists a compound that contains either Ag^+ or Cl^-. Pure water is the only compound listed that contains no common ions.

7. **(C) is correct.** The lower the K_{sp}, the more quickly the compound will precipitate out of solution. The smallest K_{sp} is for Hg_2Cl_2, that for AgCl is next, and the largest is for $PbCl_2$. Thus, the ions will precipitate out of solution in the order of II, III, I.

8. **(A) is correct.** $K_{sp} = 1.0 \times 10^{-10}$. Q is the product of the actual concentrations, $(2.3 \times 10^{-3})(1.2 \times 10^{-6}) = 2.8 \times 10^{-9}$. Because $Q > K_{sp}$, $CoCO_3$ will precipitate.

9. **(A) is correct.** $K_{sp} = 8.1 \times 10^{-12} = [Ag^+]^2[CO_3^{2-}] = [Ag^+]^2(0.025)$. Thus, $[Ag^+]^2 = 8.1 \times 10^{-12}/0.025$, or 3.2×10^{-10}, and $[Ag^+] = 1.8 \times 10^{-5}$ M.

10. **(C) is correct.** The precipitation of silver ions is promoted by the addition of chloride ions because silver chloride has a low K_{sp}. All other statements are false.

If acid is added, NH_3 will accept a proton, forming NH_4^+. As NH_4^+ increases, the equilibrium shifts to the left, forming more NH_3. If a base is added, the increase in OH^- shifts the reaction to the left.

This response correctly recognizes what a buffer solution is and shows how the listed equilibrium reaction responds to addition of acid or base.

Chemistry of the Environment

The information presented in Chapter 18 is not tested on the AP Chemistry Examination.

CHAPTER 19

Chemical Thermodynamics

Chemical thermodynamics relates degree of randomness and energy changes to the equilibria of chemical reactions. This relationship helps determine which reactions will be spontaneous.

Spontaneous Processes

▌ Events that occur without ongoing outside intervention are said to be **spontaneous.**

▌ A spontaneous process has a definite direction in which it occurs. For every process, there is an opposite process. One process is spontaneous, and the other is not. For example, on a warm day, melting is spontaneous, and freezing is not. The chemical reaction between iron and oxygen to form rust is spontaneous. The formation of iron and oxygen from rust is not spontaneous.

▌ The spontaneity of a process can depend on temperature. Depending on temperature, either the forward or the reverse process can predominate, or the processes can occur at equal rates and an equilibrium exists.

▌ In a **reversible process,** the change in the system is made in such a way that the system can be restored to its original state by exactly reversing the change. Changing ice to liquid water at 0°C is an example of a process that can be reversed simply by releasing energy instead of absorbing it.

▌ An **irreversible process** is one that cannot simply be reversed to restore the system and its surroundings to their original state. In an irreversible process, the system must take a different path back to its starting point. Ice melting at a temperature above its freezing point is an example of an irreversible process.

▌ Whenever a system is in equilibrium, the processes are reversible. In a spontaneous process, the change is irreversible.

Entropy and the Second Law of Thermodynamics

▌ **The second law of thermodynamics** states that when a process is spontaneous in one direction, it is nonspontaneous in the reverse direction.

▌ Whether or not a process occurs spontaneously depends not only on change in enthalpy but also on whether the disorder of the system increases. The degree of disorder or randomness of a system is called **entropy (S).**

▌ A spontaneous process is favored by a more random arrangement. For example, the solution process for ammonium nitrate is endothermic, so its change in enthalpy is not favorable for spontaneous solution. However, the product is more random than the original compounds, so entropy has increased. Thus, the process occurs spontaneously.

- The change in entropy, given by $\Delta S = S_{final} - S_{initial}$, depends on only the initial and final states of the system. It does not depend on the pathway by which a system changes.
- For processes at constant temperature, entropy change can be calculated by

$$\Delta S_{system} = q_{rev}/T$$

where q_{rev} is the heat transferred along the path of the process.
- For example, the change in entropy when 1 mol of ice melts at 0°C is

$$\Delta S = 1 \text{ mol} \times 6.01 \text{ kJ/mol} \times 1000 \text{ J/1 kJ} \times 1/273 \text{ K} = 22.0 \text{ J/K}$$

The heat of fusion for ice is 6.01 kJ/mol. Note that ΔS is positive because the system becomes more random. If 1 mol of liquid water freezes at that temperature, the entropy change is negative.
- The second law of thermodynamics can be summarized in terms of the entropy of the universe, the system, and the surroundings:

For a reversible process: $\Delta S_{univ} = \Delta S_{sys} + \Delta S_{surr} = 0$

For an irreversible process: $\Delta S_{univ} = \Delta S_{sys} + \Delta S_{surr} > 0$

- Note that entropy is not conserved; the universe is constantly becoming more random. Also note that the entropy of the universe increases during any spontaneous process and that entropy can increase for the universe even if it decreases within the system.
- If a system doesn't change energy or matter with its surroundings, the above equations can be simplified:

For a reversible process, isolated system: $\Delta S_{sys} = 0$

For an irreversible process, isolated system: $\Delta S_{sys} > 0$

The Molecular Interpretation of Entropy

- In a gas, the number of gas particles relates to entropy. In the following chemical reaction, entropy is greater on the right side of the equation because there are more gas particles.

$$2NH_3(g) \leftrightarrows N_2(g) + 3H_2(g)$$

The entropy change for the forward reaction is positive, and it is negative for the reverse reaction.
- Entropy increases as temperature increases because kinetic energy of the particles also increases. The following figure shows how entropy increases greatly during a phase change because the particles are freer to move.

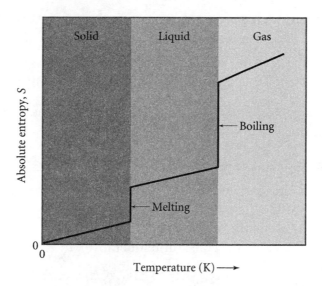

Entropy Changes in Chemical Reactions

▌ ΔS is not easily measured for a chemical reaction. However, absolute entropy, S, can be determined experimentally.

▌ Molar entropy values for substances in their standard states (1 atm, 298 K) are known as **standard molar entropies ($S°$)**. From the following table you can observe that standard molar entropy increases with increasing molar mass and with an increasing number of atoms in the formula.

STANDARD MOLAR ENTROPIES OF SELECTED SUBSTANCES AT 298 K	
Substance	**$S°$, J/mol-K**
Gases	
$H_2(g)$	130.7
$N_2(g)$	191.6
$O_2(g)$	205.2
$H_2O(g)$	188.8
$NH_3(g)$	192.5
$CH_3OH(g)$	237.6
$C_6H_6(g)$	269.2
Liquids	
$H_2O(l)$	69.9
$CH_3OH(l)$	126.8
$C_6H_6(l)$	172.8
Solids	
$Li(s)$	29.1
$Na(s)$	51.3
$K(s)$	64.7
$Fe(s)$	27.3
$FeCl_3(s)$	142.3
$NaCl(s)$	72.3

- The entropy change in a chemical reaction can be calculated by subtracting the sum of the entropies of the reactants from the sum of the entropies of the products.

$$\Delta S^\circ = \Sigma n S^\circ(\text{products}) - \Sigma m S^\circ(\text{reactants})$$

The variables n and m are the coefficients of the substances in the chemical equation.

Gibbs Free Energy; and Free Energy and Temperature

- Because the spontaneity of a reaction involves changes in both enthalpy and entropy, the equation for **Gibbs free energy** (or just **free energy**) relates the enthalpy, absolute temperature, and entropy of a state.
- For a process at any constant temperature, the free energy is defined as

$$\Delta G = \Delta H - T\Delta S$$

- The sign of ΔG provides information about the spontaneity of a reaction. If ΔG is negative, the reaction is spontaneous in the forward direction. If it is zero, the reaction is at equilibrium. If it is positive, the reaction in the forward direction is nonspontaneous, but the reaction in the reverse direction will be spontaneous.
- The equation for finding the standard free-energy change for a chemical process at 25°C is similar to that used to find the entropy change. G_f° is the standard free energy of formation. Values of G_f° for certain substances can be found in Appendix C of your textbook. Note that $G_f^\circ = 0$ for any free element that is in the state at which it occurs under standard conditions.

$$\Delta G^\circ = \Sigma n G_f^\circ(\text{products}) - \Sigma m G_f^\circ(\text{reactants})$$

Free Energy and the Equilibrium Constant

- To calculate ΔG under nonstandard conditions, use the equation $\Delta G = \Delta G^\circ + RT \ln Q$.
- If the system is at equilibrium, $\Delta G^\circ = -RT \ln K_{eq}$. Thus, if ΔG° is negative, $K_{eq} > 1$, and if $\Delta G^\circ = 0$, $K_{eq} = 1$. If ΔG° is positive, $K_{eq} < 1$. The more negative ΔG° is, the greater the value of K_{eq}. The more positive ΔG° is, the lower the value of K_{eq}.

For Additional Review

Review spontaneous and nonspontaneous reactions that are central to living systems. Compare the two types of reactions and list different mechanisms in which they occur.

Multiple-Choice Questions

1. Which one of the following processes produces a decrease in the entropy of the system?
   (A) Boiling water to form steam
   (B) Dissolution of solid KCl in water
   (C) Mixing of two gases in one container
   (D) Freezing liquid water to form ice
   (E) Sublimation of solid iodine to vapor

2. The melting point of bromine is $-7°C$, and its heat of fusion is 10.57 kJ/mol. What is the change in entropy when 2.00 mol of bromine changes from liquid to solid bromine at its melting point?
   (A) -3.02 kJ/K
   (B) -39.7 J/K
   (C) 39.7 J/K
   (D) -79.5 J/K
   (E) 79.5 J/K

3. Which of the following statements is true regarding entropy?
   (A) The entropy of the universe remains constant.
   (B) As with energy, mass, and enthalpy, entropy is conserved.
   (C) For a reversible process, $\Delta S_{sys} = -\Delta S_{surr}$.
   (D) In an isolated system, energy is still exchanged with the surroundings.
   (E) A change in entropy depends on the pathway of the change.

4. Which of the following chemical reactions has the greatest increase in entropy?
   (A) $2H_2(g) + O_2(g) \rightarrow 2H_2O(g)$
   (B) $2H_2O(g) \rightarrow 2H_2(g) + O_2(g)$
   (C) $2NH_3(g) \rightarrow N_2(g) + 3H_2(g)$
   (D) $N_2(g) + 3H_2(g) \rightarrow 2NH_3(g)$
   (E) $HCl(g) + NH_3(g) \rightarrow NH_4Cl(s)$

5. What is the entropy change for the following chemical reaction at 298 K?

   $$2H_2(g) + O_2(g) \rightarrow 2H_2O(l)$$

   (A) -196 J/mol-K
   (B) -266 J/mol-K
   (C) 266 J/mol-K
   (D) 327 J/mol-K
   (E) -327 J/mol-K

6. The ΔG values for the following phase changes at 1 atm are given. Which of the changes are spontaneous?
   I. At 283 K, $\Delta G = -250$ J/mol for $H_2O(s) \rightarrow H_2O(l)$.
   II. At 273 K, $\Delta G = 0$ J/mol for $H_2O(s) \rightarrow H_2O(l)$.
   III. At 283 K, $\Delta G = 210$ J/mol for $H_2O(s) \rightarrow H_2O(l)$.
   (A) I
   (B) II
   (C) III
   (D) I and II
   (E) I and III

7. A reaction that is not spontaneous at low temperature can become spontaneous at high temperature if
   (A) both ΔH and ΔS are positive
   (B) both ΔH and ΔS are negative
   (C) ΔH is positive and ΔS is negative
   (D) ΔH is negative and ΔS is positive
   (E) ΔH is positive and ΔS is zero

8. For which of the following choices is the standard Gibbs free energy of formation equal to zero?
   I. $H_2O(l)$
   II. $O_2(g)$
   III. $H_2(g)$
   (A) I
   (B) II
   (C) III
   (D) II and III
   (E) I, II, and III

9. For the following chemical reaction, $\Delta H°$ is $+137$ kJ/mol and $\Delta S°$ is $+120$ J/K-mol.

$$C_2H_6(g) \rightarrow C_2H_4(g) + H_2(g)$$

Which of the following statements is true about the reaction?
(A) It is spontaneous at all temperatures.
(B) It is spontaneous only at high temperatures.
(C) It is spontaneous only at low temperatures.
(D) It is nonspontaneous at all temperatures.
(E) Spontaneity cannot be predicted reliably for this reaction.

10. Use the following table of thermodynamic data to complete the statement.

Substance	ΔH_f^o (kJ/mol)	$S°$ (J/K · mol)
$PCl_3(g)$	−288.07	311.7
$PCl_3(l)$	−319.6	217

The vaporization of $PCl_3(l)$ is
(A) nonspontaneous at low temperatures and spontaneous at high temperatures
(B) spontaneous at low temperatures and nonspontaneous at high temperatures
(C) spontaneous at all temperatures
(D) nonspontaneous at all temperatures
(E) always in equilibrium with its condensation

Free-Response Question

Choose the sample of matter that has greater entropy in each pair, and explain your choice.

(a) 1 mol of $NaCl(s)$ or 1 mol of $HCl(g)$ at 25°C
(b) 2 mol of $HCl(g)$ or 1 mol of $HCl(g)$ at 25°C
(c) 1 mol of $HCl(g)$ or 1 mol of $Ar(g)$ at 25°C
(d) 1 mol of $N_2(s)$ at 24 K or 1 mol of $N_2(g)$ at 298 K

ANSWERS AND EXPLANATIONS

Multiple-Choice Questions

▌ 1. **(D) is correct.** The changing of a liquid or a solid to a vapor, the dissolving of a solute in a solvent, and the mixing of gases all make the particles more random, so these processes increase entropy. Particles become less random when changed from a liquid to a solid, so entropy decreases when this process occurs.

▌ 2. **(D) is correct.** Using the equation $\Delta S_{system} = q_{rev}/T$, $\Delta S_{system} = (2.00$ mol $\times$ 10.57 kJ/mol $\times$ 1000 J/1 kJ)/(273 − 7) K = 79.5 J/K. Because the change decreases entropy, the sign is negative.

▌ 3. **(C) is correct.** The entropy of the universe is constantly increasing, so entropy is not conserved. In an isolated system, neither matter nor energy is exchanged with the surroundings. Entropy change does not depend on the pathway of the change. However, for a reversible process, $\Delta S_{univ} = \Delta S_{sys} + \Delta S_{surr} = 0$. Because $\Delta S_{sys} + \Delta S_{surr} = 0$, $\Delta S_{sys} = -\Delta S_{surr}$.

■ **4. (C) is correct.** Entropy increases when, in a chemical reaction involving only gases, the number of gas particles increases. The number of particles decreases in answers A and D. In answer E, gases change to a solid, which decreases entropy. The number of particles increases for both answers B and C, but the increase is greater for answer C.

■ **5. (E) is correct.** Using the equation $\Delta S° = \Sigma n S°$(products) $- \Sigma m S°$ (reactants) and the information from the table in the student copy, $\Delta S° = 2(69.9$ J/mol-K$) - [2(130.7$ J/mol-K$) + 205.2$ J/mol-K$] = -327$ J/mol-K.

■ **6. (A) is correct.** For choice I, the reaction is spontaneous because $\Delta G < 0$, as is expected because ice spontaneously melts at 283 K (10°C). The system in choice II is not spontaneous because it is at equilibrium. At equilibrium, $\Delta G = 0$, and there is no net reaction. Ice and water coexist at the melting point. The reaction in choice III is not spontaneous because $\Delta G > 0$. Ice does not spontaneously melt below its melting point of 273 K.

■ **7. (A) is correct.** The equation $\Delta G = \Delta H - T\Delta S$ is used to determine the relationship. ΔG must be negative for the reaction to be spontaneous. If both ΔH and ΔS are positive, then it is logical that $\Delta H > T\Delta S$ when T is small, but $\Delta H < T\Delta S$ when T is large. If both ΔH and ΔS are negative, these relationships between ΔH and $T\Delta S$ are reversed. Answers C and E are nonspontaneous at all temperatures. Answer D is spontaneous at all temperatures.

■ **8. (D) is correct.** Gibbs free energy is zero for any free element in its standard state, so it is zero for choices II and III. Free energy is not zero for a compound.

■ **9. (B) is correct.** Using $\Delta G = \Delta H - T\Delta S$, $\Delta G = 137{,}000$ J/mol $- T(120$ J/K-mol$)$. For the reaction to be spontaneous, $\Delta G < 0$, so 137,000 J/mol $< T(120$ J/K-mol$)$. Solving this inequality, $T > 1140$ K. Thus, the reaction is spontaneous only at high temperatures.

■ **10. (C) is correct.** Using $\Delta G = \Delta H - T\Delta S$, $\Delta G = -288{,}070$ J/mol $- T(311.7$ J/K-mol$)$. The information for the formation of a liquid is not needed. For the reaction to be spontaneous, $\Delta G < 0$. Because T will always be positive, the reaction is spontaneous at any temperature.

Free-Response Question
Solution

(a) Gaseous HCl has the higher entropy because gases are more disordered than solids. (b) The sample containing 2 mol of HCl has twice the entropy of the sample containing 1 mol. (c) The HCl sample has the higher entropy because, although the molar masses are approximately equal, the HCl molecule contains more atoms per molecule. (d) The gaseous N_2 sample has the higher entropy because gases are more disordered than solids.

This response correctly compares pairs of substances in terms of the factors that increase entropy, including molecule size, molar mass, amount of a gas, and state.

CHAPTER 20

Electrochemistry

Oxidation-reduction (redox) reactions are among the most common and important chemical reactions. The transfer of electrons in redox reactions releases or absorbs energy in the form of heat or electricity. **Electrochemistry** is the study of relationships between electricity and chemical reactions.

Oxidation-Reduction Reactions

▌ It can be determined whether a chemical reaction is redox or not by examining the chemical equation for the reaction. Writing the oxidation number of each element in the equation above or below it shows whether the oxidation number of an element changes from one side of the equation to the other. If change in oxidation state indicates that electrons were transferred, the reaction is a redox reaction.

▌ In a redox reaction, both oxidation and reduction must occur. **Oxidation** occurs when electrons are lost by an atom, and **reduction** occurs when atoms gain electrons. An **oxidizing agent,** or **oxidant,** removes electrons from another substance by acquiring them itself. Similarly, a **reducing agent,** or **reductant,** is a substance that gives up electrons, thereby causing another substance to be reduced.

Balancing Oxidation-Reduction Equations

▌ The **law of conservation of mass** is obeyed when balancing a chemical equation for a redox reaction. The number of atoms of each element must be the same on both sides of the equation. However, for a chemical equation for a redox reaction, charge must also be balanced.

▌ Sometimes, redox equations can be balanced simply by balancing the atoms, and the charges balance also as a result. However, if atoms balance and charges do not, the equation is not balanced.

▌ One way to balance a redox equation is by using half-reactions. A **half-reaction** shows either the oxidation part of the reaction or the reduction part, but not both.

▌ Look at an example of how to use half-reactions to balance the following redox equation:

$$Fe(s) + CuSO_4(aq) \rightarrow Cu(s) + Fe_2(SO_4)_3(aq)$$

1. Examine the oxidation numbers for each atom, and note which ones change. If polyatomic ions stay the same on both sides of the equation, they can be considered a unit, like an atom. If they change from one side to the other, each atom in the ion must be considered. For this example, Fe^0 becomes Fe^{3+}, and Cu^{2+} becomes Cu^0.

2. Write the equations for the half-reactions. Be sure to use the same number of atoms indicated in the equation to be balanced. Indicate the number of electrons transferred if the greatest number of atoms were involved.

$$Fe^0 \rightarrow 2Fe^{3+} + 6e^- \qquad Cu^{2+} + 2e^- \rightarrow Cu^0$$

3. Balance both the atoms and the charges in each half reaction.

$$2Fe^0 \rightarrow 2Fe^{3+} + 6e^- \qquad Cu^{2+} + 2e^- \rightarrow Cu^0$$

4. Multiply these equations by numbers that will give you the lowest common number of electrons. Then, add the half reactions for the overall equation. Return any spectator ions, balancing them also.

$$2Fe^0 \rightarrow 2Fe^{3+} + 6e^-$$

$$\underline{3Cu^{2+} + 6e^- \rightarrow 3Cu^0}$$

$$2Fe^0 + 3Cu^{2+} \rightarrow 3Cu^0 + 2Fe^{3+} \Rightarrow 2Fe(s) + 3CuSO_4(aq) \rightarrow$$
$$3Cu(s) + Fe_2(SO_4)_3(aq)$$

▮ Many redox reactions occur in acidic solutions. When balancing equations for these reactions, follow the listed procedure. However, when balancing each half-reaction, first balance the elements other than H and O. Balance the O atoms by adding the appropriate number of H_2O molecules. Then, balance the H atoms by adding H^+. Then, balance charge.

▮ If the redox reaction occurs in a basic solution, the equations are balanced in a similar manner to how they are balanced in an acidic solution, but OH^- and H_2O are used. H^+ ions can be used if they are "neutralized" by an equal number of OH^- ions.

Voltaic Cells

▮ The energy released in a spontaneous redox reaction can be used to perform electrical work through a **voltaic** (or **galvanic**) cell. This cell is a device in which the transfer of electrons takes place through an external pathway rather than directly between reactants.

▮ The following figure shows an example of a voltaic cell. The Zn and the Cu serve as the **electrodes.** Oxidation occurs at the **anode,** and reduction occurs at the **cathode.** Electrons flow from the anode to the cathode through the wire. Ions migrate through a salt bridge or some type of porous barrier that connects the electrolyte solutions, keeping them neutral.

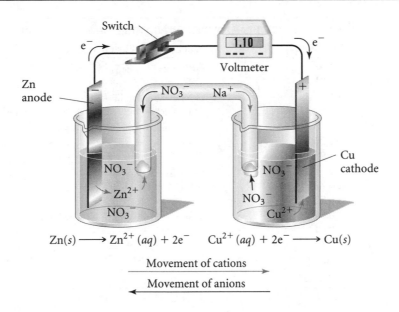

Zn(s) $\longrightarrow$ Zn^{2+} (aq) + 2e$^-$ Cu^{2+} (aq) + 2e$^-$ $\longrightarrow$ Cu(s)

Movement of cations

Movement of anions

Cell EMF

▮ The potential difference between the two electrodes of a voltaic cell provides the driving force that pushes electrons through the external circuit. This potential difference has several names—**electromotive force, emf,** E_{cell}, and **cell potential.**

▮ E_{cell} is measured in units of volts (V), and a spontaneous cell reaction requires that the cell potential be positive.

▮ The emf of a particular cell depends on conditions. Standard conditions are 25°C, 1 atm pressure for any gases, and 1 M concentrations for products and reactants in solution. For standard conditions, the emf is called the **standard emf** or the **standard cell potential,** $E°_{cell}$.

▮ The potential for an electrode is its potential for reduction, the **standard reduction potential,** $E°_{red}$. The cell potential is calculated using the following equation.

$$E°_{cell} = E°_{red}(\text{cathode}) - E°_{red}(\text{anode})$$

▮ The standard reduction potential cannot be measured directly. It is determined relative to that of a standard hydrogen electrode.

▮ The following table lists standard reduction potentials for several half-cells. Note that each reaction is written as a reduction.

STANDARD REDUCTION POTENTIALS IN WATER AT 25°C	
Potential (V)	**Reduction Half-Reaction**
+2.87	$F_2(g) + 2e^- \rightarrow 2F^-(aq)$
+1.51	$MnO_4^-(aq) + 8H^+(aq) + 5e^- \rightarrow Mn^{2+}(aq) + 4H_2O(l)$
+1.36	$Cl_2(g) + 2e^- \rightarrow 2Cl^-(aq)$
+1.33	$Cr_2O_7^{2-}(aq) + 14H^+(aq) + 6e^- \rightarrow 2Cr^{3+}(aq) + 7H_2O(l)$
+1.23	$O_2(g) + 4H^+(aq) + 4e^- \rightarrow 2H_2O(l)$
+1.06	$Br_2(l) + 2e^- \rightarrow 2Br^-(aq)$
+0.96	$NO_3^-(aq) + 4H^+(aq) + 3e^- \rightarrow NO(g) + 2H_2O(l)$
+0.80	$Ag^+(aq) + e^- \rightarrow Ag(s)$
+0.77	$Fe^{3+}(aq) + e^- \rightarrow Fe^{2+}(aq)$
+0.68	$O_2(g) + 2H^+(aq) + 2e^- \rightarrow H_2O_2(aq)$
+0.59	$MnO_4^-(aq) + 2H_2O(l) + 3e^- \rightarrow MnO_2(s) + 4OH^-(aq)$
+0.54	$I_2(s) + 2e^- \rightarrow 2I^-(aq)$
+0.40	$O_2(g) + 2H_2O(l) + 4e^- \rightarrow 4OH^-(aq)$
+0.34	$Cu^{2+}(aq) + 2e^- \rightarrow Cu(s)$
0	$2H^+(aq) + 2e^- \rightarrow H_2(g)$
−0.28	$Ni^{2+}(aq) + 2e^- \rightarrow Ni(s)$
−0.44	$Fe^{2+}(aq) + 2e^- \rightarrow Fe(s)$
−0.76	$Zn^{2+}(aq) + 2e^- \rightarrow Zn(s)$
−0.83	$2H_2O(l) + 2e^- \rightarrow H_2(g) + 2OH^-(aq)$
−1.66	$Al^{3+}(aq) + 3e^- \rightarrow Al(s)$
−2.71	$Na^+(aq) + e^- \rightarrow Na(s)$
−3.05	$Li^+(aq) + e^- \rightarrow Li(s)$

▌ The value of the standard reduction potential is independent of the amount present. For example, E°_{red} is the same for the reduction of 2 mol Br_2 as it is for 1 mol Br_2.

▌ When a voltaic cell is based on two standard half-reactions, the reaction with the most positive E°_{red} will occur at the cathode. The reaction with the less positive E°_{red} will occur at the anode. For example, in the Cu/Zn cell, the E°_{red} for Cu is more positive (+0.34 V) than that for Zn (−0.76 V), so Cu becomes the cathode, and Zn is the anode.

Spontaneity of Redox Reactions

▌ Voltaic cells use redox reactions that proceed spontaneously. It is possible to decide whether a redox reaction will be spontaneous by using half-cell potentials to calculate the emf associated with it.

$$E^\circ = E^\circ_{red} \text{ (reduction process)} - E^\circ_{red}(\text{oxidation process})$$

▌ A positive value of E° indicates a spontaneous process, and a negative value of E° indicates a nonspontaneous one.

Effect of Concentration on Cell EMF

▌ The **Nernst equation** shows how to calculate the emf under nonstandard conditions.

$$E = E^\circ - (RT/nF) \ln Q$$

E is the emf under nonstandard conditions, n is the number of electrons transferred during the reaction, F is Faraday's constant (96,500 J/V-mol), and Q is the reaction quotient.

■ The Nernst equation explains why the emf of a voltaic cell drops as it discharges. As reactants are converted to products, the value of Q increases, so the value of E decreases, eventually reaching $E = 0$, thus the cell reaction has reached equilibrium, and no net reaction is occurring in the voltaic cell.

For Additional Review

Investigate the use of the "sacrificial metals" that help prevent corrosion of other metals. Relate your findings to the reduction potentials of these metals.

Multiple-Choice Questions

1. Which of the following reactions involve oxidation reduction (redox)?
   - I. $K_2CrO_4(aq) + BaCl_2(aq) \rightarrow BaCrO_4(s) + 2KCl(aq)$
   - II. $Pb_2^{2+}(aq) + 2Br^-(aq) \rightarrow PbBr_2(s)$
   - III. $Cu(s) + S(s) \rightarrow CuS(s)$
   - (A) I
   - (B) II
   - (C) III
   - (D) II and III
   - (E) I, II, and III

2. Which element is oxidized in the chemical reaction shown by the following chemical equation?

   $3Cu(s) + 8HNO_3(aq) \rightarrow$
   $3Cu(NO_3)_2(aq) + 2NO(g) + 4H_2O(l)$

   - (A) Cu
   - (B) H
   - (C) N
   - (D) O
   - (E) The reaction is not redox.

3. Which of the following elements is the best oxidizing agent?
   - (A) H_2
   - (B) Na
   - (C) O_2
   - (D) Li
   - (E) Ca

4. What is the coefficient of Br^- when the following equation is balanced?

   $3Br_2(l) \rightarrow Br^-(aq) + BrO_3^-(aq)$ (basic)

   - (A) 1
   - (B) 2
   - (C) 3
   - (D) 4
   - (E) 5

5. What is the coefficient of MnO_4^- in the balanced form of the following redox reaction that occurs in an acidic solution?

   $MnO_4^-(aq) + SO_2(g) \rightarrow$
   $Mn^{2+}(aq) + SO_4^{2-}(aq)$

   - (A) 1
   - (B) 2
   - (C) 3
   - (D) 4
   - (E) 5

6. The electrode at which oxidation occurs is called the
   - (A) oxidizing agent
   - (B) cathode
   - (C) reducing agent
   - (D) anode
   - (E) voltaic cell

7. The purpose of the salt bridge in an electro-chemical cell is to
   (A) maintain electrical neutrality in the half-cells via migration of ions
   (B) provide a source of ions to react at the anode and cathode
   (C) provide oxygen to facilitate oxidation at the anode
   (D) provide a means for electrons to travel from the anode to the cathode
   (E) provide a means for electrons to travel from the cathode to the anode

8. What is the value of the cell potential for a cell in which the electrodes are copper and sodium?
   (A) 0.92
   (B) 2.37
   (C) −2.37
   (D) 3.05
   (E) 36.71

9. Using the standard reduction potentials from the table, determine which of the following reactions is/are spontaneous under standard conditions.
   I. $Cu(s) + 2H^+(aq) \rightarrow$
      $Cu^{2+}(aq) + H_2(g)$
   II. $Cl_2(g) + 2I^-(aq) \rightarrow$
      $2Cl^-(aq) + I_2(s)$
   III. $Fe^{2+}(aq) + Ni(s) \rightarrow$
      $Ni^{2+}(aq) + Fe(s)$
   (A) I
   (B) II
   (C) III
   (D) I and III
   (E) II and III

10. What value of n will be used in the Nernst equation for the following redox reaction?

$$2Al(s) + 6HCl(aq) \rightarrow 2AlCl_3(aq) + 3H_2(g)$$

   (A) 1
   (B) 2
   (C) 3
   (D) 6
   (E) 12

Free-Response Question

   Use standard reduction potentials for iron and magnesium to determine why magnesium is often used to protect iron from corrosion.

ANSWERS AND EXPLANATIONS

Multiple-Choice Questions

   1. (C) is correct. If the oxidation number for each element is written by its symbol in each chemical equation, it is seen that oxidation numbers don't change from one side of the equation to the other for equations I and II. In the third equation, Cu^0 changes to Cu^{2+}, and S^0 becomes S^{2-}.

   2. (A) is correct. In the equation, Cu^0 changes to Cu^{2+}, and some of the N^{5+} changes to N^{2+}. Because copper has lost electrons, copper has been oxidized.

   3. (C) is correct. Because an oxidizing agent is reduced, the element that is the best oxidizing agent is the one that is most easily reduced. Reduction involves gaining electrons. With the exception of O_2, all the elements listed are chemically metallic in nature and will tend to lose electrons instead of gaining them. O_2 tends to form negative ions by gaining electrons, so it is the strongest oxidizing agent.

▌ **4. (E) is correct.** Because this reaction occurs in a basic solution, OH^-, H_2O, and, if needed, H^+ that has an equal number of OH^- can be used to help balance the equation. The balanced equation is $3Br_2(l) + 6OH^-(aq) \rightarrow 5Br^-(aq) + BrO_3^-(aq) + H_2O(l)$.

▌ **5. (B) is correct.** Because this reaction occurs in an acidic solution, H_2O, and H^+ can be used to help balance the equation. The balanced reduction half-reaction is $8H^+ + MnO_4^- + 5e^- \rightarrow Mn^{2+} + 2H_2O$. The balanced oxidation half-reaction is $2H_2O + SO_2 \rightarrow SO_4^{2-} + 4H^+ + 2e^-$. Multiplying the reduction half-reaction by 2 and the oxidation half-reaction by 5 to make the number of electrons lost and gained equal and then adding the two equations together results in $2H_2O(l) + 2MnO_4^-(aq) + 5SO_2(g) \rightarrow 2Mn^{2+}(aq) + 5SO_4^{2-}(aq) + 4H^+(aq)$.

▌ **6. (D) is correct.** In a voltaic cell, electrons travel from the anode to the cathode. For electrons to be available from the anode, atoms at that electrode must lose electrons. Oxidation is the loss of electrons from atoms, so this is the process that occurs at the anode.

▌ **7. (A) is correct.** A salt bridge allows for migration of ions so that the half-cells remain electrically neutral. Negative ions move from the cathode half-cell to the anode half-cell, and positive ions move in the opposite direction. A wire provides a path for the electrons moving from the anode to the cathode.

▌ **8. (D) is correct.** From the values in the table, E°_{red}(cathode) $= +0.34$ V, and E°_{red}(anode) $= -2.71$ V. Note that the reaction with the more positive E°_{red} occurs at the cathode. Using the equation $E^\circ_{cell} = E^\circ_{red}$(cathode) $- E^\circ_{red}$(anode), $E^\circ_{cell} = +0.34$ V $- (-2.71$ V$) = 3.05$ V.

▌ **9. (B) is correct.** Spontaneous reactions occur when E°_{cell} is positive. Using the values from the table and the equation $E^\circ_{cell} = E^\circ_{red}$(cathode) $- E^\circ_{red}$(anode), E°_{cell} is positive only for the second reaction.

▌ **10. (D) is correct.** Each of the two Al^0 atoms loses $3e^-$ to become Al^{3+}, for a total of $6e^-$. Each of six H^+ ions gains $1e^-$ to become a hydrogen atom, for a total of $6e^-$. Because six electrons are transferred during the reaction, the value of n in the Nernst equation is 6.

Free-Response Question

The standard reduction potentials for iron and magnesium are

$$Mg^{2+} + 2e^- \rightarrow Mg \qquad E^\circ_{red} = -2.37 \text{ V}$$
$$Fe^{2+} + 2e^- \rightarrow Fe \qquad E^\circ_{red} = -0.44 \text{ V}$$

Because E°_{red} (Mg) is more negative than E°_{red} (Fe), Mg is more easily oxidized than Fe. Thus when iron and magnesium are connected, magnesium is preferentially oxidized, and iron becomes the site at which a reduction reaction occurs:

$$O_2(g) + 4H^+(aq) + 4e^- \rightarrow 2H_2O(l)$$

Thus, iron acts as a cathode and will not be oxidized until all the magnesium is used.

This response correctly uses the table of standard reduction potentials and compares the resulting standard reduction potentials for these elements. It then applies this information to determine which element is oxidized and which element is not according to the makeup of the electrodes involved.

CHAPTER 21

Nuclear Chemistry

Most of the changes that have occurred so far in your study of chemistry have been chemical changes that involve interactions among electrons. Nuclear chemistry differs in that it involves changes in an atom's nucleus.

Radioactivity

▌ The nucleus of an atom is made up of protons and neutrons, which are known as **nucleons.**

▌ Atoms of the same element that differ in the number of neutrons that they contain are called **isotopes.** Isotopes that are radioactive are called **radioisotopes.**

▌ A specific isotope of a specific element is a **nuclide.** Nuclei that are radioactive are called **radionuclides.**

▌ Because isotopes of the same element have the same atomic number, they are represented by the same symbol. However, they differ in mass number, and the symbol for the isotope must specify which isotope is under consideration. For example, cobalt with a mass number of 60 can be represented several different ways. Cobalt-60 and $^{60}_{27}$Co are probably the most common representations, but sometimes Co-60 or ^{60}Co is used.

▌ Radioactivity occurs when a nucleus emits a particle or electromagnetic radiation. The three most common types of radiation are **alpha particles (α), beta particles (β),** and **gamma radiation (γ).**

▌ An alpha particle consists of a helium nucleus, $^4_2$He. When a nuclide emits an alpha particle, its mass number decreases by four, and its atomic number decreases by two.

▌ A beta particle consists of a high-speed electron, $^{\;\;0}_{-1}$e or $^{\;\;0}_{-1}\beta$. The zero shows that these particles have negligible mass, and the -1 shows its charge. These electrons are emitted by the nucleus and are not the electrons in the shells around the nucleus. Beta emission is equivalent to changing a neutron to a proton and a beta particle. Therefore, beta emission does not change the mass number but increases the atomic number by one.

▌ Gamma rays are high-energy photons, $^0_0\gamma$ or γ. When gamma radiation is emitted, it changes neither the atomic number nor the atomic mass of the atom. Gamma radiation almost always accompanies another type of radioactive emission, and it represents the energy lost when the remaining nucleons reorganize into a stable arrangement.

▌ Two less-common types of radiation are positron emission and electron capture. A positron is identical to an electron, but it has a positive charge, ^0_1e. Electron capture involves capturing an electron from a shell. Both of these types of radiation have the same effect as changing a proton to a neutron and a positron. Thus, neither process changes the mass number of the atom, but the atomic number decreases by one.

Nuclear Equations

▌ Just as chemical reactions can be represented by chemical equations, nuclear reactions can be represented by **nuclear equations.** Just as in chemical equations, nuclear equations must show that mass and charge are conserved. In both types of equations, reactants are on the left side of the arrow, and products are on the right side. However, where atoms maintain their identity from one side of a chemical equation to the other, atoms most often change identity from one side of a nuclear equation to the other.

▌ Nuclear equations are written using symbols that show both mass and charge, such as $^{238}_{92}U$ or $^0_{-1}e$.

▌ Nuclear equations can show **radioactive decay,** which happens when a nucleus spontaneously decomposes. For example, thorium-230 undergoes alpha emission, forming radium-226. Note that the total mass (the upper numbers) is the same on both sides of the equation, as is the charge (the lower numbers).

$$^{230}_{90}Th \rightarrow {}^{226}_{88}Ra + {}^4_2He$$

▌ A nuclear equation can also show a **nuclear transmutation,** which involves a change in identity of a nucleus when it is struck by a neutron (^1_0n) or another nucleus. For example, when aluminum-27 is bombarded with an alpha particle, phosphorus-30 and a neutron form.

$$^{27}_{13}Al + {}^4_2He \rightarrow {}^{30}_{15}P + {}^1_0n$$

Rates of Radioactive Decay

▌ Different radioisotopes undergo radioactive decay at different rates. **Half-life** $(t_{1/2})$ is used to measure rate of decay because it is the time it takes for half of a sample of the radioisotope to change to a different element. Half of the sample remains after one half-life; one-fourth, $(1/2)^2$, of the sample remains after two half-lives; one-eighth, $(1/2)^3$, remains after three half-lives, and so on.

▌Some half-lives are a matter of seconds, and others are millions of years. The following table provides the half-lives of several radioisotopes.

THE HALF-LIVES AND TYPE OF DECAY FOR SEVERAL RADIOISOTOPES			
	Isotope	Half-life (yr)	Type of Decay
Natural radioisotopes	$^{238}_{92}U$	4.5×10^9	Alpha
	$^{235}_{92}U$	7.0×10^8	Alpha
	$^{232}_{90}Th$	1.4×10^{10}	Alpha
	$^{40}_{19}K$	1.3×10^9	Beta
	$^{14}_{6}C$	5715	Beta
Synthetic radioisotopes	$^{239}_{94}Pu$	24,000	Alpha
	$^{137}_{55}Cs$	30	Beta
	$^{90}_{38}Sr$	28.8	Beta
	$^{131}_{55}I$	0.022	Beta

▌Half-life is not affected by external conditions such as temperature, pressure, or state.

▌The quantitative aspects of half-life can be used in calculations to determine values such as the half-life of an isotope or the age of a sample of a radioisotope.

▌In the following equation, N_t is the number of nuclei remaining after time t, N_0 is the initial number of nuclei, and k is a number known as the **decay constant.**

$$\ln\left(\frac{N_t}{N_0}\right) = -kt$$

▌If either the half-life or the decay constant is known, the other value can be determined by the following equation.

$$k = \frac{0.693}{t_{1/2}}$$

Biological Effects of Radiation

▌Radioactivity is a nuclear change (not a chemical one), but radioactive emissions can cause chemical changes in other substances. One of the most common chemical effects of radiation can be seen in living tissue.

▌When matter absorbs radiation, the radiation can either excite or ionize the matter. Ionizing radiation is more harmful to biological systems.

▌When living tissue is exposed to radiation, water molecules absorb most of the energy. These water molecules lose electrons, forming H_2O^+, which can react with another water molecule, forming an H_3O^+ ion and an OH molecule. The highly reactive OH molecule is a **free radical** because it has unpaired electrons. These free radicals attack other molecules, forming more free radicals.

▌The amount of chemical damage done by radiation depends on the activity and energy of the radiation, the length of the exposure, and whether the source is in the body or on the outside.

▌Gamma rays are most penetrating and do the most damage from an exterior source. Alpha particles do the most damage if the source is inside the body.

For Additional Review

Find out what diseases are diagnosed and treated by high-energy radiation. List the radioisotopes that are most commonly used in radiation therapy.

Multiple-Choice Questions

1. Of the following choices, which changes the atomic number?
   (A) Alpha emission
   (B) Beta emission
   (C) Electron capture
   (D) Positron emission
   (E) All of these processes change the atomic number.

2. How does alpha decay affect a nucleus?
   (A) Atomic number is 2 less, and mass number is 2 less.
   (B) Atomic number is 1 less, and mass number is 2 less.
   (C) Atomic number is 2 less, and mass number is 4 less.
   (D) Atomic number is 2 more, and mass number is 4 more.
   (E) Atomic number is 2 more, and mass number is 2 less.

3. What other product is formed when $^{238}_{92}\text{U}$ undergoes alpha decay?
   (A) $^{234}_{90}\text{U}$
   (B) $^{234}_{90}\text{Th}$
   (C) $^{242}_{94}\text{U}$
   (D) $^{242}_{94}\text{Pu}$
   (E) $^{234}_{92}\text{U}$

4. A neutron bombards a $^{238}_{92}\text{U}$ nucleus. The product of this transmutation undergoes beta decay. What nuclide is formed by this process?
   (A) $^{239}_{92}\text{U}$
   (B) $^{238}_{93}\text{Np}$
   (C) $^{239}_{93}\text{Np}$
   (D) $^{238}_{91}\text{Pa}$
   (E) $^{239}_{91}\text{Pa}$

5. During radioactive decay, a $^{14}_{6}\text{C}$ nucleus becomes a $^{14}_{7}\text{N}$ nucleus. What type of radioactive decay has the carbon-14 nucleus undergone?
   (A) Alpha decay
   (B) Beta decay
   (C) Gamma decay
   (D) Positron decay
   (E) Electron capture

6. The half-life of a radionuclide
   (A) is constant
   (B) becomes shorter with passing time
   (C) becomes longer with passing time
   (D) becomes shorter with increased temperature
   (E) becomes longer with increased temperature

7. How much of a 150.0-mg sample of a radionuclide remains after three half-lives?
   (A) 10.00 mg
   (B) 18.75 mg
   (C) 37.50 mg
   (D) 50.00 mg
   (E) 120.0 mg

8. What is the value of the decay constant for $^{14}_{6}\text{C}$?
   (A) $1.21 \times 10^{-4} \text{ yr}^{-1}$
   (B) $2.52 \times 10^{-4} \text{ yr}^{-1}$
   (C) 0.121 yr^{-1}
   (D) 3960 yr^{-1}
   (E) 5715 yr^{-1}

9. Which of the following statements is true?
   (A) Free radicals are charged particles that do damage to biological tissue.
   (B) OH^- is an example of a free radical.
   (C) When living tissue is exposed to radiation, bone tissue absorbs most of the energy.
   (D) A free radical contains unpaired electrons, which makes it highly reactive.
   (E) Beta particles do the most damage if the radiation source is inside the body.

10. Which one of the following forms of radiation can penetrate the deepest into body tissue?
    (A) Alpha
    (B) Beta
    (C) Gamma
    (D) Positron
    (E) Proton

Free-Response Question

A sample is found to contain 1.50 mg of iodine-131. The sample is examined again later and found to contain 1.30 mg of iodine-131. How much time passed between the determinations of the amount of iodine-131 in the sample?

ANSWERS AND EXPLANATIONS

Multiple-Choice Questions

■ **1. (E) is correct.** Alpha emission decreases the atomic number by two. Beta emission increases the atomic number by one. Both electron capture and positron emission decrease the atomic number by one.

■ **2. (C) is correct.** An alpha particle contains two protons and two neutrons, so it has a mass number of 4 and a charge of $+2$. When this particle is removed from a nucleus, it reduces the mass of the nucleus by four and the atomic number by two.

■ **3. (B) is correct.** Alpha emission reduces the mass number from 238 to 234. It reduces the atomic number from 92 to 90. The element that has an atomic number of 90 is thorium, Th. Thus, the product is $^{234}_{90}Th$.

■ **4. (C) is correct.** A nuclear equation in which mass and charge are balanced is a good way to show this process. $^{238}_{92}U + ^{1}_{0}n \rightarrow ^{239}_{92}U \rightarrow ? + ^{0}_{-1}e$. Because mass is conserved, the nuclide formed must have a mass number of 239. Because charge is conserved, it must have an atomic number of 93. The element Np has an atomic number of 93. Thus, $^{239}_{93}Np$ is the nuclide formed.

■ **5. (B) is correct.** Look at a nuclear equation for the reaction: $^{14}_{6}C \rightarrow ^{14}_{7}N + ?$. The total mass is the same on both sides, so the other particle produced has a mass number of 0. The atomic number is greater by one on the right side, so the charge on the other particle produced is -1. The particle with a charge of -1 and a mass number of 0 is a beta particle, $^{0}_{-1}e$.

■ **6. (A) is correct.** The amount of a radionuclide becomes less over time, but the rate of decay remains the same. Also, half-life is not affected by external conditions, such as temperature.

■ **7. (B) is correct.** After each half-life, half the sample that was present at the beginning of the half-life remains. After one half-life, 150.0 mg/2, or 75.00 mg remains. After two half-lives, 75.00 mg/2, or 37.50 mg remains. After three half-lives, 37.50 mg/2, or 18.75 mg remains.

■ **8. (A) is correct.** The decay constant can be calculated from the half-life, $k = 0.693/t_{1/2}$. From the table in the student copy, the half-life of $^{14}_{6}C$ is 5715 yr. Thus, its decay constant is $k = 0.693/5715$ yr $= 1.21 \times 10^{-4}$ yr^{-1}.

■ **9. (D) is correct.** A free radical is a substance that contains unpaired electrons. Free radicals are usually molecules, which are not charged. OH, but not OH$^-$, is an example of a free radical. When living tissue is exposed to radiation, water absorbs most of the energy. Alpha particles do the most damage if the source is inside the body.

■ **10. (C) is correct.** Because it is electromagnetic radiation and not a particle, gamma radiation is most penetrating.

Free-Response Question
Solution

Values from the given information can be substituted for N_t and N_0 in the equation $\ln\left(\dfrac{N_t}{N_0}\right) = -kt$. From the table in the student copy, the half-life of iodine-131 is 0.022 yr. The decay constant can be calculated from this half-life by using the equation $k = \dfrac{0.693}{t_{1/2}}$;

$k = \dfrac{0.693}{0.022 \text{ yr}} = 31.5$ yr^{-1}. Thus, $\ln\left(\dfrac{1.30}{1.50}\right) = -0.143$, and

$-0.143 = -(31.5$ yr$^{-1})t$. Dividing both sides of the equation by -31.5 yr^{-1} to solve for t results in a time of 4.54×10^{-3} yr.

This response correctly identifies the equations necessary to solve for time and recognizes the source of information for half-life. It accurately uses given information and the equations to solve for the decay constant and then for the time.

Chemistry of the Nonmetals

The information presented in Chapter 22 is not tested on the AP Chemistry Examination.

CHAPTER 23

Metals and Metallurgy

Descriptive chemistry examines elements and their compounds in a systematic fashion. The location of elements on the periodic table determines many of their properties.

General Concepts: Periodic Trends and Chemical Reactions

▌ Because of the way the periodic table is organized, many trends in properties can be predicted. In general, elements in the same group have the same valence electron configuration, making the elements similar in the way they react chemically.

▌ Going from left to right across a period, electrons are added to the same shell. The increase in protons with no increase in electron shells is the basis for many trends, which are summarized in the following figure.

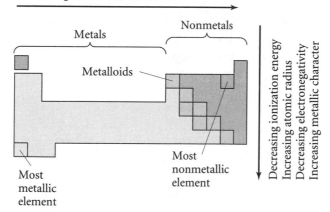

▌ One important factor that affects chemical properties is the ease with which atoms form pi bonds. The higher up in a group an atom is, the smaller the atom is, so the more easily it can form pi bonds. The pi bonds of smaller atoms are stronger than those of larger atoms in the same group.

Group 8A: The Noble Gases

▌ Because the noble gases have an exceedingly stable electron configuration, they are chemically unreactive and will undergo reaction only under rigorous conditions.

▌ Note that all noble gases have full valence shells. Such electron distributions are spherically symmetrical and particularly stable.

Group 7A: The Halogens

 ▌ Because halogens have a valence electron configuration of ns^2np^5, they need only one more electron to have a stable noble gas configuration. Thus, they have large negative electron affinities and are highly reactive, forming ions with a -1 charge.

Oxygen; and The Other Group 6A Elements: S, Se, Te, and Po

 ▌ Because group 6A elements have a valence electron configuration of ns^2np^4, they need two more electrons to have a stable noble gas configuration. Thus, they have relatively large negative electron affinities and are reactive, forming ions with a -2 charge.

 ▌ With the exception of oxygen, the elements of this group can also have positive oxidation numbers up to $+6$ and can have expanded valence shells.

Nitrogen; and The Other Group 5A Elements: P, As, Sb, and Bi

 ▌ Group 5A elements have a valence electron configuration of ns^2np^3. They can either gain three electrons or lose five electrons to have a stable noble gas configuration.

 ▌ Because they do not have a high electron affinity, these elements have a tendency to share electrons unless they are bonded to an active metal. The oxidation numbers of group 5A elements in these compounds range from -3 to $+5$.

Carbon; and The Other Group 4A Elements: Si, Ge, Sn, and Pb

 ▌ The trend from nonmetallic to metallic properties going down the group is quite evident; this group contains a nonmetal, two metalloids, and two metals.

 ▌ Because halogens have a valence electron configuration of ns^2np^2, the electronegativities of these elements are relatively low. Thus, they tend to form covalent bonds.

 ▌ Oxidation states of $+4$ and $+2$ are most common.

Metallic Bonding

 ▌ Physical properties shared by all metals include **conductivity, malleability, and ductility.** Conductivity depends on the mobility of electrons in a metal. Malleability and ductility depend on metal atoms being able to move past each other.

 ▌ A simple model of metallic bonding known as the **electron-sea model** can explain these physical properties of metals. This model theorizes that a metal consists of an array of metal cations located in a "sea" of valence electrons.

 ▌ Although the electrons are confined to the metal by an electrical attraction to the cations, they are free to move throughout the metal, and no electron is attracted to one cation more than it is to another one.

 ▌ The mobility of electrons accounts for electrical conductivity because electrons can flow from one part of the metal to another. It also explains heat conductivity because mobile electrons permit ready transfer of kinetic energy throughout the metal.

- Malleability and ductility can be explained by the fact that metal ions bond to many neighbors, and their locations can be changed without changing the nature of the metal.
- However, the electron sea model does not explain patterns in properties such as melting and boiling points, hardness, and heat of fusion.
- To explain these properties, the bonding of metals can be considered to be the overlapping of valence orbitals among several metal atoms. This overlapping of atomic orbitals leads to the formation of **molecular orbitals,** the number of which is equal to the number of atomic orbitals.
- The energies of the molecular orbitals are so close that the orbitals essentially form an **energy band,** which is formed from allowed energy states.
- This energy band is not completely filled with electrons, so it takes little energy to excite electrons in the band to unoccupied positions within the band. These excited electrons are free to move through the lattice, explaining the conductivity of metals.
- Trends such as melting point can be explained by the number of electrons present in **metal-metal bonding interactions** and those in **metal-metal antibonding interactions.**

Transition Metals

- The term **transition elements** refers to those metals whose outer d orbitals are being filled. They occupy groups 1B through 8B on the periodic table.
- Looking at the periodic table, it can be seen that the $(n + 1)s$ orbital fills before the nd orbitals for the transition metals. During chemical reactions, these metals will lose these s electrons before they lose d electrons.
- The presence of partially filled d subshells results in transition metals' exhibiting more than one stable oxidation state. Oxidation states above $+2$ are the result of successive losses of d electrons.
- Many transition metal compounds are colored.
- Several transition metal compounds exhibit **magnetic properties.** When all electrons are paired, the solid is **diamagnetic,** in which no atoms or ions have magnetic moments. Some atoms or ions are **paramagnetic,** and they contain unpaired electrons that are not influenced by neighboring electrons. When such a material is placed in a magnetic field, the magnetic moments roughly align, and the paramagnetic substance is drawn into a magnetic field. When unpaired electrons are affected by neighboring electrons, the material shows **ferromagnetism.** When a ferromagnetic material is placed in a magnetic field, the electrons align strongly with the field, and a **permanent magnet** forms. The most common ferromagnetic elements are iron, cobalt, and nickel.

For Additional Review

Draw a graphic organizer that shows the relationships among element groups, their electron configurations, and their properties.

1. What is the oxidation state of xenon in XeO_4?
   (A) +8
   (B) +6
   (C) +4
   (D) +2
   (E) 0

2. Which of the following elements has the highest ionization energy?
   (A) B
   (B) Cl
   (C) I
   (D) Mn
   (E) Na

3. Which of the listed elements is the most nonmetallic?
   (A) As
   (B) Br
   (C) F
   (D) N
   (E) O

4. Element X forms the compound LiX. Which of the following elements could be element X?
   (A) Ar
   (B) As
   (C) Cl
   (D) N
   (E) O

5. Which of the following nitrogen compounds is unlikely to form?
   (A) Ca_3N_2
   (B) K_3N
   (C) N_2O_3
   (D) N_2O_5
   (E) N_2O_7

6. Which of the following properties of metals is based more on the electrons in the metallic bond than on the cation?
   I. Conductivity
   II. Ductility
   III. Malleability
   (A) I
   (B) II
   (C) III
   (D) II and III
   (E) I, II, and III

7. What subshell is the most likely source of the two electrons lost by a copper atom when it forms a Cu^{2+} ion?
   (A) $3s$
   (B) $3d$
   (C) $4s$
   (D) $4d$
   (E) $4p$

8. Which of the following choices shows the behavior of a paramagnetic material?

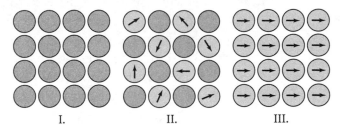

I.   II.   III.

   (A) I
   (B) II
   (C) III
   (D) II and III
   (E) None of the above

9. If four atomic orbitals overlap, how many molecular orbitals form?
   (A) 1 molecular orbitals
   (B) 2 molecular orbitals
   (C) 4 molecular orbitals
   (D) 8 molecular orbitals
   (E) 12 molecular orbitals

10. Which of the following statements is NOT true about transition metals?
   (A) They frequently have more than one common oxidation state.
   (B) Their compounds are frequently colored.
   (C) Their compounds frequently exhibit magnetic properties.
   (D) They are found in the *d*-block of the periodic table.
   (E) They typically have low melting points.

Free-Response Question

What oxidation numbers would you expect for an element that has a valence configuration of ns²np²? Explain your answer.

ANSWERS AND EXPLANATIONS

Multiple-Choice Questions

1. **(A) is correct.** Oxygen is in group 6A, so its oxidation number is -2. Because four oxygen atoms are in the molecule and the molecule is electrically neutral, Xe must have an oxidation state of $+8$ to balance the $4 \times (-2)$, or -8, charges contributed by the oxygen atoms.

2. **(B) is correct.** Ionization energy increases from left to right across a period and up a group. Thus, the elements in the upper right part of the periodic table have the highest ionization energy. Chlorine is closest to this position.

3. **(C) is correct.** Metallic properties increase from right to left across a period and from top to bottom in a group. Thus, the most nonmetallic elements are in the upper right part of the periodic table. Fluorine is in the upper right corner of the periodic table.

4. **(C) is correct.** Li, an alkali metal, forms Li^+. Thus, it will form a compound in a $1:1$ ratio with an element that forms a -1 ion. The group that forms -1 ions is the halogens, group 7A. The only halogen listed is Cl.

5. **(E) is correct.** Because nitrogen is in group 5A, it can have oxidation numbers from -3 to $+5$. All the compounds listed have an oxidation number within this range, with the exception of answer E. Nitrogen has an oxidation number of $+7$ in this compound.

6. **(A) is correct.** Conductivity is based on mobility of electrons. Current flows because electrons move, and heat is conducted because moving electrons transfer kinetic energy. Ductility and malleability are based on the fact that the cations in a metal can be moved out of position when force is applied to them.

7. **(C) is correct.** Following the standard pattern of the electrons' filling in subshells, copper has an $[Ar]4s^23d^9$ electron configuration. It will lose its *s* electrons before it loses the *d* electrons. Thus, copper will lose its 4s electrons first.

■ **8. (B) is correct.** In a paramagnetic material, unpaired electrons usually are not affected by neighboring electrons. Figure II shows unpaired electrons that are not aligned.

■ **9. (C) is correct.** One molecular orbital forms for every atomic orbital that overlaps. If four atomic orbitals overlap, four molecular orbitals form.

■ **10. (E) is correct.** All the statements are true with the exception of *E*. Transition metals typically have high melting points.

Free-Response Question

The most stable electron configuration is one that contains eight valence electrons. The atoms of this element contain four electrons. They can achieve a stable configuration either by gaining four electrons or by losing four electrons. Thus, the oxidation numbers are most likely +4 or −4. An oxidation number of +2 is also possible, because it will lose its *s* electrons before it loses its *p* electrons.

This response recognizes the implication of electron configuration on oxidation number. It accurately determines possible oxidation states based on electron configuration.

CHAPTER 24

Chemistry of Coordination Compounds

Compounds of the transition metals are associated with **metal complexes,** which are complex assemblies of metals surrounded by molecules and ions.

Metal Complexes

▌ Compounds that contain metal complexes are **coordination compounds.** The molecules or ions that surround the metal in a complex are known as **ligands.** Ligands are usually either anions or polar molecules, and each one has at least one unshared pair of valence electrons. **Hydrates** are examples of complex ions in which the ligand is water. The central metal and the ligands bound to it form the **coordination sphere** of the complex.

▌ Swiss chemist Alfred Werner proposed an explanation of what happens when coordination compounds form. According to his theory, metal ions exhibit both **primary and secondary valences.** The primary valence is the oxidation number of the metal, and the secondary valence is the number of atoms directly bonded to the metal ion, which is also called the **coordination number.**

▌ The coordination number of some central metals is constant. For example, the coordination number of Cr^{3+} is always six. The most common coordinate numbers are four and six. Coordination number can be influenced by the size of the metal ion and the size of the ligands. For larger ligands, the coordination number is smaller.

▌ Four-coordinate complexes are usually either tetrahedral or square planar in shape. Tetrahedral is most common. Most six-coordinate complexes are octahedrons.

▌ The following table shows an example of some complexes formed from cobalt, chlorine, and ammonia. Note in the modern formulation that, in each case, six ligands attach to the central metal.

PROPERTIES OF SOME AMMONIA COMPLEXES OF COBALT(III)				
Original Formulation	Color	Ions per Formula Unit	"Free" Cl⁻ Ions per Formula Unit	Modern Formulation
$CoCl_3 \cdot 6NH_3$	Orange	4	3	$[Co(NH_3)_6]Cl_3$
$CoCl_3 \cdot 5NH_3$	Purple	3	2	$[Co(NH_3)_5Cl]Cl_2$
$CoCl_3 \cdot 4NH_3$	Green	2	1	trans-$[Co(NH_3)_4Cl_2]Cl$
$CoCl_3 \cdot 4NH_3$	Violet	2	1	cis-$[Co(NH_3)_4Cl_2]Cl$

▍ Werner's explanation also clarified why the two formulations with identical formulas are different colors. The types of atoms are the same, but their arrangement differs. Werner proposed that if the Cl^- ligands are next to each other, the result is different than if they were on opposite sides of the molecule from each other. He called the form where the Cl^- ligands are beside each other the *cis* form of the complex, and the *trans* form occurs when these ligands are opposite each other.

▍ The bond between a ligand and a metal ion is an example of an interaction between a Lewis base and a Lewis acid. Because the ligands have unshared electrons, they can donate a pair of electrons, acting as a Lewis base. Metal ions act as Lewis acids because they have empty valence orbitals and can accept a pair of electrons.

▍ The properties of a complex ion are different from the atoms that form it. Color is the most obvious property that differs. Ease of oxidation and reduction are also affected.

▍ As in compounds and polyatomic ions, charge is conserved in complex ions. The charge of a complex ion equals the sum of the charges on the central ion and the ligands.

▍ The atom of the ligand bound directly to the metal is called the **donor atom**. For example, if water is a ligand, oxygen is the donor atom.

Ligands with More than One Donor Atom

▍ **Monodentate ligands** possess a single donor atom. **Polydentate ligands** (also known as **chelating agents**) have two or more donor atoms.

▍ Polydentate ligands can wrap around a metal ion and bond with it in different locations. Complexes formed from polydentate ligands are usually more stable than those that form from monodentate ligands.

Isomerism

▍ **Isomers** are compounds that have the same composition but have atoms that are arranged differently. Isomers usually differ somewhat in their properties.

▍ Isomers are of two different types. **Structural isomers** have different bonds. **Stereoisomers** have the same bonds, but the bonds have different spatial arrangements.

▍ Structural isomers are either **linkage isomers** or **coordination-sphere isomers**. Linkage isomers are relatively rare and occur when two different atoms in the ligand can be donor atoms. For example, NO_2^- can coordinate through either a nitrogen atom or an oxygen atom. Coordination-sphere isomers differ in the ligands that directly bond to the metal ion. $[Cr(H_2O)_6]Cl_3$, $[Cr(H_2O)_5Cl]Cl_2 \cdot H_2O$, and $[Cr(H_2O)_4Cl_2]Cl \cdot 2H_2O$ are coordination-sphere isomers.

■ One type of stereoisomer is also called a **geometric isomer,** and it is the most common form of isomerism. Geometric isomers exist in *cis* and *trans* forms, as previously described.

■ Another type of stereoisomer is **optical isomerism.** Optical isomers are mirror images of each other. Most of the properties of optical isomers are identical. They are distinguished from each other by their reaction to polarized light.

For Additional Review

Evaluate why an aqueous solution would be pale blue versus deep blue. What is the relationship between visible spectrum showing colors and presence of ions in aqueous solutions?

Multiple-Choice Questions

1. The coordination sphere of a complex consists of
   (A) the central metal ion only
   (B) the ligands only
   (C) the central metal ion and the ligands bonded to it
   (D) the primary and secondary valences
   (E) coordination numbers

2. A ligand with a single donor atom is called a
   (A) bidentate
   (B) chelate
   (C) linkage
   (D) monodentate
   (E) polydentate

3. Which of the following choices is NOT likely to be a ligand?
   (A) H_2O
   (B) NH_3
   (C) Br^-
   (D) CO_2
   (E) CN^-

4. What is the oxidation number of the antimony atom in the $[SbF_6]^-$ ion?
   (A) $+1$
   (B) -1
   (C) $+5$
   (D) -5
   (E) $+6$

5. What is the coordination number in $[PtBr(NH_3)_3]^+$
   (A) 1
   (B) 2
   (C) 3
   (D) 4
   (E) 6

6. For which of the following ligands is the coordination number likely to be largest for a relatively small metal ion?
   I. H_2O
   II. NH_3
   III. F^-
   (A) I
   (B) II
   (C) III
   (D) The same for II and III
   (E) The same for I and III

7. In what type of isomers are the bonds the same but the spatial arrangements of the atoms are different?
   (A) Structural isomers
   (B) Linkage isomers
   (C) Coordination-sphere isomers
   (D) Stereoisomers
   (E) Resonance structures

8. What shape is $[Fe(CN)_6]^{4-}$ most likely to be?
   (A) Cubic
   (B) Hexagonal
   (C) Octahedral
   (D) Square planar
   (E) Tetrahedral

9. In which type of isomer do all forms of the isomer have the same properties?
   (A) Coordination-sphere isomers
   (B) Geometric isomers
   (C) Linkage isomers
   (D) Optical isomers
   (E) Structural isomers

10. In one form of $[Ni(H_2O)_2(NH_3)_4]^{2+}$, two of the NH_3 ligands are at the top and bottom of the molecule. The other two NH_3 ligands are on opposite sides of the metal ion from each other. What type of isomer has this configuration?
    (A) *Cis*
    (B) *Trans*
    (C) Optical
    (D) Linkage
    (E) Polydentate

Free-Response Question

Why can't the $[Ni(NH_3)_6]^{2+}$ ion exist in cis *and* trans *forms?*

ANSWERS AND EXPLANATIONS

Multiple-Choice Questions

▌ **1. (C) is correct.** Neither the central metal ion nor the ligands by themselves form the coordination sphere. The collective central metal ion and the ligands attached to it form the coordination sphere.

▌ **2. (D) is correct.** Ligands can be monodentate or polydentate, with bidentate being a form of polydentate. Monodentate ligands are those with a single donor atom. Polydentate ligands have more than one donor atom.

▌ **3. (D) is correct.** Ligands are either polar molecules or anions. H_2O and NH_3 are polar molecules. Br^- and CN^- are anions. CO_2 is a nonpolar molecule and is not likely to be a ligand.

▌ **4. (C) is correct.** Charge is conserved, so the oxidation number for Sb plus six times the charge on F^- equals the charge on the complex ion, -1. Thus, $x + 6(-1) = -1$, and $x = +5$.

▌ **5. (D) is correct.** The coordination number is the number of ligands attached to the metal ion. In this ion, one Br^- ion and three NH_3 molecules are attached to Pt, so the coordination number is $1 + 3$, or 4.

6. (C) is correct. More small than large ligands can fit around a metal ion. Thus, the coordination number is likely to be greater for smaller ligands. F^- is the smallest ligand listed.

7. (D) is correct. Structural isomers, which include linkage and coordination-sphere isomers, have different bonds. The bonds are the same but their spatial arrangements differ in stereoisomers.

8. (C) is correct. Complex ions with six ligands are most often octahedrals. This complex ion contains six ligands.

9. (D) is correct. Properties differ somewhat between most isomers. However, optical isomers are mirror images of each other and their properties are the same.

10. (B) is correct. Because the two NH_3 ligands are opposite each other, the arrangement is *trans*. If the NH_3 ligands were next to each other, the arrangement would be *cis*.

Free Response Question

The $[Ni(NH_3)_6]^{2+}$ ion cannot exist in *cis* and *trans* forms because all the ligands are identical. To have *cis* and *trans* forms, there must be four of one type of ligand and two of another type. In *trans* isomers, identical ligands are opposite each other. In *cis* forms, identical ligands are next to each other.

This response correctly defines cis *and* trans *isomers. It then accurately evaluates the complex ion given to determine why it cannot exist in these forms.*

CHAPTER 25

The Chemistry of Life: Organic and Biological Chemistry

The study of most carbon compounds constitutes a separate branch of chemistry known as **organic chemistry.**

Some General Characteristics of Organic Molecules

▌ Bonding arrangements are important in determining the overall shape of organic molecules and determining how they will react. In almost all cases, carbon forms four bonds with other atoms. C—H bonds occur in most organic molecules. C—C bonds usually form the backbone of the molecule, and H atoms are on the surface.

▌ When all bonds of a carbon atom are single bonds, the electron pairs form a tetrahedron. The presence of a double bond makes the shape trigonal planar. A linear molecule results from a triple bond or more than one double bond.

Introduction to Hydrocarbons

▌ Compounds containing only carbon and hydrogen are **hydrocarbons.**

▌ **Alkanes** are hydrocarbons that contain only single bonds. The general formula for an alkane is C_nH_{2n+2}. The following table lists the formulas and names of the first ten hydrocarbons. Note that the names consist of a prefix that indicates the number of carbon atoms present and the suffix *-ane*.

FIRST SEVERAL MEMBERS OF THE STRAIGHT-CHAIN ALKANE SERIES			
Molecular Formula	Condensed Structural Formula	Name	Boiling Point (°C)
CH_4	CH_4	Methane	−161
C_2H_6	CH_3CH_3	Ethane	−89
C_3H_8	$CH_3CH_2CH_3$	Propane	−44
C_4H_{10}	$CH_3CH_2CH_2CH_3$	Butane	−0.5
C_5H_{12}	$CH_3CH_2CH_2CH_2CH_3$	Pentane	36
C_6H_{14}	$CH_3CH_2CH_2CH_2CH_2CH_3$	Hexane	68
C_7H_{16}	$CH_3CH_2CH_2CH_2CH_2CH_2CH_3$	Heptane	98
C_8H_{18}	$CH_3CH_2CH_2CH_2CH_2CH_2CH_2CH_3$	Octane	125
C_9H_{20}	$CH_3CH_2CH_2CH_2CH_2CH_2CH_2CH_2CH_3$	Nonane	151
$C_{10}H_{22}$	$CH_3CH_2CH_2CH_2CH_2CH_2CH_2CH_2CH_2CH_3$	Decane	174

▌ Alkanes can be straight chains of carbon atoms. Hydrocarbons that contain four or more carbon atoms can also be **branched.** For example, the following diagram shows two forms of butane.

$$CH_3 - CH_2 - CH_2 - CH_3 \quad \text{and} \quad CH_3 - \underset{\underset{CH_3}{|}}{CH} - CH_3$$

▌ The following steps summarize the procedures used to name alkanes, including those that are branched.

1. Find the longest continuous chain of carbon atoms, and use the name of this chain as the base name of the compound. (Groups attached to the main chain are called **substituents**).
2. Number the carbon atoms in the longest chain, beginning with the end of the chain that is nearest to a substituent.
3. Name and give the location of each substituent group. A substituent group that is formed by removing an H atom from a hydrocarbon is named using the prefix for the hydrocarbon and the suffix-*yl*.
4. When two or more substituents are present, list them in alphabetical order. If more than one unit of the same substituent is in the molecule, a prefix (*di*-for two, *tri*-for three, and so on) indicates the number of units present.

▌ As an example, note how the following hydrocarbon is named.

3-Ethyl-2,4,5-trimethylheptane

▌ Alkanes can also form rings. These hydrocarbons are called **cycloalkanes,** and they have the general formula of C_nH_{2n}. Cycloalkanes are named by placing the prefix *cyclo*-before the name as given by the number of carbon atoms in the ring. For example, a ring containing six carbon atoms and all single bonds is named cyclohexane.

▌ **Alkenes** are unsaturated hydrocarbons that contain at least one double bond. Alkenes having only one double bond have the general formula C_nH_{2n}. The longest chain of an alkene is named like an alkane, except the suffix used is -*ene*. In locating the double bond and branches, numbering starts at the end of the chain that gives the double bond the lower number. If more than one double bond is present, each one is numbered, and a prefix indicating the number of double bonds (*di*-, *tri*-, and so on) is placed before the-*ene* ending.

- **Alkynes** are unsaturated hydrocarbons that contain at least one triple bond. Alkynes having only one triple bond have the general formula C_nH_{2n-2}. Alkynes are named like alkenes, but the suffix used is *-yne*.
- The most characteristic reactions of alkenes and alkynes are **addition reactions,** in which the multiple bond is broken and a reactant is added to the two carbon atoms that formed the multiple bond.

Functional Groups

- The site of reactivity in an organic molecule is the **functional group** (see on the previous page) because it determines how an organic molecule behaves.
- The following table summarizes common functional groups in organic compounds.

Common Functional Groups in Organic Compounds

Functional Group	Type of Compound	Suffix or Prefix	Example	Systematic Name (common name)
$\diagdown$C=C$\diagup$	Alkene	*-ene*	H, H on C=C with H, H	Ethene (Ethylene)
—C≡C—	Alkyne	*-yne*	H—C≡C—H	Ethyne (Acetylene)
—C—Ö—H	Alcohol	*-ol*	H—C—Ö—H (with H above and below C)	Methanol (Methyl alcohol)
—C—Ö—C—	Ether	*ether*	H—C—Ö—C—H (with H above and below each C)	Dimethyl ether
—C—Ẍ: (X = halogen)	Haloalkane	*halo-*	H—C—Cl: (with H above and below C)	Chloromethane (Methyl chloride)
—C—N̈—	Amine	*-amine*	H—C—C—N̈—H (with H above and below each C)	Ethylamine
:O: ‖ —C—H	Aldehyde	*-al*	H—C—C—H (with H below C and :O: above second C)	Ethanal (Acetaldehyde)
:O: ‖ —C—C—C—	Ketone	*-one*	H—C—C—C—H (with H above and below, :O: above middle C)	Propanone (Acetone)
:O: ‖ —C—Ö—H	Carboxylic acid	*-oic acid*	H—C—C—Ö—H (with H above and below first C, :O: above second C)	Ethanoic acid (Acetic acid)
:O: ‖ —C—Ö—C—	Ester	*-oate*	H—C—C—Ö—C—H (with H above and below, :O: above)	Methyl ethanoate (Methyl acetate)
:O: ‖ —C—N̈—	Amide	*-amide*	H—C—C—N̈—H (with H above and below, :O: above)	Ethanamide (Acetamide)

For Additional Review

Make an events chain showing how to name a branched alkyne. Choose an example of a branched alkyne, and name it.

Multiple-Choice Questions

1. Hydrocarbons containing only single bonds between the carbon atoms are called
   (A) alkenes
   (B) alkynes
   (C) aromatics
   (D) alkanes
   (E) ketones

2. Hydrocarbons containing carbon-carbon triple bonds are called
   (A) alkanes
   (B) aromatic
   (C) alkynes
   (D) alkenes
   (E) cyclic

3. How many structural isomers of heptane exist?
   (A) 2
   (B) 4
   (C) 6
   (D) 8
   (E) 10

4. Alkenes have the general formula
   (A) C_nH_{2n}
   (B) C_nH_{2n-2}
   (C) C_nH_{2n+2}
   (D) C_nH_n
   (E) $C_{2n}H_n$

5. What is the name of the following alkane?

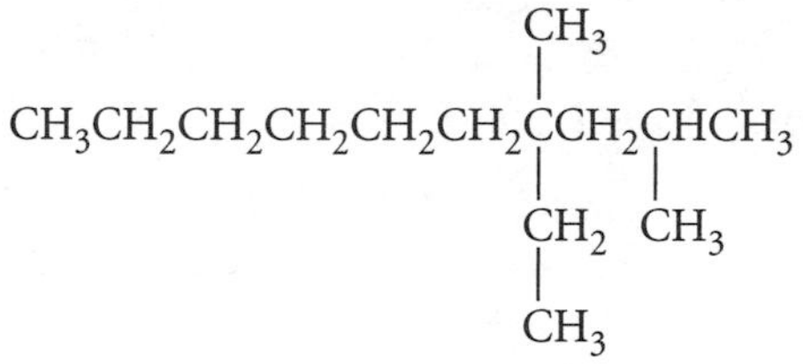

$$CH_3CH_2CH_2CH_2CH_2CH_2\overset{\overset{\displaystyle CH_3}{|}}{C}CH_2\overset{\overset{\displaystyle }{|}}{C}HCH_3$$

with CH_2 below the C (attached to CH_3) and CH_3 below the CH.

   (A) 4-ethyl-2,4-dimethyldecane
   (B) 2,4-dimethyl-4-ethyldecane
   (C) 7-ethyl-7,9-dimethyldecane
   (D) 7,9-dimethyl-7-ethyldecane
   (E) 3-isopropyl-3-methylnonane

6. Which of the following compounds is an alkyne?
   (A) C_3H_8
   (B) C_3H_6
   (C) C_6H_6
   (D) $C_{17}H_{32}$
   (E) C_2H_8

7. What is the name of the following hydrocarbon?

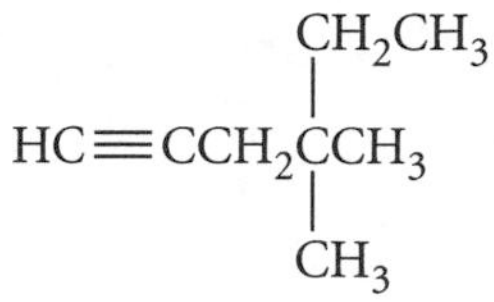

$$HC\equiv CCH_2\overset{\overset{\displaystyle CH_2CH_3}{|}}{C}CH_3$$

with CH_3 below the C.

   (A) 2-ethyl-2-methyl-4-pentyne
   (B) 3,3-dimethyl-5-hexyne
   (C) 4-ethyl-4-methyl-1-pentyne
   (D) 4,4-dimethyl-1-hexyne
   (E) 4,4-methyl-1-hexyne

8. Which one of the following is *not* an alcohol?
   (A) Acetone
   (B) Glycerol
   (C) Ethanol
   (D) Cholesterol
   (E) Ethylene glycol

9. How many C atoms are present in 2,3-diethyl-5-methylcyclononane?
   (A) 8 C atoms
   (B) 13 C atoms
   (C) 14 C atoms
   (D) 28 C atoms
   (E) 42 C atoms

10. Which of the following compounds does not contain a C=O bond?
    (A) Ketone
    (B) Aldehyde
    (C) Ester
    (D) Amide
    (E) Ether

Free-Response Question

> *From what you know about alkenes and* cis *and* trans *isomers, explain the structure of the* cis *and* trans *isomers of 2-pentene.*

ANSWERS AND EXPLANATIONS

Multiple-Choice Questions

1. **(D) is correct.** Alkanes is the only answer listed that includes only single bonds. Ketones and alkenes contain double bonds, alkynes contain a triple bond, and aromatics contain a benzene ring.

2. **(C) is correct.** Alkanes contain only single bonds, and aromatic compounds contain benzene rings. Alkenes contain double bonds. Cyclic compounds could contain a triple bond, but this situation is rare. All alkynes contain at least one triple bond.

3. **(D) is correct.** Heptane contains one isomer with a 7-carbon chain, two isomers with 6-carbon chains, four isomers with 5-carbon chains, and one isomer with a 4-carbon chain for a total of eight isomers of heptane.

4. **(A) is correct.** Alkenes contain two hydrogen atoms for each carbon atom, two more hydrogen atoms for the end carbons, less two hydrogen atoms for the double bond. The overall composition is given by the formula C_nH_{2n}.

5. **(A) is correct.** The longest carbon chain contains 10 atoms, so the base name is decane. The first substituent group is located on the second carbon from the right. Methyl groups are on carbon atoms 2 and 4, and an ethyl group is also on atom 4. Alphabetically, the substituents would list ethyl first. *Di-* is used with the methyl prefix because two methyl groups are present in the molecule.

6. **(D) is correct.** Alkynes contain two hydrogen atoms for each carbon atom, two more hydrogen atoms for the end carbons, less four hydrogen atoms for the triple bond. The overall composition is given by the formula C_nH_{2n-2}, and only answer D fits this formula.

7. **(D) is correct.** The longest carbon chain consists of six atoms and a triple bond, so the base of the name is hexyne. The triple bond is located on the first carbon. Two methyl groups are on the fourth carbon atom, so the prefix *di-* is used.

8. **(A) is correct.** All alcohols end in *-ol*, and answer A is the only one that does not end in *-ol*.

▌**9. (C) is correct.** There are nine carbon atoms in the ring. Two ethyl groups, each with two carbon atoms, and one methyl group, which contains one carbon atom, gives a total of five carbon atoms in the branches. The total number of carbon atoms is 9 + 5, or 14.

▌**10. (E) is correct.** Examining the table that shows functional groups shows that all the answers but ether contain a $C=O$ bond. Ether contains $C-O$ bonds, but they are not double bonds.

Free-Response Question
Solution

The *cis* isomer, as seen in coordination compounds, contains like ligands next to each other. *Trans* isomers have like ligands opposite each other. For unsaturated hydrocarbons, what is attached to the carbon atoms surrounding the double bond is considered. H atoms are placed side-by-side for the *cis* isomer and opposite each other for the *trans* isomer.

This response transfers concepts from a previous chapter to the structures of a hydrocarbon. It correctly distinguishes between cis *and* trans *isomers in coordination compound, and it applies this relationship to the concept of isomers of hydrocarbons based on the location of the double bond.*

Part III

Sample Tests with Answers and Explanations

On the following pages are two sample examinations that approximate the actual AP Chemistry Examination in format, types of questions, and content. Set aside three hours to take each test. To best prepare yourself for actual AP exam conditions, use only the allowed amounts of time for Section I and Section II.

MATERIAL IN THE FOLLOWING TABLE MAY BE USEFUL IN ANSWERING THE QUESTIONS IN THIS SECTION OF THE EXAMINATION.

PERIODIC TABLE OF THE ELEMENTS

1A 1																	8A 18
1 **H** 1.0079	2A 2											3A 13	4A 14	5A 15	6A 16	7A 17	2 **He** 4.0026
3 **Li** 6.941	4 **Be** 9.012											5 **B** 10.811	6 **C** 12.011	7 **N** 14.007	8 **O** 16.00	9 **F** 19.00	10 **Ne** 20.179
11 **Na** 22.99	12 **Mg** 24.30	3B 3	4B 4	5B 5	6B 6	7B 7	8B 8	9	10	1B 11	2B 12	13 **Al** 26.98	14 **Si** 28.09	15 **P** 30.974	16 **S** 32.06	17 **Cl** 35.453	18 **Ar** 39.948
19 **K** 39.10	20 **Ca** 40.08	21 **Sc** 44.96	22 **Ti** 47.90	23 **V** 50.94	24 **Cr** 52.00	25 **Mn** 54.938	26 **Fe** 55.85	27 **Co** 58.93	28 **Ni** 58.69	29 **Cu** 63.55	30 **Zn** 65.39	31 **Ga** 69.72	32 **Ge** 72.59	33 **As** 74.92	34 **Se** 78.96	35 **Br** 79.90	36 **Kr** 83.80
37 **Rb** 85.47	38 **Sr** 87.62	39 **Y** 88.91	40 **Zr** 91.22	41 **Nb** 92.91	42 **Mo** 95.94	43 **Tc** (98)	44 **Ru** 101.1	45 **Rh** 102.91	46 **Pd** 106.42	47 **Ag** 107.87	48 **Cd** 112.41	49 **In** 114.82	50 **Sn** 118.71	51 **Sb** 121.75	52 **Te** 127.60	53 **I** 126.91	54 **Xe** 131.29
55 **Cs** 132.91	56 **Ba** 137.33	57 **La** 138.91	72 **Hf** 178.49	73 **Ta** 180.95	74 **W** 183.85	75 **Re** 186.21	76 **Os** 190.2	77 **Ir** 192.2	78 **Pt** 195.08	79 **Au** 196.97	80 **Hg** 200.59	81 **Tl** 204.38	82 **Pb** 207.2	83 **Bi** 208.98	84 **Po** (209)	85 **At** (210)	86 **Rn** (222)
87 **Fr** (223)	88 **Ra** 226.02	89 **Ac** 227.03	104 **Rf** (261)	105 **Db** (262)	106 **Sg** (263)	107 **Bh** (264)	108 **Hs** (265)	109 **Mt** (268)	110 **Ds** (269)	111 **Uuu** (272)	112 **Uub** (277)						

58 **Ce** 140.12	59 **Pr** 140.91	60 **Nd** 144.24	61 **Pm** (145)	62 **Sm** 150.4	63 **Eu** 151.97	64 **Gd** 157.25	65 **Tb** 158.93	66 **Dy** 162.50	67 **Ho** 164.93	68 **Er** 167.26	69 **Tm** 168.93	70 **Yb** 173.04	71 **Lu** 174.97
90 **Th** 232.04	91 **Pa** 231.04	92 **U** 238.03	93 **Np** (237)	94 **Pu** (244)	95 **Am** (243)	96 **Cm** (247)	97 **Bk** (247)	98 **Cf** (251)	99 **Es** (252)	100 **Fm** (257)	101 **Md** (258)	102 **No** (259)	103 **Lr** (262)

Practice Test 1

Chemistry Section I
Part A

Time—1 hour and 30 minutes
Number of questions—75
Percent of total grade—45

NO CALCULATORS MAY BE USED WITH SECTION I.

Note: For all questions, assume that the temperature is 298 K, the pressure is 1.00 atmosphere, and solutions are aqueous unless otherwise specified.

Throughout the test the following symbols and abbreviations have the definitions specified unless otherwise noted.

T = temperature	M = molar
P = pressure	m = molal
V = volume	L, mL = liter(s), milliliter(s)
S = entropy	g = gram(s)
H = enthalpy	nm = nanometer(s)
G = free energy	atm = atmosphere(s)
R = molar gas constant	J, kJ = joule(s), kilojoule(s)
n = number of moles	V = volt(s)
	mol = mole(s)

Directions: Each set of lettered choices below refers to the numbered statements immediately following it. Select the one lettered choice that best fits each statement and then fill in the corresponding oval on the answer sheet. A choice may be used once, more than once, or not at all in each set.

Questions 1–4 refer to the following elements.

(A) Silver and gold
(B) Zinc and mercury
(C) Aluminum and gallium
(D) Chlorine and bromine
(E) Carbon and oxygen

1. In their standard states at 25°C, are a gas and a liquid respectively
2. Exist in well-known allotropic forms
3. Are coinage metals
4. Are members of the halogen family

Questions 5–8 refer to molecular geometry.

(A) Tetrahedral
(B) Square-planar
(C) Trigonal-bipyramidal
(D) Trigonal-pyramidal
(E) Octahedral

5. The geometry of PCl_5
6. The geometry of NH_3
7. The geometry of XeF_4
8. The geometry of CCl_4

Questions 9–12 refer to organic chemistry.

(A) Alcohol
(B) Alkane
(C) Alkene
(D) Alkyne
(E) Amine

9. C_2H_5OH
10. C_2H_6
11. C_2H_2
12. C_2H_4

Questions 13–16 refer to the following substances.

(A) Fluorine
(B) Sulfur trioxide
(C) Silver chloride
(D) Sodium oxide
(E) Ozone

13. Is an allotrope of oxygen
14. Is a basic oxide
15. Is the most reactive element
16. Is an acidic oxide important in acid rain

Questions 17–18 refer to the following choices.

(A) N
(B) Cl
(C) Ne
(D) Mg
(E) Rb

17. Which element is the most electronegative?
18. Which element has the most possible oxidation states?

Chemistry Section I
Part B

Directions: Each of the questions or incomplete statements below is followed by five suggested answers or completions. Select the one that is best in each case and then fill in the corresponding oval on the answer sheet.

19. Magnesium is more active than cobalt, and hydrogen lies below both of them in the activity series. These facts indicate that
    (A) cobalt is the most easily oxidized
    (B) magnesium is the most easily oxidized
    (C) neither metal reacts with acids
    (D) water is produced when the metals react with hydrogen ion
    (E) gas is produced when the metals react with hydrogen ion

20. What is the mass of Cu produced if 10.0 g of Cu_2S reacts with 16.0 g of O_2 as follows? (Mass of one mole: Cu, 63.5 g; O, 16.0 g; S, 32.1 g.)

$$Cu_2S + O_2 \rightarrow 2Cu + SO_2$$

    (A) 31.8 g
    (B) 63.5 g
    (C) 3.99 g
    (D) 7.98 g
    (E) 33.6 g

21. Predict the number of subshells in the fourth shell, that is $n = 4$.
    (A) 0, 1, 2, 3, and 4
    (B) 0, 1, and 4
    (C) 0, 1, 2, and 3
    (D) 0, 1, and 2
    (E) 1 and 2

22. For which of the following reactions would you expect S to be less than zero?
    (A) $H_2O(l) \rightarrow H_2O(g)$
    (B) $CO(g) + \frac{1}{2}O_2(g) \rightarrow CO_2(g)$
    (C) $2SO_3(g) \rightarrow 2SO_2(g) + O_2(g)$
    (D) $CO_2(s) \rightarrow CO_2(g)$
    (E) $2AgCl(s) \rightarrow 2Ag(s) + Cl_2(g)$

23. Which occur(s) when NaOH is added to an aqueous buffer solution containing NH_3 and NH_4Cl?
    I. pH of solution increases
    II. NH_4^+ concentration increases
    III. NH_3 concentration increases

    (A) I only
    (B) II only
    (C) III only
    (D) I and III
    (E) II and III

24. Which of the following salts would form an acidic solution in water?
    I. NH_4Cl
    II. $Fe(NO_3)_3$
    III. KCl

    (A) I only
    (B) II only
    (C) III only
    (D) I and II
    (E) II and III

25. Which of the following substances should have the highest normal boiling point?
(A) CH_3Cl
(B) CH_3Br
(C) CH_3I
(D) CH_4
(E) CH_3OH

26. What is the coefficient in front of BF_3 when the following equation is balanced?

$$BF_3 + NaBH_3 \rightarrow NaBF_3 + B_2H_6$$

(A) 2
(B) 3
(C) 4
(D) 5
(E) 6

27. Which of the following statements about the properties of a gas are true when the temperature is increased at constant volume?
   I. Pressure increases.
   II. Pressure decreases.
   III. Average molecular speed increases.

(A) I only
(B) II only
(C) III only
(D) I and III
(E) II and III

28. In C_6H_5Cl (chlorobenzene), which of the following intermolecular forces operate in the liquid phase?
   I. Ion-ion
   II. Dipole-dipole
   III. London dispersion

(A) I only
(B) II only
(C) III only
(D) I and III
(E) II and III

29. Which of the following alcohols form(s) a ketone when oxidized?
(A) 1-propanol
(B) Methanol
(C) 2-methyl-2-propanol
(D) 2-propanol
(E) All of the above

30. Which of the following descriptions of elements is NOT true?
(A) Rb is an active metal that forms a +1 cation in aqueous solution.
(B) I_2 is a grayish-black solid that readily forms a purple vapor.
(C) Pb is a bluish-gray, soft, and dense metal.
(D) H shows only nonmetallic properties.
(E) All of the above

31. Which of the following shows the atoms and ions Mg^{2+}, Ca^{2+}, and Ca in order of decreasing size?
(A) $Ca > Ca^{2+} > Mg^{2+}$
(B) $Ca > Mg^{2+} > Ca^{2+}$
(C) $Mg^{2+} > Ca > Ca^{2+}$
(D) $Mg^{2+} > Ca^{2+} > Ca$
(E) $Ca > Ca^{2+} = Mg^{2+}$

32. In which molecule would you expect the central atom to use sp^3d^2 hybrid orbitals?
(A) PF_5
(B) SF_6
(C) CO_2
(D) SiO_2
(E) SO_3

33. What is the molarity of an aqueous HBr solution if 35.00 mL is neutralized with 70.00 mL of a 0.500 M NaOH solution?
(A) 0.250 M
(B) 0.500 M
(C) 0.750 M
(D) 1.00 M
(E) 2.000 M

Questions 34–35 refer to redox reactions that involve electrochemistry.

34. For the unbalanced redox reaction

$$Ag_2S(s) + NO_3^-(aq) \rightarrow Ag^+(aq) + S(s) + NO(g)$$

in acidic solution, what is the balanced reduction half-reaction?
   (A) $Ag_2S(s) \rightarrow 2Ag^+(aq) + S(s) + 2e^-$
   (B) $S^{2-}(s) \rightarrow S(s) + 2e^-$
   (C) $NO_3^-(aq) + 4H^+(aq) + 3e^- \rightarrow NO(g) + 2H_2O$
   (D) $2H^+(aq) + 2e^- \rightarrow H_2(g)$
   (E) $NO_3^-(aq) + 2H^+(aq) + e^- \rightarrow NO(g) + 2OH^-$

35. For the unbalanced redox reaction

$$Cl_2(g) \rightarrow ClO_4^-(aq) + Cl^-(aq)$$

in basic solution, what is the balanced oxidation half-reaction?
   (A) $Cl_2 + 2e^- \rightarrow Cl^-$
   (B) $Cl_2 + 4O_2 + 2e^- \rightarrow 2ClO_4^-$
   (C) $Cl_2 + 8H_2O \rightarrow 2ClO_4^- + 16H^+ + 14e^-$
   (D) $Cl_2 + 16OH^- \rightarrow 2ClO_4^- + 8H_2O + 14e^-$
   (E) $Cl_2 + 8OH^- \rightarrow 2ClO_4^- + Cl_2 + 6e^-$

36. Using the tables of average bond energies below, the ΔH for the reaction is how many kJ?

$$C\equiv O(g) + 2H_2(g) \rightarrow H_3C-O-H(g)$$

Bond	C–O	C=O	C≡O
D (kJ/mol)	358	799	1072

Bond	C–H	H–H	O–H
D (kJ/mol)	413	436	463

   (A) +276
   (B) −276
   (C) +735
   (D) −735
   (E) −116

37. Given the following table of thermodynamic data, complete the sentence below.

Substance	ΔH_f° (kJ/mol)	S° (J/K · mol)
$PCl_3(g)$	−288.07	311.7
$PCl_3(l)$	−319.6	217

The vaporization of $PCl_3(l)$ is
   (A) nonspontaneous at low temperature and spontaneous at high temperature
   (B) spontaneous at low temperature and nonspontaneous at high temperature
   (C) spontaneous at all temperatures
   (D) nonspontaneous at all temperatures
   (E) none of the above, since not enough information is given to draw a conclusion

38. Which of the following describes an atom that is oxidized?
   (A) It loses electrons and becomes more positively charged.
   (B) It loses electrons and becomes more negatively charged.
   (C) It gains electrons and becomes more positively charged.
   (D) It gains electrons and becomes more negatively charged.
   (E) None of the above

39. The vapor pressure of a liquid will decrease if
   (A) the volume of the vapor above the liquid is increased
   (B) the volume of the liquid is decreased
   (C) the temperature is decreased
   (D) the surface area of the liquid is decreased
   (E) a more volatile liquid is added

GO ON TO THE NEXT PAGE

40. Which of the following has the largest ionic radius?
    (A) Be^{2+}
    (B) Mg^{2+}
    (C) Ca^{2+}
    (D) Sr^{2+}
    (E) Ba^{2+}

41. The solubility of $BaCO_3$ in water is increased by which of the following?
    I. Adding HNO_3
    II. Increasing pH of the solution
    III. Decreasing pH of the solution
    (A) I
    (B) II
    (C) III
    (D) I and II
    (E) I and III

42. What is the coefficient of Fe^{3+} when the following equation is balanced?

    $CN^- + Fe^{3+} \rightarrow CNO^- + Fe^{2+}$ (*basic soln*)

    (A) 1
    (B) 2
    (C) 3
    (D) 4
    (E) 5

43. What is the electron configuration for a Ca^{2+} ion?
    (A) $[Ar]4p^2$
    (B) $[Ar]$
    (C) $[Kr]4s^2$
    (D) $[Ar]4s^2$
    (E) $[Br]4s^2$

44. The standard Gibbs free energy of formation is zero for which of the following?
    I. $H_2O(l)$
    II. $O(g)$
    III. $H_2(g)$
    (A) I
    (B) II
    (C) III
    (D) II and III
    (E) I, II, and III

45. A certain liquid has a density of 2.67 g/cm^3. What volume (in L) would 1340 g of this liquid occupy?
    (A) 1.99×10^{-3}
    (B) 50.2
    (C) 3.58
    (D) 35.8
    (E) 0.502

46. Which of the following expresses the temperature 422.35 K in degrees Celsius and then in degrees Fahrenheit?
    (A) 792.23°C, 519.08°F
    (B) 149.20°C, 300.56°F
    (C) 695.50°C, 354.39°F
    (D) 50.89°C, 324.04°F
    (E) 22.78°C, 98.60°F

47. Combustion of a 1.031-g sample of a compound containing only carbon, hydrogen, and oxygen produced 2.265 g of CO_2 and 1.236 g of H_2O. What is the empirical formula of the compound?
    (A) C_3H_8O
    (B) C_3H_5O
    (C) $C_6H_{16}O_2$
    (D) $C_3H_9O_3$
    (E) $C_3H_6O_3$

48. What is the weight percentage of Al in Al_2O_3?
    (A) 26.46%
    (B) 20.93%
    (C) 52.92%
    (D) 47.08%
    (E) 62.64%

49. Which of the following statements correctly describes the responses of alpha, beta, and gamma radiation to an electric field?
    (A) Both beta and gamma are deflected, whereas alpha shows no response.
    (B) Both alpha and gamma are deflected in the same direction, whereas beta shows no response.
    (C) Both alpha and beta are deflected in the same direction, whereas gamma shows no response.
    (D) Alpha and beta are deflected in opposite directions, whereas gamma shows no response.
    (E) Only alpha is deflected, whereas beta and gamma show no response.

50. Which of the following pairs of elements should be the most similar in chemical properties?
    (A) C and O
    (B) B and As
    (C) I and Br
    (D) K and Kr
    (E) Cs and He

51. Which of the following compounds produces a basic solution when dissolved in water?
    (A) SO_2
    (B) Na_2O
    (C) CO_2
    (D) OF_2
    (E) O_2

52. The only noble gas that does not have the ns^2np^6 valence electron configuration is
    (A) radon
    (B) neon
    (C) helium
    (D) krypton
    (E) none of the above

53. A _____ ΔH corresponds to an _____ process.
    (A) negative; endothermic
    (B) negative; exothermic
    (C) positive; exothermic
    (D) zero; exothermic
    (E) zero; endothermic

54. Which element is oxidized in the reaction shown below?

    $$Fe(CO)_5(l) + 2HI(g) \rightarrow Fe(CO)_4I_2(s)$$
    $$+ CO(g) + H_2(g)$$

    (A) Fe
    (B) C
    (C) O
    (D) H
    (E) I

55. Which of the following statements correctly names and defines the law that states that "the volume of a fixed amount of gas maintained at constant pressure is directly proportional to its absolute temperature"?
    (A) Charles's law gives the temperature-volume relationship.
    (B) Boyle's law gives the temperature-volume relationship.
    (C) Charles's law gives the temperature-pressure relationship.
    (D) Dalton's law gives the temperature-volume relationship.
    (E) Avogadro's law gives the temperature-pressure relationship.

GO ON TO THE NEXT PAGE

56. One difference between first- and second-order reactions is that
    (A) the half-life of a first-order reaction does not depend on $[A]_0$, but the half-life of a second-order reaction does depend on $[A]_0$
    (B) the rate of a first-order reaction does not depend on reactant concentrations, but the rate of a second-order reaction does depend on reactant concentrations
    (C) the rate of a first-order reaction depends on reactant concentrations, but the rate of a second-order reaction does not depend on reactant concentrations
    (D) a first-order reaction can be catalyzed, but a second-order reaction cannot be catalyzed
    (E) the half-life of a first-order reaction depends on $[A]_0$, but the half-life of a second-order reaction does not depend on $[A]_0$

57. Which of the following units is appropriate for a first-order reaction rate constant?
    (A) $M\,s^{-1}$
    (B) s^{-1}
    (C) mol/L
    (D) $M^{-1}s^{-1}$
    (E) $L\,mol^{-1}\,s^{-1}$

58. According to the table shown below, the value of $\Delta S°$ for the reaction 2C (s, diamond) $+O_2(g) \rightarrow 2CO(g)$ is
    (A) -185.9 J/K
    (B) $+185.9$ J/K
    (C) -9.5 J/K
    (D) $+9.5$ J/K
    (E) -195.7 J/K

	C(s, diamond)	$O_2(g)$	CO(g)
S (J K^{-1} mol^{-1})	2	205	198

59. A reaction that is not spontaneous at low temperature can become spontaneous at high temperature if ΔH and ΔS are
    (A) + and + respectively
    (B) − and − respectively
    (C) + and − respectively
    (D) − and + respectively
    (E) + and 0 respectively

60. Consider a solution containing 0.100 M fluoride ions and 0.126 M hydrogen fluoride. The concentration of fluoride ions after the addition of 5.00 mL of 0.01000 M HCl to 25.0 mL of this solution is
    (A) 0.0850 M
    (B) 0.00167 M
    (C) 0.0980 M
    (D) 0.0817 M
    (E) 0.00253 M

61. The common-ion effect refers to the observation that
    (A) some ions, such as $Na^+(aq)$, frequently appear in solutions but do not participate in solubility equilibria
    (B) common ions, such as $Na^+(aq)$, do not affect equilibrium constants
    (C) the selective precipitation of a metal ion, such as Ag^+, is promoted by the addition of solubility
    (D) ions such as K^+ and Na^+ are common ions, so that their values in equilibrium constant expressions are always 1.00
    (E) common ions precipitate all counter-ions

62. Under what conditions can it be said absolutely that a system is at equilibrium at constant pressure and temperature?
    (A) $\Delta H = 0$
    (B) $\Delta H > 0$
    (C) $\Delta G = 0$
    (D) $\Delta G > 0$
    (E) $\Delta S > 0$

63. Which of the following factors affect equilibrium concentrations?
    I. Magnitude of equilibrium constant
    II. Initial concentration of products and reactants
    III. Temperature
    (A) I only
    (B) II only
    (C) III only
    (D) I and III
    (E) I, II, and III

64. Under suitable conditions, it is sometimes possible to form solutions that contain a greater amount of solute than what is needed to form a saturated solution. Such solutions are called
    (A) isotonic
    (B) unsaturated
    (C) supersaturated
    (D) saturated
    (E) polyunsaturated

65. Write the equilibrium-constant expressions for the following reaction:

$$CO_2(g) + H_2(g) \rightleftarrows CO(g) + H_2O(l)$$

    (A) $K_{eq} = P_{CO}/P_{CO_2} \cdot P_{H_2}$
    (B) $K_{eq} = P_C/P_{CO} \cdot P_{H_2}$
    (C) $K_{eq} = P_{CO}/P_{H_2}$
    (D) $K_{eq} = P_{H_2}/P_{CO}$
    (E) $K_{eq} = P_{HCl}/P_N$

66. Isotopes of hydrogen
    (A) have the same atomic number and different mass numbers
    (B) have the same atomic number and the same mass number
    (C) have different atomic numbers and different mass numbers
    (D) have different atomic numbers and the same mass number
    (E) are exactly alike

67. Which of the following pairs of terms accurately characterizes typical metal oxides and typical nonmetal oxides?
    (A) Basic; amphoteric
    (B) Basic; acidic
    (C) Amphoteric; basic
    (D) Acidic; basic
    (E) Amphoteric; acidic

68. What is the relative pH for the following substances: human blood, tears, egg white, seawater, and baking soda?
    (A) pH = 3.0 − 4.0
    (B) pH = 1.0 − 2.0
    (C) pH = 7.0 − 8.0
    (D) pH = 10.0 − 12.0
    (E) pH = 9.0 − 10.0

69. In which of the following is it true that the bonds are the same but the spatial arrangement of the atoms is different?
    (A) Structural isomers
    (B) Linkage isomers
    (C) Coordination-sphere isomers
    (D) Stereo isomers
    (E) Resonance structures

70. The half-life of a radionuclide
    (A) is constant
    (B) gets shorter with passing time
    (C) gets longer with passing time
    (D) gets shorter with increased temperature
    (E) gets longer with increased temperature

71. Which of the following combinations of quantum numbers for an electron is NOT permissible?
    (A) $n = 5, l = 2, m_l = 0$
    (B) $n = 3, l = 2, m_l = 3$
    (C) $n = 4, l = 3, m_l = -2$
    (D) $n = 1, l = 0, m_l = 0$
    (E) $n = 2, l = 1, m_l = -1$

GO ON TO THE NEXT PAGE

72. Hydrocarbons containing only single bonds between the carbon atoms are called
(A) alkenes
(B) alkynes
(C) aromatics
(D) alkanes
(E) ketones

73. A given atom has an atomic mass of 23 and an atomic number of 11. Which of the following statements about its atomic structure is NOT correct?
(A) Its number of protons is 11.
(B) Its number of electrons is 11.
(C) Eight electrons are in its outermost energy shell.
(D) The number of neutrons is 12.
(E) Most of its mass is in the nucleus.

74. Consider the following reaction at equilibrium:

$$2NH_3(g) \rightleftarrows N_2(g) + 3H_2(g) \quad \Delta H = 92.4 \text{ kJ}$$

Le Châtelier's principle predicts that adding $N_2(g)$ to the system will result in
(A) a decrease in the concentration of $NH_3(g)$
(B) a decrease in the concentration of $H_2(g)$
(C) an increase in the value of the equilibrium constant
(D) a lower partial pressure of N_2
(E) removal of all of the $H_2(g)$

75. The solubility of $MnSO_4 \cdot H_2O$ in water at 20°C is 70.0 g per 100.0 mL of water. A solution at 20°C that is 4.22 M in $MnSO_4 \cdot H_2O$ is best described as what kind of solution? (The formula mass of $MnSO_4 \cdot H_2O$ is 168.97 g/mol.)
(A) Hydrated
(B) Solvated
(C) Saturated
(D) Unsaturated
(E) Supersaturated

END OF SECTION I

IF YOU FINISH BEFORE TIME IS CALLED, YOU MAY CHECK YOUR WORK ON THIS SECTION. DO NOT GO ON TO SECTION II UNTIL YOU ARE TOLD TO DO SO.

Chemistry
Section II

Time—1 hour and 30 minutes
Percent of total grade—55

INFORMATION IN THE TABLE BELOW AND IN THE FOLLOWING TABLES MAY BE USEFUL IN ANSWERING THE QUESTIONS IN THIS SECTION OF THE EXAMINATION.

PERIODIC TABLE OF THE ELEMENTS

1A 1																		8A 18
1 **H** 1.0079	2A 2												3A 13	4A 14	5A 15	6A 16	7A 17	2 **He** 4.0026
3 **Li** 6.941	4 **Be** 9.012												5 **B** 10.811	6 **C** 12.011	7 **N** 14.007	8 **O** 16.00	9 **F** 19.00	10 **Ne** 20.179
11 **Na** 22.99	12 **Mg** 24.30	3B 3	4B 4	5B 5	6B 6	7B 7	8	⎡8B⎤ 9	10	1B 11	2B 12		13 **Al** 26.98	14 **Si** 28.09	15 **P** 30.974	16 **S** 32.06	17 **Cl** 35.453	18 **Ar** 39.948
19 **K** 39.10	20 **Ca** 40.08	21 **Sc** 44.96	22 **Ti** 47.90	23 **V** 50.94	24 **Cr** 52.00	25 **Mn** 54.938	26 **Fe** 55.85	27 **Co** 58.93	28 **Ni** 58.69	29 **Cu** 63.55	30 **Zn** 65.39		31 **Ga** 69.72	32 **Ge** 72.59	33 **As** 74.92	34 **Se** 78.96	35 **Br** 79.90	36 **Kr** 83.80
37 **Rb** 85.47	38 **Sr** 87.62	39 **Y** 88.91	40 **Zr** 91.22	41 **Nb** 92.91	42 **Mo** 95.94	43 **Tc** (98)	44 **Ru** 101.1	45 **Rh** 102.91	46 **Pd** 106.42	47 **Ag** 107.87	48 **Cd** 112.41		49 **In** 114.82	50 **Sn** 118.71	51 **Sb** 121.75	52 **Te** 127.60	53 **I** 126.91	54 **Xe** 131.29
55 **Cs** 132.91	56 **Ba** 137.33	57 **La** 138.91	72 **Hf** 178.49	73 **Ta** 180.95	74 **W** 183.85	75 **Re** 186.21	76 **Os** 190.2	77 **Ir** 192.2	78 **Pt** 195.08	79 **Au** 196.97	80 **Hg** 200.59		81 **Tl** 204.38	82 **Pb** 207.2	83 **Bi** 208.98	84 **Po** (209)	85 **At** (210)	86 **Rn** (222)
87 **Fr** (223)	88 **Ra** 226.02	89 **Ac** 227.03	104 **Rf** (261)	105 **Db** (262)	106 **Sg** (263)	107 **Bh** (264)	108 **Hs** (265)	109 **Mt** (268)	110 **Ds** (269)	111 **Uuu** (272)	112 **Uub** (277)							

58 **Ce** 140.12	59 **Pr** 140.91	60 **Nd** 144.24	61 **Pm** (145)	62 **Sm** 150.4	63 **Eu** 151.97	64 **Gd** 157.25	65 **Tb** 158.93	66 **Dy** 162.50	67 **Ho** 164.93	68 **Er** 167.26	69 **Tm** 168.93	70 **Yb** 173.04	71 **Lu** 174.97
90 **Th** 232.04	91 **Pa** 231.04	92 **U** 238.03	93 **Np** (237)	94 **Pu** (244)	95 **Am** (243)	96 **Cm** (247)	97 **Bk** (247)	98 **Cf** (251)	99 **Es** (252)	100 **Fm** (257)	101 **Md** (258)	102 **No** (259)	103 **Lr** (262)

GO ON TO THE NEXT PAGE

STANDARD REDUCTION POTENTIALS IN AQUEOUS SOLUTION AT 25°C

Half-reaction			$E°$(V)
$F_2(g) + 2e^-$	$\rightarrow$	$2F^-$	2.87
$Co^{3+} + e^-$	$\rightarrow$	Co^{2+}	1.82
$Au^{3+} + 3e^-$	$\rightarrow$	$Au(s)$	1.50
$Cl_2(g) + 2e^-$	$\rightarrow$	$2Cl^-$	1.36
$O_2(g) + 4H^+ + 4e^-$	$\rightarrow$	$2H_2O(l)$	1.23
$Br_2(l) + 2e^-$	$\rightarrow$	$2Br^-$	1.07
$2Hg^{2+} + 2e^-$	$\rightarrow$	Hg_2^{2+}	0.92
$Hg^{2+} + 2e^-$	$\rightarrow$	$Hg(l)$	0.85
$Ag^+ + e^-$	$\rightarrow$	$Ag(s)$	0.80
$Hg_2^{2+} + 2e^-$	$\rightarrow$	$2Hg(l)$	0.79
$Fe^{3+} + e^-$	$\rightarrow$	Fe^{2+}	0.77
$I_2(s) + 2e^-$	$\rightarrow$	$2I^-$	0.53
$Cu^+ + e^-$	$\rightarrow$	$Cu(s)$	0.52
$Cu^{2+} + 2e^-$	$\rightarrow$	$Cu(s)$	0.34
$Cu^{2+} + e^-$	$\rightarrow$	Cu^+	0.15
$Sn^{4+} + 2e^-$	$\rightarrow$	Sn^{2+}	0.15
$S(s) + 2H^+ + 2e^-$	$\rightarrow$	$H_2S(g)$	0.14
$2H^+ + 2e^-$	$\rightarrow$	$H_2(g)$	0.00
$Pb^{2+} + 2e^-$	$\rightarrow$	$Pb(s)$	−0.13
$Sn^{2+} + 2e^-$	$\rightarrow$	$Sn(s)$	−0.14
$Ni^{2+} + 2e^-$	$\rightarrow$	$Ni(s)$	−0.25
$Co^{2+} + 2e^-$	$\rightarrow$	$Co(s)$	−0.28
$Tl^+ + e^-$	$\rightarrow$	$Tl(s)$	−0.34
$Cd^{2+} + 2e^-$	$\rightarrow$	$Cd(s)$	−0.40
$Cr^{3+} + e^-$	$\rightarrow$	Cr^{2+}	−0.41
$Fe^{2+} + 2e^-$	$\rightarrow$	$Fe(s)$	−0.44
$Cr^{3+} + 3e^-$	$\rightarrow$	$Cr(s)$	−0.74
$Zn^{2+} + 2e^-$	$\rightarrow$	$Zn(s)$	−0.76
$Mn^{2+} + 2e^-$	$\rightarrow$	$Mn(s)$	−1.18
$Al^{3+} + 3e^-$	$\rightarrow$	$Al(s)$	−1.66
$Be^{2+} + 2e^-$	$\rightarrow$	$Be(s)$	−1.70
$Mg^{2+} + 2e^-$	$\rightarrow$	$Mg(s)$	−2.37
$Na^+ + e^-$	$\rightarrow$	$Na(s)$	−2.71
$Ca^{2+} + 2e^-$	$\rightarrow$	$Ca(s)$	−2.87
$Sr^{2+} + 2e^-$	$\rightarrow$	$Sr(s)$	−2.89
$Ba^{2+} + 2e^-$	$\rightarrow$	$Ba(s)$	−2.90
$Rb^+ + e^-$	$\rightarrow$	$Rb(s)$	−2.92
$K^+ + e^-$	$\rightarrow$	$K(s)$	−2.92
$Cs^+ + e^-$	$\rightarrow$	$Cs(s)$	−2.92
$Li^+ + e^-$	$\rightarrow$	$Li(s)$	−3.05

ADVANCED PLACEMENT CHEMISTRY EQUATIONS AND CONSTANTS

ATOMIC STRUCTURE

$$E = h\nu \qquad c = \lambda\nu$$

$$\lambda = \frac{h}{mv} \qquad p = mv$$

$$E_n = \frac{-2.178 \times 10^{-18}}{n^2} \text{ joule}$$

EQUILIBRIUM

$$K_a = \frac{[H^+][A^-]}{[HA]}$$

$$K_b = \frac{[OH^-][HB^+]}{[B]}$$

$$K_w = [OH^-][H^+] = 1.0 \times 10^{-14} \text{ @ } 25°C$$
$$= K_a \times K_b$$

$$pH = -\log[H^+], \quad pOH = -\log[OH^-]$$

$$14 = pH + pOH$$

$$pH = pK_a + \log\frac{[A^-]}{[HA]}$$

$$pOH = pK_b + \log\frac{[HB^+]}{[B]}$$

$$pK_a = -\log K_a, \quad pK_b = -\log K_b$$

$$K_p = K_c(RT)^{\Delta n}$$

where Δn = moles product gas – moles reactant gas

THERMOCHEMISTRY/KINETICS

$$\Delta S° = \sum S° \text{ products} - \sum S° \text{ reactants}$$

$$\Delta H° = \sum \Delta H_f° \text{ products} - \sum \Delta H_f° \text{ reactants}$$

$$\Delta G° = \sum \Delta G_f° \text{ products} - \sum \Delta G_f° \text{ reactants}$$

$$\Delta G° = \Delta H° - T\Delta S°$$
$$= -RT \ln K = -2.303\, RT \log K$$
$$= -n\mathscr{F}E°$$

$$\Delta G = \Delta G° + RT \ln Q = \Delta G° + 2.303\, RT \log Q$$

$$q = mc\Delta T$$

$$C_p = \frac{\Delta H}{\Delta T}$$

$$\ln[A]_t - \ln[A]_0 = -kt$$

$$\frac{1}{[A]_t} - \frac{1}{[A]_0} = kt$$

$$\ln k = \frac{-E_a}{R}\left(\frac{1}{T}\right) + \ln A$$

E = energy

ν = frequency

λ = wavelength

p = momentum

v = velocity

n = principal quantum number

m = mass

Speed of light, $c = 3.0 \times 10^8 \text{ m s}^{-1}$

Planck's constant, $h = 6.63 \times 10^{-34} \text{ J s}$

Boltzmann's constant, $k = 1.38 \times 10^{-23} \text{ J K}^{-1}$

Avogadro's number $= 6.022 \times 10^{23} \text{ mol}^{-1}$

Electron charge, $e = -1.602 \times 10^{-19}$ coulomb

1 electron volt per atom $= 96.5 \text{ kJ mol}^{-1}$

Equilibrium Constants

K_a (weak acid) $\qquad K_p$ (gas pressure)

K_b (weak base) $\qquad K_c$ (molar concentrations)

K_w (water)

$S°$ = standard entropy

$H°$ = standard enthalpy

$G°$ = standard free energy

$E°$ = standard reduction potential

T = temperature

n = moles

m = mass

q = heat

c = specific heat capacity

C_p = molar heat capacity at constant pressure

E_a = activation energy

k = rate constant

A = frequency factor

Faraday's constant, $\mathscr{F} = 96,500$ coulombs per mole of electrons

Gas constant, $R = 8.31 \text{ J mol}^{-1} \text{ K}^{-1}$
$$= 0.0821 \text{ L atm mol}^{-1} \text{ K}^{-1}$$
$$= 8.31 \text{ volt coulomb mol}^{-1} \text{ K}^{-1}$$

GASES, LIQUIDS, AND SOLUTIONS

$$PV = nRT$$

$$\left(P + \frac{n^2a}{V^2}\right)(V - nb) = nRT$$

$$P_A = P_{total} \times X_A, \text{ where}$$

$$X_A = \frac{\text{moles A}}{\text{total moles}}$$

$$P_{total} = P_A + P_B + P_C + \cdots$$

$$n = \frac{m}{M}$$

$$K = {}^\circ C + 273$$

$$\frac{P_1V_1}{T_1} = \frac{P_2V_2}{T_2}$$

$$D = \frac{m}{V}$$

$$u_{rms} = \sqrt{\frac{3kT}{m}} = \sqrt{\frac{3RT}{M}}$$

$$KE \text{ per molecule} = \frac{1}{2}mv^2$$

$$KE \text{ per mole} = \frac{3}{2}RT$$

$$\frac{r_1}{r_2} = \sqrt{\frac{M_2}{M_1}}$$

$$\text{molarity, } M = \text{moles solute per liter solution}$$

$$\text{molality} = \text{moles solute per kilogram solvent}$$

$$\Delta T_f = iK_f \times \text{molality}$$

$$\Delta T_b = iK_b \times \text{molality}$$

$$\pi = MRT$$

$$A = abc$$

OXIDATION-REDUCTION; ELECTROCHEMISTRY

$$Q = \frac{[C]^c[D]^d}{[A]^a[B]^b}, \text{ where } a\,A + b\,B \rightarrow c\,C + d\,D$$

$$I = \frac{q}{t}$$

$$E_{cell} = E^\circ_{cell} - \frac{RT}{n\mathscr{F}} \ln Q$$

$$= E^\circ_{cell} - \frac{0.0592}{n} \log Q \ @ \ 25^\circ C$$

$$\log K = \frac{nE^\circ}{0.0592}$$

P = pressure
V = volume
T = temperature
n = number of moles
D = density
m = mass
v = velocity

u_{rms} = root-mean-square speed
KE = kinetic energy
r = rate of effusion
M = molar mass
π = osmotic pressure
i = van't Hoff factor
K_f = molal freezing-point depression constant
K_b = molal boiling-point elevation constant
A = absorbance
a = molar absorptivity
b = path length
c = concentration
Q = reaction quotient
I = current (amperes)
q = charge (coulombs)
t = time (seconds)
E° = standard reduction potential
K = equilibrium constant

Gas constant, R = 8.31 J mol^{-1} K^{-1}
$= 0.0821$ L atm mol^{-1} K^{-1}
$= 8.31$ volt coulomb mol^{-1} K^{-1}

Boltzmann's constant, $k = 1.38 \times 10^{-23}$ J K^{-1}
K_f for H_2O = 1.86 K kg mol^{-1}
K_b for H_2O = 0.512 K kg mol^{-1}
1 atm = 760 mm Hg
$= 760$ torr
STP = 0.000°C and 1.000 atm
Faraday's constant, $\mathscr{F}$ = 96,500 coulombs per mole of electrons

Chemistry

Part A

Time—40 minutes

YOU MAY USE YOUR CALCULATOR FOR PART A.

CLEARLY SHOW THE METHOD USED AND STEPS INVOLVED IN ARRIVING AT YOUR ANSWERS. It is to your advantage to do this, because you may earn partial credit if you do, and you will receive little or no credit if you do not. Attention should be paid to significant figures. Be sure to write all your answers to the questions on the lined pages following each question in the booklet with the pink cover. Do NOT write your answers on the green insert.

Answer Question 1 below. The Section II score weighting for this question is 20 percent.

1.

$$Ca(OH)_2(s) \leftrightarrow Ca^{2+}(aq) + 2OH^-(aq)$$

A saturated solution of calcium hydroxide is prepared at 25 C. ($K_{sp} = 6.5 \times 10^{-6}$ @ 25°C).

(a) Write the solubility-product-constant expression for the reaction above.

(b) Determine the molar solubility of $Ca(OH)_2$ at 25 C.

(c) Determine the pH of the solution.

(d) Discuss the effect on the equilibrium position when the following are added to the $Ca(OH)_2$ solution.
   (i) 0.1 *M* $CaCl_2$ solution
   (ii) 0.1 *M* HCl solution
   (iii) 0.1 *M* NaCl solution

(e) What is the molar solubility of $Ca(OH)_2$ at 25°C in a solution that is 1.00 *M* $CaCl_2$?

Answer EITHER Question 2 OR Question 3 below. Only one of these two questions will be graded. If you start both questions, be sure to cross out the question you do not want graded. The Section II score weighting for the question you choose is 20 percent.

2. Answer the following questions regarding electrochemistry.
   (a) Assume that the three metals Zn, Fe, and Na are at standard conditions.
      (i) Write the balanced equation for the oxidation half-reaction for each metal.
      (ii) Calculate the standard potential, $E°_{red}$.
      (iii) Determine which is the most active metal. Explain.
   (b) Given the reactions $Fe^{2+} + Sn \rightarrow Fe + Sn^{2+}$ or $Sn^{2+} + Fe \rightarrow Sn + Fe^{2+}$:
      (i) Write the balanced equation for the oxidation half-reaction.
      (ii) Calculate the standard potential, $E°_{red}$.
      (iii) Determine which reaction is spontaneous.
      (iv) Identify the anode and cathode for the reaction that spontaneously occurs in a voltaic cell.

3. $$2NO(g) + 2H_2(g) \rightarrow N_2(g) + 2H_2O(g)$$

A rate study was conducted on the above reaction at 25°C. Data was collected on initial concentrations of the reactants, and the rate of appearance of nitrogen gas is presented below.

Experiment	Initial [NO] (M)	Initial [H$_2$] (M)	Initial Rate of Appearance of N$_2$ (M/s)
1	0.10	0.10	1.23×10^{-3}
2	0.10	0.20	2.46×10^{-3}
3	0.20	0.30	1.48×10^{-2}

   (a) Determine the initial rate of disappearance of $NO(g)$ in experiment 1.
   (b) Determine the overall order of the reaction. Explain your reasoning.
   (c) For the reaction,
      (i) write the rate law that is consistent with the data, and
      (ii) calculate the specific rate constant, k, and specify units.
   (d) The following one-step mechanism was proposed for the reaction:

   $$2NO(g) + 2H_2(g)$$
   $$\rightarrow N_2(g) + H_2O(g) \quad slow$$

Is this proposed mechanism consistent with the experimental data analysis that you have completed? Explain.

Chemistry

Part B

NO CALCULATORS MAY BE USED WITH PART B.

Answer Question 4 below. The Section II score weighting for this question is 15 percent.

4. Write the formulas to show the reactants and the products for any FIVE of the laboratory situations described below. Answers to more than five choices will not be graded. In all cases a reaction occurs. Assume that all solutions are aqueous. You do not need to balance the equations.

   (a) A 0.2 barium nitrate solution is added to an alkaline 0.2 M potassium chromate solution.

   (b) Carbon dioxide is passed over hot, solid sodium oxide.

   (c) Methylamine gas is bubbled into distilled water.

   (d) A mixture of powdered aluminum metal and powdered iron(III) oxide are heated strongly.

   (e) A solution of 0.5 M sulfuric acid has solid lead(II) carbonate added to it.

   (f) Liquid bromine is shaken with a 0.5 M sodium iodide solution.

   (g) Solid ammonium nitrate is heated in a laboratory to temperatures above 300 degrees Celsius.

   (h) Calcium oxide powder is added to distilled water.

Your responses to the rest of the questions in this part will be graded on the basis of the accuracy and relevance of the information cited. Explanations should be clear and well organized. Examples and equations may be included in your responses where appropriate. Specific answers are preferable to broad, diffuse responses.

Answer BOTH Question 5 AND Question 6 below. Both of these questions will be graded. The Section II score weighting for these questions is 30 percent (15 percent each).

5. Answer the following questions in terms of oxidation-reduction reactions and periodic trends.
   (a) Using standard reduction potentials, determine whether the following reactions are spontaneous under standard conditions.
       (i) $Cu(s) + 2H^+(aq)$
           $\rightarrow Cu^{2+}(aq) + H_2(g)$
       (ii) $Cl_2(g) + 2I^-(aq)$
            $\rightarrow 2Cl^-(aq) + I_2(s)$
   (b) Write the elements in the following groups in order of increasing (smallest to largest) value of the stated property. Explain using chemical principles.
       (i) Electronegativity: S, Na, Al, Cs
       (ii) Metallic character: Ca, Cl, Al
       (iii) Tendency to form pi bonds: C, Si, N
       (iv) Atomic radius: Sr, Ca, Ba
       (v) Electrical conductivity: Ge, Na, S
       (vi) Ionic character: H_2S, KBr, F_2

6. $BaCl_2$, $AgNO_3$, $Al_2(SO_4)_3$

   The chemicals above were prepared as aqueous solutions with equal concentrations. As a person doing an experiment, what would you expect to observe when the following events occur in the laboratory?
   (a) Hg_2^{2+} ions are introduced to each solution.
   (b) Cl^- ions are introduced to each solution.
   (c) The freezing point of each solution is determined and compared.

Answer EITHER Question 7 OR Question 8. Only one of these two questions will be graded. If you start both questions, be sure to cross out the question you do not want graded. The Section II score weighting for the question you choose is 15 percent.

7. Explain how the current arrangement of the periodic table of elements is due to the following characteristics. (Include specifics; it is acceptable to write the answer as a short essay.)
   (a) Groups and periods
   (b) Metals, metalloids, and nonmetals
   (c) Atomic number
   (d) Atomic mass
   (d) Elemental activity
   (e) Valence electrons

8. Answer the following questions, using appropriate chemical principles.
   (a) Ice cubes can appear cloudy because of dissolved gases that are present at freezing. Account for the fact that—to make clear ice cubes—it is preferable to use hot water over cold water.
   (b) Account for the fact that helium balloons deflate more rapidly than do the same size balloons filled with air.
   (c) Rock-salt mixed with ice is used as a freezing mixture in home ice cream makers. Account for the fact that the slushy salt-ice mixture remains fluid at temperatures well below 0°C.
   (d) Account for the fact that when ice at the freezing temperature is compressed, it liquefies, whereas when CO_2 is compressed, it solidifies.

END OF EXAMINATION

ANSWERS AND EXPLANATIONS

Multiple-Choice Questions

▌ 1. **(D) is correct.** At 25°C, chlorine is a gas, and bromine is a liquid. Even though mercury is a liquid, zinc is a solid.

▌ 2. **(A) is correct.** Allotropes are different forms of the same element. Diamond and graphite are allotropes of carbon; dioxygen (O_2) and ozone (O_3) are allotropes of oxygen.

▌ 3. **(E) is correct.** Silver, gold, zinc, and mercury are all transition metals. "Coinage metals" are the metals that are used to mint coins. Silver and gold are the "coinage metals."

▌ 4. **(D) is correct.** Members of the group containing F, Cl, Br, and I are halogens.

▌ 5. **(C) is correct.** PCl_5 has five bonding atoms. Therefore it has a trigonal-bipyramidal geometry.

$$
\begin{array}{c}
\quad\quad F \\
\quad\quad | \quad / F \\
F - P \\
\quad\quad | \quad \backslash F \\
\quad\quad F
\end{array}
$$

▌ 6. **(D) is correct.** NH_3 has three bonding atoms and one orbital with a lone pair of electrons. Therefore it has a trigonal-pyramidal geometry.

$$
\begin{array}{c}
\ddot{N} \\
/ \; | \; \backslash \\
H \quad H \quad H
\end{array}
$$

▌ 7. **(B) is correct.** XeF_4 has four bonding atoms and two orbitals with lone pairs of electrons. Therefore it has a square-planar geometry.

$$
\begin{array}{c}
F \qquad F \\
\backslash \quad \ddot{} \quad / \\
Xe \\
/ \quad \ddot{} \quad \backslash \\
F \qquad F
\end{array}
$$

▌ 8. **(A) is correct.** CCl_4 has four bonding atoms. Therefore it has a tetrahedral geometry.

$$
\begin{array}{c}
Cl \\
| \\
C \\
/ \; | \; \backslash \\
Cl \quad Cl \quad Cl
\end{array}
$$

▌ 9. **(A) is correct.** Alcohols, such as butyl alcohol, include an OH in the carbon chain.

▌ 10. **(B) is correct.** Alkanes have the general molecular formula C_nH_{2n+2}, such as butane, C_6H_6.

▌ 11. **(D) is correct.** Alkynes, C_nH_{2n-2}, include butyne, C_2H_2.

▌ 12. **(C) is correct.** Alkenes conform to C_nH_{2n}—for example, butene, C_2H_4.

13. (E) is correct. Ozone, O_3, is an allotrope of oxygen.

14. (D) is correct. Metal oxides typically yield basic solutions when dissolved in water.

15. (A) is correct. Fluorine has the lowest bond energy in the halogens. This makes it more reactive.

16. (B) is correct. Sulfur trioxide is an acid oxide. It reacts with rainwater to form H_2SO_4.

17. (B) is correct. Electronegativity is the measure of strength of the attraction an atom has for the electrons of another atom in a chemical bond. Though neon seems to match this description, it is unable to form chemical bonds; therefore it has no electronegativity. The halogen chlorine is the next best candidate.

18. (B) is correct. Chlorine has the most oxidation states. Remember, chlorine can take on both positive and negative oxidation states, such as $1-$, $1+$, $3+$, $4+$, $5+$, $6+$, $7+$.

19. (B) is correct. You have studied oxidation-reduction reactions and the trends that the periodic table offers. In this answer, magnesium is the element that is most easily oxidized.

20. (D) is correct. Determine the limiting reactant based on the number of moles (Cu_2S, 1/16 mol vs. O_2, ½ mol). Since both reactants have the same molar ratios, the limiting reactant is Cu_2S. Complete the stoichiometry, and the mass of Cu produced is 7.98 g. See the math below:

$$10 \text{ g Cu}_2\text{S} \times \frac{1 \text{ mol Cu}_2\text{S}}{159.1 \text{ g Cu}_2\text{S}} \times \frac{2 \text{ mol Cu}}{1 \text{ mol Cu}_2\text{S}} \times \frac{63.5 \text{ g Cu}}{1 \text{ mol Cu}} = 7.98 \text{ g Cu}$$

21. (C) is correct. There are four subshells in the fourth shell, corresponding to the four possible values of l (0, 1, 2, and 5).

22. (B) is correct. When S is less than zero, the entropy is decreasing. The only reaction that has a decrease in entropy is shown in answer B, where 1½ gaseous particles are reacting to form one gaseous particle.

23. (D) is correct. Adding base to a buffer decreases $[H^+]$ and thereby increases the pH of the solution. Also, NH_4^+ reacts to form NH_3.

24. (D) is correct. The following salts would form an acidic solution in water: NH_4Cl and $Fe(NO_3)_3$.

25. (E) is correct. Normally the heaviest compound in a related series will have the highest boiling point, because London dispersion forces increase with increasing weight. However, CH_3OH has the highest boiling point, because hydrogen bonds also exist between CH_3OH molecules.

26. (A) is correct. The balanced equation is $2BF_3 + 2NaBH_3 \rightarrow 2NaBF_3 + 2B_2H_6$. Therefore, the coefficient of BF_3 is 2.

27. (D) is correct. The characteristics and properties of gases yield certain theories. Only statements I and III are correct, since pressure increases and average molecular speed decreases.

28. (E) is correct. You have learned about intermolecular forces operating in different phases. The only two correct statements are III and IV—dipole-dipole and London dispersion.

29. (D) is correct. Alcohol is a functional group to hydrocarbons. Alcohol forms a ketone to 2-propanol when oxidized. Ketones are classified as having a C=O bond between two carbons. The 2-propanol is the only compound that is available to form a ketone. The 2-methyl-2-propanol does not have the structure that supports a ketone formation when oxidized.

30. (D) is correct. The periodic table provides information on trends, such as metallic and nonmetallic properties. Using this information, you should realize that "H shows only nonmetallic properties" is a giveaway as the answer. Even though it is considered a "nonmetal," it can still react with metallic properties (i.e., the placement of hydrogen on the activity series of metals).

31. (A) is correct. Cations are smaller than their parent atoms, so Ca^{2+} is smaller than the Ca atom. Since Ca is below Mg in group 2A of the periodic table, Ca^{2+} is larger than Mg^{2+}. Consequently, $Ca > Ca^{2+} > Mg^{2+}$.

32. (B) is correct. Molecular geometry and bonding theories allow you to evaluate hybrid orbitals. SF_6 has a central atom that uses the sp^3d^2 hybrid orbitals.

33. (D) is correct. In aqueous reactions and solution stoichiometry, you have practiced determining molarity. Be careful of significant digits. The molarity is 1.00 M. For a 1 : 1 reaction, like this one, molarity can be determined using the following equation: $M_aV_a = M_bV_b$; where "a" = acid and "b" = base. Completing the math, $M_a = (0.500\ M * 70.00\ \text{mL})/35.00\ \text{mL} = 1.00\ M$.

34. (C) is correct. Redox reactions have electron transfers between the products and the reactants. Clues to solve the problem: "acidic solution" = H^+ in the equation, "reduction" = element has gained electrons. Nitrogen's oxidation state has changed from 5+ on the reactants side to 2+ on the product side; therefore it has gained electrons.

35. (D) is correct. Again, redox reactions have electron transfers between the products and the reactants. Clues to solve the problem: "basic solution" = OH^- in the equation, "oxidation" = element has lost electrons. Chlorine's oxidation state has changed from 0 on the reactants side to 7+ (ClO_4^-) on the product side; therefore, it has lost electrons. Answer C is a correctly balanced reaction, but it is in an acidic solution.

36. (E) is correct. The enthalpy change for the reaction is determined by the equation: $\Delta H = \Sigma D_{broken} - \Sigma D_{formed}$. Determine the bonds that are breaking and the bonds that are forming. The setup is:

$$\Delta H = \Sigma D_{broken} - \Sigma D_{formed}$$
$$\text{Bonds broken: 1 C} \equiv \text{O and 2 H—H}$$
$$\text{Bonds formed: 3 C—H, 1 C—O, and 1 O—H}$$
$$\Delta H = (1072 + 2(436)) - (3(413) + 358 + 463)$$
$$\Delta H = -116\ \text{kJ}$$

37. (A) is correct. In thermodynamics, you will often need to analyze and evaluate information given in tables. From the information presented here, you can assess that the response is nonspontaneous at low temperature and spontaneous at high temperature. Spontaneity is based on the value of ΔG, "$-\Delta G$" = spontaneous and "$+\Delta G$" = nonspontaneous, $\Delta G_{reaction} = \Delta H_{reaction} -$

$T\Delta S_{reaction}$. The "reaction" in this case is represented as $PCl_3(l) \rightarrow PCl_3(g)$, therefore:

$$\Delta G = (-288.07 \text{ kJ} - (-319.6 \text{ kJ})) - T(0.3117 \text{ kJ/K} - 0.217 \text{ kJ/K})$$
$$\Delta G = 31.53 \text{ kJ} - T(0.0947 \text{ kJ/K})$$

Therefore, since ΔH is positive for the reaction and ΔS is positive, at low temperatures the reaction is nonspontaneous and at high temperatures the reaction is spontaneous.

38. (A) is correct. This is a basic definition that describes an atom that is oxidized. The atom loses electrons and becomes more positively charged.

39. (C) is correct. Lowering the temperature of a liquid decreases its vapor pressure, because intermolecular forces become stronger relative to kinetic energy of particles.

40. (E) is correct. According to the basic periodic trends, ionic size increases going down a family.

41. (E) is correct. Acid addition (decreasing pH) causes the reaction $H^+(aq) + CO_3^{2-}(aq) \rightarrow HCO_3^-(aq)$ to occur, thereby shifting the following equilibrium to the right: $BaCO_3(s) \rightleftarrows Ba^{2+}(aq) + CO_3^{2-}(aq)$.

42. (B) is correct. In electrochemistry, you should be able to balance oxidation-reduction equations. In balancing the equation, you can determine that the coefficient of Fe is 2.

43. (D) is correct. First write the electron configuration of the parent atom. Calcium's atomic number is 20, and its electron configuration is $[\text{Ar}]4s^2$. To form a 2+ ion, the two outer electrons must be removed, giving an ion that is isoelectric with Ar. $Ca^{2+} = [\text{Ar}]$

44. (C) is correct. In addition to concepts such as Gibbs free energy, three different choices are given. In this case it is H_2 gas only that would provide the right answer. Remember that Gibb's free energy is always zero for an element that appears as it would in natural form (i.e., hydrogen is naturally occurring as a diatomic gas).

45. (E) is correct. Density = mass/volume; therefore volume = mass/density

$$1340 \text{ g}/2.67 \text{ g/cm}^3 = 502 \text{ cm}^3$$
$$1 \text{ cm}^3 = 1\text{mL}, 1000 \text{ mL} = 1 \text{ L}$$
$$\text{therefore } 502 \text{ cm}^3 = 0.502 \text{ L}$$

46. (B) is correct. Conversions between K and C temperatures are C = K − 273.15; therefore 422.35 K = 149.20°C. The only answer that contains 149.20°C is answer *B*.

47. (A) is correct. Use the law of conservation of mass to determine the empirical formula of the compound. All of the carbon found in the CO_2 comes from the original sample, and the same is true for the hydrogen in the H_2O. Once you determine the mass of C and H in the products, the mass that is left over is the oxygen in the original sample.

$$2.265 \text{ g CO}_2 \times \frac{1 \text{ mol CO}_2}{44 \text{ g CO}_2} \times \frac{1 \text{ mol C}}{1 \text{ mol CO}_2} \times \frac{12.01 \text{ g C}}{1 \text{ mol C}} = 0.618 \text{ g C}$$

$$1.236 \text{ g } H_2 \times \frac{1 \text{ mol } H_2O}{18 \text{ g } H_2O} \times \frac{2 \text{ mol } H}{1 \text{ mol } H_2O} \times \frac{1.00 \text{ g } H}{1 \text{ mol } H} = 0.137 \text{ g } H$$

$$\text{mass } O = 1.031 \text{ } g - (0.618 \text{ } g + 0.137 \text{ } g) = 0.276 \text{ g } O$$

Once all masses are determined, convert them to moles and divide by the lowest mole amount (basic empirical formula determination).

$$0.618 \text{ g } C \times \frac{1 \text{ mol } C}{12.01 \text{ g } C} = 0.0515 \text{ mol } C/0.0173 = 3 \text{ mol } C$$

$$0.137 \text{ g } H \times \frac{1 \text{ mol } H}{1.00 \text{ g } H} = 0.137 \text{ mol } H/0.0173 = 8 \text{ mol } H$$

$$0.276 \text{ g } O \times \frac{1 \text{ mol } O}{15.99 \text{ g } O} = 0.0173 \text{ mol } O/0.0173 \text{ } 5 \text{ } 1 \text{ mol } O$$

Therefore, C_3H_8O is the answer.

■ **48. (C) is correct.** % Al = mass Al/mass $Al_2O_3 \times 100\% = 54/102 \times 100\% = 52.9\%$

■ **49. (D) is correct.** Alpha and beta particles have opposite charges; they will deflect in opposite directions. Gamma radiation has no charge; it does not deflect.

■ **50. (C) is correct.** Look for elements that are in the same family or ones that are close to each other on the periodic table; these are the ones that share the same properties.

■ **51. (B) is correct.** Metallic oxides form basic solutions, whereas nonmetallic oxides form acidic solutions.

■ **52. (C) is correct.** Helium follows the *duet* rule since it has only two electrons, whereas the other noble gases have the full octet.

■ **53. (B) is correct.** Think in terms of context clues. We know that when $\Delta H =$ "−", the process is exothermic, and when $\Delta H =$ "+" the process is endothermic. Which choice fits this knowledge?

■ **54. (A) is correct.** Oxidation is losing electrons, Fe has lost electrons, and H has gained electrons. Consequently, Fe must be the correct answer.

■ **55. (A) is correct.** It is Charles's law that gives the temperature-volume relationship. Boyle's law states that the volume of a fixed quantity of gas maintained at constant temperature is inversely proportional to the pressure. Boyle's law is based on a pressure-volume relationship.

■ **56. (A) is correct.** First-order reactions rely only on the rate constant to determine ½-life, whereas second-order reactions depend on $[A]_0$.

■ **57. (B) is correct.** Determining the units in a kinetics problem can be tricky. Always remember that the units for rate are $M \text{ s}^{-1}$. In this case:

$$M \text{ s}^{-1} = X [M]$$
$$M \text{ s}^{-1}/M = X [M]/M$$
$$\text{s}^{-1} = X \text{ (units for the rate constant)}$$

58. (B) is correct. $\Delta S = S_{products} - S_{reactants}$. Remember when doing problems like this that you have to worry about the number of moles of each species present.

$$\Delta S = (2 \text{ mole} * 197.9 \text{ J/K} * \text{mole}) - ((2 \text{ mole} * 2.4 \text{ J/K} * \text{mole})$$
$$+ (1 \text{ mole} * 205.0 \text{ J/K} * \text{mole}))$$

$$\Delta S = 395.8 \text{ J/K} - 209.8 \text{ J/K}$$

$$\Delta S = 186 \text{ J/K}$$

59. (A) is correct. $\Delta G = \Delta H - T\Delta S$. When $\Delta G =$ "+", the reaction is nonspontaneous; when $\Delta G =$ "−", the reaction is spontaneous. The only way to have nonspontaneous at low temperatures and spontaneous at high temperatures is to have the signs for both ΔH and ΔS be "+".

60. (D) is correct. This is a common-ion effect problem. The addition of 5×10^{-5} mol of H^+ (5.0 mL of 0.01 M HCl) to the solution leads to the decrease of F^- by the same amount of moles. The concentration of the F^- is now determined by dividing the number of moles by the new volume (30 mL—25 from the HF and 5 mL from the HCl); 2.45×10^{-3} mol/0.030 L = 0.0817 M.

61. (C) is correct. Additional aspects of aqueous equilibria include the precipitation and separation of ions. Specifically, this question concerns selective precipitation, which is the common-ion effect.

62. (C) is correct. Chemical thermodynamics has taught us about spontaneous processes. The conditions under which one can absolutely say a system is at equilibrium at constant pressure and temperature is when $\Delta G = 0$.

63. (E) is correct. The following factors will affect equilibrium concentrations: magnitude of equilibrium constant, initial concentrations of products and reactants, and temperature. The larger the K_{eq}, the greater is the amount of products; the smaller the K_{eq}, the greater is the amount of reactants. Initial concentrations will always affect the equilibrium concentrations. Temperature is the only factor that can change both the equilibrium concentrations and the K_{eq}.

64. (C) is correct. A solution that is in equilibrium with undissolved solute is saturated. If you dissolve less solute than is needed to form a saturated solution, the solution is unsaturated. The correct answer is supersaturated.

65. (A) is correct. $K_{eq} = P_{CO}/P_{CO_2} \cdot P_{H_2}$. You need to employ the law of mass action. Remember to omit any pure liquids, pure solids, or solvents from the expression. Because H_2O appears in the reaction as a pure liquid, its concentration does not appear in the equilibrium-constant.

66. (A) is correct. Definition of an isotope is "same number of protons, different number of neutrons." Since protons and neutrons determine the mass of the atom, and protons determine the atomic number, answer A is the only plausible choice. Don't get tripped up by the distracters.

67. (B) is correct. Metal oxides are basic and nonmetallic oxides are acidic when introduced to water. You should remember this from reaction prediction.

68. (C) is correct. pH = 7.0 − 8.0 is the correct response. The molar concentration of $H^+(aq)$ in an aqueous solution is usually very small. For convenience, we usually express $[H^+]$ in terms of pH. The pH of a neutral solution is 7.00 at 25°C. Human blood, tears, egg white, and seawater are at pH 7.0, and baking soda is at pH 8.0.

▌ **69. (D) is correct.** Steroisomers have the same bond arrangement but different appearances in the structural formula.

▌ **70. (A) is correct.** A central part of nuclear chemistry is rates of radioactive decay. You should be able to make calculations based on half-life.

▌ **71. (B) is correct.** The value of m_l cannot be greater than the value of l. Thus, $n = 3, l = 2$, and $m_l = 3$ are not permissible. The other combinations of quantum numbers for an electron are permissible.

▌ **72. (D) is correct.** Alkanes are single-bonded carbon compounds.

▌ **73. (C) is correct.** By definition, atomic number is the number of protons or electrons in a neutral atom. With 11 electrons, its electron arrangement is 2-8-1 over three energy levels. If the atomic number is 23, however, 12 neutrons must add to 11 protons for this total mass. Note its outer level has 1 electron.

▌ **74. (B) is correct.** Le Châtelier's principle states that stresses placed on a system at equilibrium will be reduced in the direction opposing the stress. When N_2 is added to the system, there is an increase in NH_3 and a decrease in H_2.

▌ **75. (E) is correct.** Convert the solubility (70 g/100 mL) to a concentration (4.14 M). 4.22 M is more concentrated than the 4.14 M "saturated" solution, so the 4.22 M solution must be supersaturated.

Free-Response Questions

Part A

1. (a) $K_{sp} = [Ca^{2+}][OH^-]^2$ — Remember that for every one Ca^{2+} in solution, there are two OH^-, so the term is squared. Also, $Ca(OH)_2$ is not included, since it is a solid.

1. (b) Molar solubility is determined by the ion available in lowest concentration in solution. For this problem, molar solubility is equal to the $[Ca^{2+}]$.

$$\text{Let } x = [Ca^{2+}]$$
$$\text{Let } 2x = [OH^-]$$
$$K_{sp} = 6.5 \times 10^{-6} = [x][2x]^2$$
$$6.5 \times 10^{-6} = 4x^3$$
$$1.65 \times 10^{-6} = x^3$$
$$\sqrt[3]{1.65 \times 10^{-6}} = x$$
$$0.0118 \text{ M} = x = [Ca^{2+}]$$

1. (c) This problem can be completed two ways—the hard way and the easy way. AP Chemistry Exam readers want to see the easy way, since it requires you to tie in the information from part (b) of the problem instead of starting all over again. Also, in problems like this, it is good to state the obvious—the equations that you will need to solve the problem.

$$pH + pOH = 14$$
$$pOH = -\log[OH^-]$$

Easy Way:

$$\text{From part b} \rightarrow [OH^-] = 2x = 0.0236 \text{ M}$$

(always make this statement and write it in the answer)

$$\text{pOH} = -\log [0.0236]$$

$$\text{pOH} = 1.627$$

$$\text{pH} = 14 - 1.627 = 12.373$$

Hard Way:

Rearrange K_{sp} equation to solve for $[OH^-]$, then plug it in to the pOH and pH equations.

1. (d) (i) Shift to the reactants (shift $\leftarrow$). (*Either answer is appropriate, but don't just draw an arrow pointing left.*) Based on Le Châtelier's principle, the addition of the common-ion (Ca^{2+}) in the product shifts the equilibrium position back to the reactants to decrease the stress on the system.

   (ii) Shift to the products (shift $\rightarrow$). The addition of the H^+ leads to a reaction involving the OH^- in the product ($H^+ + OH^- \rightarrow H_2O$); the water formation reduces the $[OH^-]$. This leads to the production of more products to reestablish equilibrium.

   (iii) No shift. Neither ion (Na^+ or Cl^-) is common to the solution; thus, there is no effect on the equilibrium position.

1. (e) Common-ion effect problem—set up the ICE (**I**nitial – **C**hange– **E**quilibrium) chart to start.

$$Ca(OH)_2(s) \rightarrow Ca^{2+}(aq) + 2OH^-(aq)$$

I	1.0	
C	$+x$	$+2x$
E	$1.0 + x$	$2x$

x for $[Ca^{2+}]$ can be neglected due to the initial concentration present.

(*more than three orders of magnitude difference from the K_{sp} value*)

$$K_{sp} = [Ca^{2+}][OH^-]^2$$

$$6.5 \times 10^{-6} = [1.0][2x]^2$$

$$6.5 \times 10^{-6} = 4x^2$$

$$1.625 \times 10^{-6} = x^2$$

$$\sqrt{1.65 \times 10^{-6}} = x$$

$$1.27 \times 10^{\times 3} \text{ M} = x$$

Molar solubility has been decreased by an order of 10.

2. (a) Solution

Analyze

You are given three metals and asked to determine their standard reduction potentials and to determine which is the most active metal.

Plan

An active metal is one that is easily oxidized (is a good reducing agent). The more negative the standard reduction potential, the more active the metal is. Thus, you look for the most negative standard reduction potential.

Solve

(i and ii). The balanced standard reduction potential for the oxidation half reaction and the E°_{red} is

$$Na^+(aq) + e^- \rightarrow Na(s) \qquad E^\circ_{red} = -2.71 \text{ V}$$
$$Zn^{2+}(aq) + 2e^- \rightarrow Zn(s) \qquad E^\circ_{red} = -0.76 \text{ V}$$
$$Fe^{2+}(aq) + 2e^- \rightarrow Fe(s) \qquad E^\circ_{red} = -0.44 \text{ V}$$

(iii). Sodium metal is the most active metal, because it has the largest negative standard potential, -2.71 V.

2. (b) Solution

Analyze and Plan

You need to determine which reaction has a positive standard emf. You need to reverse the half-reaction with the more negative standard reduction potential. If you do this and add the half-reactions, you determine the spontaneous reaction.

Solve

(i and ii). The standard reduction potential and E°_{red} for the following are

$$Fe^{2+}(aq) + 2e^- \rightarrow Fe(s) \qquad E^\circ_{red} = -0.44 \text{ V}$$
$$Sn^{2+}(aq) + 2e^- \rightarrow Sn(s) \qquad E^\circ_{red} = -0.14 \text{ V}$$

Solve

(iii and iv). The half-reaction with the more reduction potential involves iron. You will reverse this one.

Anode:	$Fe \rightarrow Fe^{2+}(aq) + 2e^-$	$E^\circ_{red} = -0.44 \text{ V}$
Cathode:	$Sn^{2+}(aq) + 2e^- \rightarrow Sn(s)$	$E^\circ_{red} = -0.14 \text{ V}$
	$Sn^{2+} + Fe \rightarrow Sn + Fe^{2+}$	$E^\circ_{rxn} = E^\circ_{cathode} - E^\circ_{anode}$

$$E^\circ_{rxn} = E^\circ_{cathode} - E^\circ_{anode}$$
$$= -0.14 \text{ V} - (-0.44 \text{ V})$$
$$E^\circ_{rxn} = 0.30 \text{ V}.$$

The balanced chemical reaction has a positive standard emf, which means it is spontaneous at standard conditions.

3. (a) ½ rate of appearance of N_2 = rate of disappearance of NO
This is due to the molar ratios in the equation. You could set up the problem also in terms of the disappearance of H_2, since it would be the same ratio.

$$\frac{1}{2}R_{appearN2} = R_{disappear\ NO}$$
$$\frac{1}{2}(1.23 \times 10^{-3}\ M \cdot s^{-1}) = R_{disappear\ NO}$$
$$6.15 \times 10^{-4}\ M \cdot s^{-1} = R_{disappear\ NO}$$

3. (b) **Plan**
In order to determine the rate order for the overall reaction, the rate order for each reactant must be determined. The rate orders are calculated using the formula:

$$\frac{Rate_x}{Rate_y} = \frac{k_x[NO]^m[H_2]^n}{k_y[NO]^m[H_2]^n}$$

They can be determined also by visual inspection of the data.

Solve
Rate order for $[H_2]$—By comparing experiments 1 and 2, [NO] is constant and $[H_2]$ is doubled. The rate of the reaction doubles; therefore the reaction is first order with respect to $[H_2]$.

Rate order for [NO]—By comparing experiments 1 and 3, [NO] is doubled and $[H_2]$ is tripled. In order to calculate the rate order, the mathematical equation must be used.

$$\frac{Rate_3}{Rate_1} = \frac{k_3[NO]^m[H_2]}{k_1[NO]^m[H_2]}$$

$$\frac{1.48 \times 10^{-2}}{1.23 \times 10^{-3}} = \frac{k_3[0.20]^m[0.30]}{k_1[0.10]^m[0.10]}$$

$$12 = (2^m)(3)$$
$$4 = 2^m$$
$$2 = m$$

The reaction is second order with respect to [NO].

Overall rate order for the reaction equals 3. Rate order [NO] + rate order $[H_2]$ = overall order.

3. (c) (i) Rate = $k[NO]^2[H_2]$
(ii) When determining the value and the units of the rate constant, use the information for one of the experiments and plug it in to the rate law proposed in the previous step. Using the information from experiment 1:

$$1.23 \times 10^{-3}\ M\ s^{-1} = k[0.10\ M]^2[0.10\ M]$$

$$1.23 \times 10^{-3} \, M \cdot s^{-1}/0.001 \, M^3 = k$$
$$1.23 \, M^{-2} \cdot s^{-1} = k$$
$$\text{(units can also be } L^2 \, mol^{-2} \, s^{-1})$$

3. (d) No. Based on the information from part (b), the reaction is second order for [NO] and first order for [H_2]. The proposed mechanism states that based on molecularity, the reaction is second order with respect to [H_2].

Part B

4. Solution

Analyze and Plan
You are asked to pick five choices out of eight given laboratory situations.

Solve
(a) $Ba^{2+} + CrO_4^{2-} \rightarrow BaCrO_4$
(b) $CO_2 + Na_2O \rightarrow Na_2CO_3$
(c) $CH_3NH_2 + H_2O \rightarrow CH_3NH_3^+ + OH^-$
(d) $Fe_2O_3 + Al \rightarrow Al_2O_3 + Fe$
(e) $PbCO_3 + H^+ + HSO_4^-$ (or SO_4^{2-})
　　　$\rightarrow PbSO_4 + CO_2 + H_2O$ (or HCO_3^-)
(f) $Br_2 + I^- \rightarrow Br^- + I_2$
(g) $NH_4NO_3 \rightarrow N_2 + O_2 + H_2O$　or　$NH_4NO_3 \rightarrow N_2O + H_2O$
(h) $CaO + H_2O \rightarrow Ca(OH)_2$

5. (a) Solution

Analyze and Plan
To determine whether a redox reaction is spontaneous under standard conditions, you need first to write its reduction and oxidation half-reactions. You can then use the standard reduction potentials to calculate the standard emf, $E°$, for the reaction. Finally, the sign of $E°$, if positive, indicates that the reaction is spontaneous.

Solve
(i). In this reaction Cu is oxidized to Cu^{2+} and H^+ is reduced to H_2. The corresponding half-reactions and associated standard reduction potentials are

Reduction:	$2H^+(aq) + 2e^- \rightarrow H_2(g)$	$E°_{red} = 0 \, V$
Oxidation:	$Cu(s) \rightarrow Cu^{2+}(aq) + 2e^-$	$E°_{red} = +0.34 \, V$

Note that for the oxidation process, you use standard reduction potentials for the reduction of Cu^{2+} to Cu. You now calculate $E°$ by using the following equation.

$$E° = E°_{red} \text{ (reduction process)} - E°_{red}\text{(oxidation process)}$$
$$E° = (0 \, V) - (0.34 \, V) = -0.34 \, V$$

Because the value of $E°$ is negative, the reaction is not spontaneous in the direction written. Copper metal does not react with acids in this fashion. The reverse reaction, however, is spontaneous: Cu^{2+} can be reduced by H_2.

(ii). Follow the procedures that you used for copper. To determine whether a redox reaction is spontaneous, you need to write its reduction and oxidation half-reactions, and then to calculate $E°$ for the reaction. The reaction is spontaneous if there is a positive sign for $E°$.

Reduction:	$Cl_2(g) + 2e^- \rightarrow 2Cl^-(aq)$	$E°_{red} = +1.36$ V
Oxidation:	$2I^-(aq) \rightarrow I_2(s) + 2e^-$	$E°_{red} = +0.54$ V

In this case, the standard emf, $E°$, for this reaction is positive, because $E° = (1.36 \text{ V}) - (0.54) = +0.82$ V. Because the value of $E°$ is positive, this reaction is spontaneous.

5. (b) Solution

Analyze and Plan

You are given a list of physical properties of elements, and for each you are asked to write the elements given in increasing order of the indicated physical property.

Solve

 (i) Electronegativity: Cs < Na < Al < S (increases from left to right in a period and decreases down a family)
 (ii) Metallic character: Cl < Al < Ca (decreases from left to right across the periodic table)
 (iii) Tendency to form pi bonds: Si < N < C (first member of a nonmetal family may form pi bonds)
 (iv) Atomic radius: Ca < Sr < Ba (increases down a family)
 (v) Electrical conductivity: S < Ge < Na (increases with the metallic character)
 (vi) Ionic character: F_2 < H_2S < KBr (increases with increasing difference in electronegativity values between the bonded atoms)

6. (a) Introduction of Hg_2^{2+} ions to solutions of $BaCl_2$, $AgNO_3$, and $Al_2(SO_4)_3$:

$BaCl_2$ − formation of a precipitate (Hg_2Cl_2)

$AgNO_3$ − no precipitate formation (Hg_2NO_3 is soluble in water)

$Al_2(SO_4)_3$ − formation of a precipitate (Hg_2SO_4)

6. (b) Introduction of Cl^- ions into solutions of $BaCl_2$, $AgNO_3$, $Al_2(SO_4)_3$:

$BaCl_2$ − no precipitate formation (Cl^- is a common ion)

$AgNO_3$ − precipitate formation (AgCl)

$Al_2(SO_4)_3$ − non precipitate formation ($AlCl_3$ is soluble in water)

6. (c) Determination of freezing point of each solution (basic colligative property problem):

Freezing point depression is a colligative property. The amount of particles in solution will determine the extent of the depression. $Al_2(SO_4)_3$ produces 5 particles in solution, $BaCl_2$ produces 3 particles in solution, and $AgNO_3$ produces 2 particles in solution. When the freezing points of the solutions are compared, they can be arranged in order of increasing freezing point depression: $AgNO_3 > BaCl_2 > Al_2(SO_4)_3$

7. Solution

Solve

The periodic table organizes about 110 elements (metals and nonmetals) systematically by arranging the elements in order of increasing atomic number. The smaller group of nonmetals is organized to the right of a step-line separating them from the larger group of metals. Seven horizontal rows or periods also produce the vertical columns of elements termed families. Each cell of the table centers the element's symbol with atomic number to the upper right and atomic mass to the lower left.

For the families, Roman numerals also signify the number of valence electrons. Distinct metals have three or fewer outer shell electrons with the most active further down in a family. Metals add energy shells further down a family. Valence electrons become further away from the nucleus and thus are more easily oxidized. A metal's activity is related to its ease of oxidation or electron loss. Nonmetals are more active near the top of their given family.

8. Solution

Solve

8. (a) Gases are more soluble in liquids at lower temperatures. For the ice cubes made with hot water, most of the gases have already bubbled out of solution.

8. (b) Helium has a much lighter molecule than do the components of air. As a result of this and of Graham's law, you know that the lighter He molecule will effuse more quickly from the balloons than air will do.

8. (c) Rock salt, when it dissolves, lowers the freezing point of water (because of the colligative property of the freezing point depression). This allows for the slushy mixture to cool below the normal freezing temperature of ice.

8. (d) Ice is a rare substance that actually expands and becomes less dense as it freezes. As a result, applying pressure to solid ice at the freezing temperature will cause it to become slightly denser and melt. On the other hand, CO_2 is more representative of most other substances that are denser at colder temperatures. Substances like CO_2 will solidify when compressed.

MATERIAL IN THE FOLLOWING TABLE MAY BE USEFUL IN ANSWERING THE QUESTIONS IN THIS SECTION OF THE EXAMINATION.

PERIODIC TABLE OF THE ELEMENTS

1A 1																	8A 18
1 **H** 1.0079	2A 2											3A 13	4A 14	5A 15	6A 16	7A 17	2 **He** 4.0026
3 **Li** 6.941	4 **Be** 9.012											5 **B** 10.811	6 **C** 12.011	7 **N** 14.007	8 **O** 16.00	9 **F** 19.00	10 **Ne** 20.179
11 **Na** 22.99	12 **Mg** 24.30	3B 3	4B 4	5B 5	6B 6	7B 7	8	8B 9	10	1B 11	2B 12	13 **Al** 26.98	14 **Si** 28.09	15 **P** 30.974	16 **S** 32.06	17 **Cl** 35.453	18 **Ar** 39.948
19 **K** 39.10	20 **Ca** 40.08	21 **Sc** 44.96	22 **Ti** 47.90	23 **V** 50.94	24 **Cr** 52.00	25 **Mn** 54.938	26 **Fe** 55.85	27 **Co** 58.93	28 **Ni** 58.69	29 **Cu** 63.55	30 **Zn** 65.39	31 **Ga** 69.72	32 **Ge** 72.59	33 **As** 74.92	34 **Se** 78.96	35 **Br** 79.90	36 **Kr** 83.80
37 **Rb** 85.47	38 **Sr** 87.62	39 **Y** 88.91	40 **Zr** 91.22	41 **Nb** 92.91	42 **Mo** 95.94	43 **Tc** (98)	44 **Ru** 101.1	45 **Rh** 102.91	46 **Pd** 106.42	47 **Ag** 107.87	48 **Cd** 112.41	49 **In** 114.82	50 **Sn** 118.71	51 **Sb** 121.75	52 **Te** 127.60	53 **I** 126.91	54 **Xe** 131.29
55 **Cs** 132.91	56 **Ba** 137.33	57 **La** 138.91	72 **Hf** 178.49	73 **Ta** 180.95	74 **W** 183.85	75 **Re** 186.21	76 **Os** 190.2	77 **Ir** 192.2	78 **Pt** 195.08	79 **Au** 196.97	80 **Hg** 200.59	81 **Tl** 204.38	82 **Pb** 207.2	83 **Bi** 208.98	84 **Po** (209)	85 **At** (210)	86 **Rn** (222)
87 **Fr** (223)	88 **Ra** 226.02	89 **Ac** 227.03	104 **Rf** (261)	105 **Db** (262)	106 **Sg** (263)	107 **Bh** (264)	108 **Hs** (265)	109 **Mt** (268)	110 **Ds** (269)	111 **Uuu** (272)	112 **Uub** (277)						

58 **Ce** 140.12	59 **Pr** 140.91	60 **Nd** 144.24	61 **Pm** (145)	62 **Sm** 150.4	63 **Eu** 151.97	64 **Gd** 157.25	65 **Tb** 158.93	66 **Dy** 162.50	67 **Ho** 164.93	68 **Er** 167.26	69 **Tm** 168.93	70 **Yb** 173.04	71 **Lu** 174.97
90 **Th** 232.04	91 **Pa** 231.04	92 **U** 238.03	93 **Np** (237)	94 **Pu** (244)	95 **Am** (243)	96 **Cm** (247)	97 **Bk** (247)	98 **Cf** (251)	99 **Es** (252)	100 **Fm** (257)	101 **Md** (258)	102 **No** (259)	103 **Lr** (262)

Practice Test 2

Chemistry Section I
Part A

Time—1 hour and 30 minutes
Number of questions—75
Percent of total grade—45

NO CALCULATORS MAY BE USED WITH SECTION I.

Note: For all questions, assume that the temperature is 298 K, the pressure is 1.00 atmosphere, and solutions are aqueous unless otherwise specified.

Throughout the test the following symbols and abbreviations have the definitions specified unless otherwise noted.

T = temperature	M = molar
P = pressure	m = molal
V = volume	L, mL = liter(s), milliliter(s)
S = entropy	g = gram(s)
H = enthalpy	nm = nanometer(s)
G = free energy	atm = atmosphere(s)
R = molar gas constant	J, kJ = joule(s), kilojoule(s)
n = number of moles	V = volt(s)
	mol = mole(s)

Directions: Each set of lettered choices below refers to the numbered statements immediately following it. Select the one lettered choice that best fits each statement and then fill in the corresponding oval on the answer sheet. A choice may be used once, more than once, or not at all in each set.

Questions 1–4 refer to the pH of given solutions.

(A) A solution with a pH of 1
(B) A solution with a pH greater than 1 and less than 7
(C) A solution with a pH of 7
(D) A solution with a pH greater than 7 and less than 13
(E) A solution with a pH greater than 13

For NH_3, $K_b = 1.8 \times 10^{-5}$
For CH_3COOH, $K_a = 1.8 \times 10^{-5}$

1. A solution prepared by mixing equal volumes of 0.2-molar NaOH and 0.2-molar CH_3COOH
2. A solution prepared by mixing equal volumes of 0.2 M NaCl and 0.2 M HCl
3. A solution prepared by mixing equal volumes of 0.2 M NaOH and 0.2 M HNO_3
4. A solution prepared by mixing equal volumes of 0.2 M NH_3 and 0.2 M HCl

Questions 5–8 refer to the following terms.

(A) Activation energy
(B) Standard entropy of formation (S_f°)
(C) Enthalpy of reaction (ΔH_{rxn}°)
(D) Total entropy of change for the universe ($\Delta S_{universe}$)
(E) Free-energy formation (ΔG_f°)

5. Is always greater than or equal to zero
6. Is defined as zero for pure elements in their standard state
7. Indicates the amount of disorder in a pure substance at the standard state
8. Is always negative for an exothermic reaction

Questions 9–12 refer to the following choices at room temperature.

(A) Grayish solid
(B) Greenish-yellow gas
(C) Pale yellow gas
(D) Reddish-brown gas
(E) Reddish-brown liquid

9. Br_2
10. Cl_2
11. F_2
12. I_2

Questions 13–16 refer to the following theories.

(A) Atomic theory
(B) Kinetic molecular theory
(C) VSEPR theory
(D) Transition-state theory
(E) Quantum theory

13. Incorporates the activation energy
14. Used to determine, predict, or explain molecular geometry
15. Used to explain the effects of temperature on reaction kinetics
16. Best explains paramagnetism

Questions 17–18 refer to the following elements.

(A) Nitrogen
(B) Sodium
(C) Aluminum
(D) Oxygen
(E) Magnesium

17. Gives a yellow flame test and is used in street light lamps
18. Reacts with oxygen to form acidic oxides

Chemistry Section I
Part B

Directions: Each of the questions or incomplete statements below is followed by five suggested answers or completions. Select the one that is best in each case and then fill in the corresponding oval on the answer sheet.

19. Copper does not react with hydrochloric acid, whereas manganese does. This means
    (A) that copper is more active than hydrogen
    (B) that manganese is less active than hydrogen
    (C) that chloride ion will react with copper
    (D) that manganese is higher in the activity series than copper
    (E) none of the above

20. What mass (in grams) of hydrogen is produced by the reaction of 4.73 g of magnesium with 1.83 g of water?
    $(Mg(s) + 2H_2O(l) \rightarrow Mg(OH)_2(aq) + H_2(g))$
    (A) 0.102
    (B) 0.0162
    (C) 0.0485
    (D) 0.219
    (E) 0.204

21. A compound containing an oxygen atom in the +2 oxidation state is
    (A) O_2F_2
    (B) OF_2
    (C) H_2O
    (D) Li_2O
    (E) K_2O_2

22. Which reaction produces an increase in the entropy of the system?
    (A) $Ag^+(aq) + Cl^-(aq) \rightarrow AgCl(s)$
    (B) $CO_2(s) \rightarrow CO_2(g)$
    (C) $H_2(g) + Cl_2(g) \rightarrow 2HCl(g)$
    (D) $N_2(g) + 3H_2(g) \rightarrow 2NH_3(g)$
    (E) $H_2O(l) \rightarrow H_2O(s)$

23. Based on quantum numbers, with $n = 4$, give the label for each of the subshells in the level.
    (A) Its subshells are labeled $4s$, $4p$, and $4d$.
    (B) Its subshells are labeled $4s$, $4p$, $4d$, and $4f$.
    (C) Its subshells are labeled $4s$, $4p$, and $4f$.
    (D) Its subshells are labeled $3s$, $3p$, $4d$, and $4f$.
    (E) Its subshells are labeled $3s$, $4p$, $4d$, and $4f$.

24. When KNO_3 dissolves in water at room temperature, ΔH is positive for the dissolution process. Given this information, what can you conclude?
    (A) $\Delta G > 0$ for the dissolution process.
    (B) $\Delta G = 0$ for the dissolution process.
    (C) The dissolution of salts in water is always a spontaneous process.
    (D) $\Delta S > 0$ for the dissolution process.
    (E) $\Delta S < 0$ for the dissolution process.

25. Which of the following binary compounds would you expect to be the most acidic?
    (A) NaH
    (B) CH_4
    (C) SnH_4
    (D) H_2O
    (E) H_2S

GO ON TO THE NEXT PAGE

26. A catalyst increases the rate of a reaction by doing which of the following?
    (A) Increasing reactant concentrations
    (B) Increasing temperature
    (C) Decreasing temperature
    (D) Increasing activation energy of the reaction
    (E) Decreasing activation energy of the reaction

27. Which of the following statements is/are true?
    I. Deviations in the behavior of gases from the ideal-gas equation occur because gas molecules occupy a finite volume in a container.
    II. Deviations in the behavior of gases from the ideal-gas equation occur because attractions between gas molecules exist.
    III. Deviations in the behavior of gases from the ideal-gas equation decrease with increasing temperature.

    (A) I only
    (B) II only
    (C) I and II
    (D) II and III
    (E) I, II, and III

28. Which of the following statements about crystalline solids is/are NOT true?
    I. Molecules or atoms in molecular solids are held together via intermolecular forces.
    II. Metallic solids have atoms in the points of the crystal lattice.
    III. Ionic solids have formula units in the point of the crystal lattice.

    (A) I
    (B) II
    (C) III
    (D) I and III
    (E) None of the above

29. A compound with —COOH is representative of which functional group?
    (A) Aldehyde
    (B) Ethers
    (C) Cycloalkane
    (D) Carboxylic acid
    (E) None of the above

30. Which type of crystalline solid is SO_2 most like to form?
    (A) Ionic
    (B) Molecular
    (C) Atomic
    (D) Metallic
    (E) Amorphous

31. A burning splint will burn more vigorously in pure oxygen than in air because
    (A) oxygen is a reactant in combustion, and the concentration of oxygen is higher in pure oxygen than it is in air
    (B) oxygen is a catalyst for combustion
    (C) oxygen is a product of combustion
    (D) nitrogen is a product of combustion, and the system reaches equilibrium at a lower temperature
    (E) nitrogen is a reactant in combustion, and its low concentration in pure oxygen catalyzes the combustion

32. The hybridizations of nitrogen in NF_3 and NH_3 are
    (A) sp^2 and sp^2 respectively
    (B) sp and sp^3 respectively
    (C) sp^3 and sp respectively
    (D) sp^3 and sp^3 respectively
    (E) sp^2 and sp^3 respectively

33. What is the molarity of a solution consisting of 1.25 g of NaOH in enough water to form 250 mL of solution?
    (A) 1.25 M
    (B) 0.800 M
    (C) 8.00 M
    (D) 1.25×10^{-4} M
    (E) 0.125 M

34. Which of the following statements is NOT true about hydrogen gas?
    (A) Forces between H_2 molecules are weak.
    (B) It is a color gas at room temperature and pressure.
    (C) It is an effective reducing agent for many metal oxides.
    (D) The H—H bond is weak.
    (E) Ignition of H_2 in air produces H_2O.

35. Water vapor is a mixture of
    (A) $CH_4(g)$ and $H_2O(g)$
    (B) $CO(g)$ and $H_2O(g)$
    (C) $CO(g)$ and $H_2(g)$
    (D) $C(s)$ and $H_2O(g)$
    (E) $CO_2(g)$ and $H_2(g)$

36. Which of the expressions below represents the correct rate law of the reaction?

$$2A + B \rightarrow C$$

Experiment	A	B	Initial Rate (Mole/L • Sec)
1	1	1	1.2
2	2	1	4.8
3	1	2	2.4
4	3	1	10.8
5	1	3	3.6

    (A) Rate $= K[A][B]$
    (B) Rate $= K[A]^2[B]$
    (C) Rate $= K[A]$
    (D) Rate $= K[B]$
    (E) Rate $= K[A]^2[B]^2$

37. A reaction occurred in which A reacted with a large excess of B to form C. The concentrations of the reactants were measured periodically and recorded in the chart below. Based on the data in the chart, which of the following statements is NOT true?

Time (Min)	[A] M	[B] M
0	0.50	6.00
10	0.36	6.00
20	0.25	6.00
30	0.18	6.00
40	0.13	6.00

    (A) The reaction is first order in [A].
    (B) The reaction is first order overall.
    (C) The rate of the reaction is constant over time.
    (D) The half-life of reactant [A] is 20 minutes.
    (E) The graph of ln[A] will be a straight line.

38. A neutralization reaction between an acid and a metal hydroxide produces
    (A) water and a salt
    (B) hydrogen gas
    (C) oxygen gas
    (D) sodium hydroxide
    (E) ammonia

39. What is the valence-electron configuration for Se^{2-}?
    (A) $2s^2 2p^4$
    (B) $2s^2 2p^6$
    (C) $4s^2 4p^4$
    (D) $4s^2 4p^6$
    (E) $3s^2 3p^2$

GO ON TO THE NEXT PAGE

40. Of the following molecules, which has the largest dipole moment?
    (A) HF
    (B) HCl
    (C) HBr
    (D) HI
    (E) HAt

41. How much heat is required to convert 100 g of water at 40°C to water vapor at 100°C? The heat of capacity of water is 4.184 J/g-°C, and the heat required to vaporize water is 2.26 kJ/g.
    (A) 227 kJ
    (B) 418 kJ
    (C) 226 kJ
    (D) 25.1 kJ
    (E) 251 kJ

42. When the equation $Al(NO_3)_3 + Na_2S \rightarrow Al_2S_3 + NaNO_3$ is balanced, the coefficients are
    (A) 2, 3, 1, 6
    (B) 2, 1, 3, 2
    (C) 1, 1, 1, 1
    (D) 4, 6, 3, 2
    (E) 2, 3, 2, 3

43. Which of the following reactions is a redox reaction?
    I. $Kr_2CrO_4 + BaCl_2 \rightarrow BaCrO_4 + 2KCl$
    II. $Pb^{2+} + 2Br^- \rightarrow PbBr_2$
    III. $Cu + S \rightarrow CuS$
    (A) I
    (B) II
    (C) III
    (D) I and III
    (E) II and III

44. Which of the following xenon compounds is/are polar?
    I. XeF_4
    II. XeO_4
    III. $XeOF_4$
    (A) I
    (B) II
    (C) III
    (D) I and III
    (E) II and III

45. One edge of a cube is measured and found to be 13 cm. The volume of the cube in m^3 is
    (A) 2.2×10^{-3}
    (B) 2.2×10^{-6}
    (C) 2.2
    (D) 2.2×10^3
    (E) 2.2×10^6

46. Which of the following is NOT a physical property of water?
    (A) It is a liquid at room temperature.
    (B) It can be decomposed into oxygen and hydrogen gases.
    (C) It boils at 100°C at 1 atm pressure.
    (D) It freezes at 0°C at 1 atm pressure.
    (E) It has a density of 1.00 g/cm^3.

47. The formula of nitrobenzene is $C_6H_5NO_2$. The molecular mass of this compound is
    (A) 107.11 amu
    (B) 43.03 amu
    (C) 109.10 amu
    (D) 123.11 amu
    (E) 3.06 amu

48. Using a periodic table, arrange the following atoms in order of increasing first ionization energy: Ne, Na, P, Ar, K.
    (A) Ne < Na < P < Ar < K
    (B) Na < Ne < P < K < Ar
    (C) Ne < P < Na < K < Ar
    (D) K < Na < P < Ar < Ne
    (E) K = Na, P < Ne < Ar

49. Why are the atomic masses in the periodic table NOT integral numbers. (For example, carbon is listed as 12.01115 instead of as 12.00000.)
    (A) Our technology does not allow for exact measurement of such a small quantity.
    (B) Atoms gain and lose electrons easily, and that changes their masses significantly.
    (C) Atomic masses listed in the periodic table are weighted averages of naturally occurring isotopes.
    (D) Atomic masses are measured in real samples that are always contaminated with other elements.
    (E) There is a theoretical uncertainty in the masses of atoms.

50. Both methane and ethane are made up of carbon and hydrogen. In methane, there are 12.0 g of carbon for every 4.00 g of hydrogen, a ratio of 3 : 1 by mass. In ethane, there are 24.0 g of carbon for every 6.00 g of hydrogen, a ratio of 4 : 1 by mass. This is a statement of the law of
    (A) constant composition
    (B) multiple proportions
    (C) conservation of matter
    (D) conservation of mass
    (E) octaves

51. In which set of elements would all members be expected to have very similar chemical properties?
    (A) O, S, Se
    (B) N, O, F
    (C) Na, Mg, K
    (D) S, Se, Si
    (E) Ne, Na, Mg

52. A chemist uses a cylinder with a piston and gas inlet valve. Consider the following change: Inject an additional gas through the gas inlet valve. What will be the consequences for the pressure of the gas and for the number of moles of gas present?
    (A) The pressure of the gas will decrease, and the number of moles of gas present will decrease.
    (B) The pressure of the gas will increase, and the number of moles of gas present will increase.
    (C) The pressure of the gas will decrease, and the number of moles of gas present will increase.
    (D) There will be no changes in the pressure of the gas or in the number of moles.
    (E) The pressure of the number of moles of gas will stay the same, and the pressure of the gas will decrease.

53. ΔE is always positive when a system
    (A) absorbs heat and does work
    (B) gives off heat and does work
    (C) absorbs heat and has work done on it
    (D) gives off heat and has work done on it
    (E) none of the above, since ΔE is always negative

54. Which of the following is NOT true about the Bohr model of the hydrogen atom?
    (A) Electrons decay into the nucleus.
    (B) The model cannot account for the ionization of an electron.
    (C) An electron in a stable Bohr orbit does not emit radiation continuously.
    (D) An electron may remain in an orbit indefinitely.
    (E) The hydrogen atom absorbs radiant energy in multiples of $h\dot{v}$.

GO ON TO THE NEXT PAGE

55. The standard cell potential (ΔE°_{cell}) of the reaction

$$Cl_2(g) + 2I^-(aq) \rightarrow 2Cl^-(aq) + I_2(s)$$

is $+0.82$ V. The value of ΔG° for the reaction is
(A) -24 kJ/mol
(B) $+24$ kJ/mol
(C) -160 kJ/mol
(D) $+160$ kJ/mol
(E) -50 kJ/mol

56. The primary source of the specificity of enzymes is
(A) their polarity, which matches that of their specific substrate
(B) their delocalized electron cloud
(C) their bonded transition metal, which is specific to the target substrate
(D) their locations within the cell
(E) their shape, which relates to the lock-and-key model

57. The rate law for a reaction is:

$$\text{rate} = k\,[A][B]^2.$$

Which of the following statements is NOT true?
(A) The reaction is first order in $[A]$.
(B) The reaction is second order in $[B]$.
(C) The reaction is second order overall.
(D) k is the reaction rate constant.
(E) If $[B]$ is doubled, the reaction rate will increase by a factor of 4.

58. For the reaction

$$C_2H_6(g) \rightarrow C_2H_4(g) + H_2(g)$$

ΔH° is $+137$ kJ/mol and ΔS° is $+120$ J/K · mol. This reaction is
(A) spontaneous at all temperatures
(B) spontaneous only at high temperatures
(C) spontaneous only at low temperatures
(D) nonspontaneous at all temperatures
(E) unreliable

59. Which of the following has the largest ionic radius?
(A) Be^{2+}
(B) Mg^{2+}
(C) Ca^{2+}
(D) Sr^{2+}
(E) Ba^{2+}

60. A 50.0-mL sample of an aqueous H_2SO_4 solution is titrated with a 0.375 M NaOH solution. The equivalence point is reached with 62.5 mL of the base. The concentration of H_2SO_4 is
(A) 0.234 M
(B) 0.469 M
(C) 0.150 M
(D) 0.300 M
(E) 0.938 M

61. The boiling point of water is known to be lower at high elevations. This is because
(A) water is more dense at high elevations
(B) hydrogen bonds are weaker at high elevations
(C) the heat of fusion is lower at high elevations
(D) the atmospheric pressure is higher at high elevations
(E) the atmospheric pressure is lower at high elevations

62. Given that a reaction is exothermic and has an activation energy of 50 kJ/mol, which of the following statements are correct?
   I. The reverse reaction has an activation energy greater than 50 kJ/mol.
   II. The reaction rate increases with temperature.
   III. The reaction rate decreases with temperature.
(A) I
(B) II
(C) III
(D) I and II
(E) I and III

63. According to the ideal-gas equation, which of the following statements is true?
    (A) If gases are mixed, the partial pressure of each lowers the partial pressure of the others.
    (B) For Boyle's law to apply, a gas must be kept at constant pressure.
    (C) The volume of a gas is not changed if it is heated from 0°C to 100°C and at the same volume if the pressure is increased from 750 torr to 850 torr.
    (D) The volume of a gas doubles when the centigrade temperature doubles if all other variables are held constant.
    (E) The volume of a gas decreases by a factor of 2 when the pressure is doubled if all other variables are held constant.

64. Which of the following statements is true under any condition for a reaction that is spontaneous at any temperature?
    (A) ΔG and ΔH are negative, and ΔS is positive.
    (B) ΔG and ΔH are positive, and ΔS is negative.
    (C) ΔG and ΔS are positive, and ΔH is negative.
    (D) ΔG, ΔH and ΔS are all positive.
    (E) ΔG, ΔH and ΔS are all negative.

65. In an experiment, data was collected to analyze the density of an unknown solid. The data gathered included 7.50 grams as the mass of the sample and 2.5 milliliters as the volume of the sample. The density of the sample was then reported as how many grams per milliliter?
    (A) 0.30
    (B) 3.00
    (C) 3.3
    (D) 0.33
    (E) 3.0

66. What is the oxidation state of xenon in XeO_4?
    (A) +8
    (B) +6
    (C) +4
    (D) +2
    (E) 0

67. All of the following statements concerning the alkali metals are true EXCEPT
    (A) they form ions that are soluble in water
    (B) they form ions with a +1 oxidation state
    (C) the electronegativity of alkali metals decreases as their atomic number increases
    (D) the first ionization number of alkali metals decreases as their atomic number increases
    (E) they are strong oxidizing agents

68. Which of the following sets of quantum numbers is NOT possible?
    (A) 3   2   0   1/2
    (B) 5   0   0   1/2
    (C) 3   2   −2   −1/2
    (D) 4   3   1   1/2
    (E) 2   2   −1   1/2

69. Which of the following cannot be a reducing agent?
    (A) Ag
    (B) I^-
    (C) Cl^-
    (D) Fe^{3+}
    (E) Cr^{3+}

GO ON TO THE NEXT PAGE

70. Alpha decay produces a new nucleus whose atomic number is
    (A) 2 less and mass number is 2 less than the atomic number and mass number of the original nucleus
    (B) 1 less and mass number is 2 less than the atomic number and mass number of the original nucleus
    (C) 2 less and mass number is 4 less than the atomic number and mass number of the original nucleus
    (D) 2 more and mass number is 4 more than the atomic number and mass number of the original nucleus
    (E) 2 more and mass number is 2 less than the atomic number and mass number of the original nucleus

71. Which one of the following forms of radiation can penetrate the deepest into body tissue?
    (A) Alpha
    (B) Beta
    (C) Gamma
    (D) Positron
    (E) Proton

72. Hydrocarbons containing carbon-carbon triple bonds are called
    (A) alkanes
    (B) aromatic hydrocarbons
    (C) alkynes
    (D) alkenes
    (E) olefins

73. Which one of the following is NOT true about transition metals?
    (A) They frequently have more than one common oxidation state.
    (B) Their compounds are frequently colored.
    (C) Their compounds frequently exhibit magnetic properties.
    (D) They are found in the d-block of the periodic table.
    (E) They typically have low melting points.

74. How is the reaction quotient used to determine whether a system is at equilibrium?
    (A) The reaction quotient must be satisfied for equilibrium to be achieved.
    (B) At equilibrium, the reaction quotient is undefined.
    (C) The reaction is at equilibrium when $Q < K_{eq}$.
    (D) The reaction is at equilibrium when $Q > K_{eq}$.
    (E) The reaction is at equilibrium when $Q = K_{eq}$.

75. When sodium hydroxide is added to a solution of saturated calcium hydroxide, which of the following precipitates would you expect to form?
    (A) Calcium
    (B) Sodium
    (C) Water
    (D) Sodium hydroxide
    (E) Calcium hydroxide

END OF SECTION I

IF YOU FINISH BEFORE TIME IS CALLED, YOU MAY CHECK YOUR WORK ON THIS SECTION. DO NOT GO ON TO SECTION II UNTIL YOU ARE TOLD TO DO SO.

Chemistry Section II

Time—1 hour and 30 minutes
Percent of total grade—55

INFORMATION IN THE TABLE BELOW AND IN THE FOLLOWING TABLES MAY BE USEFUL IN ANSWERING THE QUESTIONS IN THIS SECTION OF THE EXAMINATION.

PERIODIC TABLE OF THE ELEMENTS

1A 1																		8A 18
1 H 1.0079	2A 2												3A 13	4A 14	5A 15	6A 16	7A 17	2 He 4.0026
3 Li 6.941	4 Be 9.012												5 B 10.811	6 C 12.011	7 N 14.007	8 O 16.00	9 F 19.00	10 Ne 20.179
11 Na 22.99	12 Mg 24.30	3B 3	4B 4	5B 5	6B 6	7B 7	8	8B 9	10	1B 11	2B 12		13 Al 26.98	14 Si 28.09	15 P 30.974	16 S 32.06	17 Cl 35.453	18 Ar 39.948
19 K 39.10	20 Ca 40.08	21 Sc 44.96	22 Ti 47.90	23 V 50.94	24 Cr 52.00	25 Mn 54.938	26 Fe 55.85	27 Co 58.93	28 Ni 58.69	29 Cu 63.55	30 Zn 65.39		31 Ga 69.72	32 Ge 72.59	33 As 74.92	34 Se 78.96	35 Br 79.90	36 Kr 83.80
37 Rb 85.47	38 Sr 87.62	39 Y 88.91	40 Zr 91.22	41 Nb 92.91	42 Mo 95.94	43 Tc (98)	44 Ru 101.1	45 Rh 102.91	46 Pd 106.42	47 Ag 107.87	48 Cd 112.41		49 In 114.82	50 Sn 118.71	51 Sb 121.75	52 Te 127.60	53 I 126.91	54 Xe 131.29
55 Cs 132.91	56 Ba 137.33	57 La 138.91	72 Hf 178.49	73 Ta 180.95	74 W 183.85	75 Re 186.21	76 Os 190.2	77 Ir 192.2	78 Pt 195.08	79 Au 196.97	80 Hg 200.59		81 Tl 204.38	82 Pb 207.2	83 Bi 208.98	84 Po (209)	85 At (210)	86 Rn (222)
87 Fr (223)	88 Ra 226.02	89 Ac 227.03	104 Rf (261)	105 Db (262)	106 Sg (263)	107 Bh (264)	108 Hs (265)	109 Mt (268)	110 Ds (269)	111 Uuu (272)	112 Uub (277)							

58 Ce 140.12	59 Pr 140.91	60 Nd 144.24	61 Pm (145)	62 Sm 150.4	63 Eu 151.97	64 Gd 157.25	65 Tb 158.93	66 Dy 162.50	67 Ho 164.93	68 Er 167.26	69 Tm 168.93	70 Yb 173.04	71 Lu 174.97
90 Th 232.04	91 Pa 231.04	92 U 238.03	93 Np (237)	94 Pu (244)	95 Am (243)	96 Cm (247)	97 Bk (247)	98 Cf (251)	99 Es (252)	100 Fm (257)	101 Md (258)	102 No (259)	103 Lr (262)

GO ON TO THE
NEXT PAGE

STANDARD REDUCTION POTENTIALS IN AQUEOUS SOLUTION AT 25°C			
Half-reaction			$E°(V)$
$F_2(g) + 2e^-$	$\rightarrow$	$2F^-$	2.87
$Co^{3+} + e^-$	$\rightarrow$	Co^{2+}	1.82
$Au^{3+} + 3e^-$	$\rightarrow$	$Au(s)$	1.50
$Cl_2(g) + 2e^-$	$\rightarrow$	$2Cl^-$	1.36
$O_2(g) + 4H^+ + 4e^-$	$\rightarrow$	$2H_2O(l)$	1.23
$Br_2(l) + 2e^-$	$\rightarrow$	$2Br^-$	1.07
$2Hg^{2+} + 2e^-$	$\rightarrow$	Hg_2^{2+}	0.92
$Hg^{2+} + 2e^-$	$\rightarrow$	$Hg(l)$	0.85
$Ag^+ + e^-$	$\rightarrow$	$Ag(s)$	0.80
$Hg_2^{2+} + 2e^-$	$\rightarrow$	$2Hg(l)$	0.79
$Fe^{3+} + e^-$	$\rightarrow$	Fe^{2+}	0.77
$I_2(s) + 2e^-$	$\rightarrow$	$2I^-$	0.53
$Cu^+ + e^-$	$\rightarrow$	$Cu(s)$	0.52
$Cu^{2+} + 2e^-$	$\rightarrow$	$Cu(s)$	0.34
$Cu^{2+} + e^-$	$\rightarrow$	Cu^+	0.15
$Sn^{4+} + 2e^-$	$\rightarrow$	Sn^{2+}	0.15
$S(s) + 2H^+ + 2e^-$	$\rightarrow$	$H_2S(g)$	0.14
$2H^+ + 2e^-$	$\rightarrow$	$H_2(g)$	0.00
$Pb^{2+} + 2e^-$	$\rightarrow$	$Pb(s)$	−0.13
$Sn^{2+} + 2e^-$	$\rightarrow$	$Sn(s)$	−0.14
$Ni^{2+} + 2e^-$	$\rightarrow$	$Ni(s)$	−0.25
$Co^{2+} + 2e^-$	$\rightarrow$	$Co(s)$	−0.28
$Tl^+ + e^-$	$\rightarrow$	$Tl(s)$	−0.34
$Cd^{2+} + 2e^-$	$\rightarrow$	$Cd(s)$	−0.40
$Cr^{3+} + e^-$	$\rightarrow$	Cr^{2+}	−0.41
$Fe^{2+} + 2e^-$	$\rightarrow$	$Fe(s)$	−0.44
$Cr^{3+} + 3e^-$	$\rightarrow$	$Cr(s)$	−0.74
$Zn^{2+} + 2e^-$	$\rightarrow$	$Zn(s)$	−0.76
$Mn^{2+} + 2e^-$	$\rightarrow$	$Mn(s)$	−1.18
$Al^{3+} + 3e^-$	$\rightarrow$	$Al(s)$	−1.66
$Be^{2+} + 2e^-$	$\rightarrow$	$Be(s)$	−1.70
$Mg^{2+} + 2e^-$	$\rightarrow$	$Mg(s)$	−2.37
$Na^+ + e^-$	$\rightarrow$	$Na(s)$	−2.71
$Ca^{2+} + 2e^-$	$\rightarrow$	$Ca(s)$	−2.87
$Sr^{2+} + 2e^-$	$\rightarrow$	$Sr(s)$	−2.89
$Ba^{2+} + 2e^-$	$\rightarrow$	$Ba(s)$	−2.90
$Rb^+ + e^-$	$\rightarrow$	$Rb(s)$	−2.92
$K^+ + e^-$	$\rightarrow$	$K(s)$	−2.92
$Cs^+ + e^-$	$\rightarrow$	$Cs(s)$	−2.92
$Li^+ + e^-$	$\rightarrow$	$Li(s)$	−3.05

Source: *1999 AP® Chemistry Released Exam.* Copyright © 1999 by College Board. Reproduced with permission. All rights reserved. http://www.apcentral.collegeboard.com/

ADVANCED PLACEMENT CHEMISTRY EQUATIONS AND CONSTANTS

ATOMIC STRUCTURE

$$E = h\nu \qquad c = \lambda\nu$$

$$\lambda = \frac{h}{mv} \qquad p = mv$$

$$E_n = \frac{-2.178 \times 10^{-18}}{n^2} \text{ joule}$$

EQUILIBRIUM

$$K_a = \frac{[H^+][A^-]}{[HA]}$$

$$K_b = \frac{[OH^-][HB^+]}{[B]}$$

$$K_w = [OH^-][H^+] = 1.0 \times 10^{-14} \text{ @ } 25°C$$

$$= K_a \times K_b$$

$$pH = -\log[H^+], pOH = -\log[OH^-]$$

$$14 = pH + pOH$$

$$pH = pK_a + \log\frac{[A^-]}{[HA]}$$

$$pOH = pK_b + \log\frac{[HB^+]}{[B]}$$

$$pK_a = -\log K_a, pK_b = -\log K_b$$

$$K_p = K_c(RT)^{\Delta n}$$

where Δn = moles product gas – moles reactant gas

THERMOCHEMISTRY/KINETICS

$$\Delta S° = \sum S° \text{ products} - \sum S° \text{ reactants}$$

$$\Delta H° = \sum \Delta H_f° \text{ products} - \sum \Delta H_f° \text{ reactants}$$

$$\Delta G° = \sum \Delta G_f° \text{ products} - \sum \Delta G_f° \text{ reactants}$$

$$\Delta G° = \Delta H° - T\Delta S°$$

$$= -RT \ln K = -2.303 \, RT \log K$$

$$= -n \mathscr{F} E°$$

$$\Delta G = \Delta G° + RT \ln Q = \Delta G° + 2.303 \, RT \log Q$$

$$q = mc\Delta T$$

$$C_p = \frac{\Delta H}{\Delta T}$$

$$\ln[A]_t - \ln[A]_0 = -kt$$

$$\frac{1}{[A]_t} - \frac{1}{[A]_0} = kt$$

$$\ln k = \frac{-E_a}{R}\left(\frac{1}{T}\right) + \ln A$$

E = energy

ν = frequency

λ = wavelength

p = momentum

v = velocity

n = principal quantum number

m = mass

Speed of light, $c = 3.0 \times 10^8 \text{ m s}^{-1}$

Planck's constant, $h = 6.63 \times 10^{-34} \text{ J s}$

Boltzmann's constant, $k = 1.38 \times 10^{-23} \text{ J K}^{-1}$

Avogadro's number $= 6.022 \times 10^{23} \text{ mol}^{-1}$

Electron charge, $e = -1.602 \times 10^{-19}$ coulomb

1 electron volt per atom $= 96.5 \text{ kJ mol}^{-1}$

Equilibrium Constants

K_a (weak acid)

K_b (weak base)

K_w (water)

K_p (gas pressure)

K_c (molar concentrations)

$S°$ = standard entropy

$H°$ = standard enthalpy

$G°$ = standard free energy

$E°$ = standard reduction potential

T = temperature

n = moles

m = mass

q = heat

c = specific heat capacity

C_p = molar heat capacity at constant pressure

E_a = activation energy

k = rate constant

A = frequency factor

Faraday's constant, $\mathscr{F} = 96,500$ coulombs per mole of electrons

Gas constant, $R = 8.31 \text{ J mol}^{-1} \text{ K}^{-1}$

$$= 0.0821 \text{ L atm mol}^{-1} \text{ K}^{-1}$$

$$= 8.31 \text{ volt coulomb mol}^{-1} \text{ K}^{-1}$$

GASES, LIQUIDS, AND SOLUTIONS

$$PV = nRT$$

$$\left(P + \frac{n^2a}{V^2}\right)(V - nb) = nRT$$

$$P_A = P_{total} \times X_A, \text{ where}$$

$$X_A = \frac{\text{moles A}}{\text{total moles}}$$

$$P_{total} = P_A + P_B + P_C + \cdots$$

$$n = \frac{m}{M}$$

$$K = °C + 273$$

$$\frac{P_1V_1}{T_1} = \frac{P_2V_2}{T_2}$$

$$D = \frac{m}{V}$$

$$u_{rms} = \sqrt{\frac{3kT}{m}} = \sqrt{\frac{3RT}{M}}$$

$$KE \text{ per molecule} = \frac{1}{2}mv^2$$

$$KE \text{ per mole} = \frac{3}{2}RT$$

$$\frac{r_1}{r_2} = \sqrt{\frac{M_2}{M_1}}$$

molarity, M = moles solute per liter solution

molality = moles solute per kilogram solvent

$$\Delta T_f = iK_f \times \text{molality}$$

$$\Delta T_b = iK_b \times \text{molality}$$

$$\pi = MRT$$

$$A = abc$$

OXIDATION-REDUCTION; ELECTROCHEMISTRY

$$Q = \frac{[C]^c[D]^d}{[A]^a[B]^b}, \text{ where } a\,A + b\,B \rightarrow c\,C + d\,D$$

$$I = \frac{q}{t}$$

$$E_{cell} = E°_{cell} - \frac{RT}{n\mathscr{F}} \ln Q$$

$$= E°_{cell} - \frac{0.0592}{n} \log Q \text{ @ } 25°C$$

$$\log K = \frac{nE°}{0.0592}$$

P = pressure
V = volume
T = temperature
n = number of moles
D = density
m = mass
v = velocity

u_{rms} = root-mean-square speed
KE = kinetic energy
r = rate of effusion
M = molar mass
π = osmotic pressure
i = van't Hoff factor
K_f = molal freezing-point depression constant
K_b = molal boiling-point elevation constant
A = absorbance
a = molar absorptivity
b = path length
c = concentration
Q = reaction quotient
I = current (amperes)
q = charge (coulombs)
t = time (seconds)
$E°$ = standard reduction potential
K = equilibrium constant

Gas constant, R = 8.31 J mol^{-1} K^{-1}

= 0.0821 L atm mol^{-1} K^{-1}

= 8.31 volt coulomb mol^{-1} K^{-1}

Boltzmann's constant, k = 1.38 × 10^{-23} J K^{-1}

K_f for H$_2$O = 1.86 K kg mol^{-1}

K_b for H$_2$O = 0.512 K kg mol^{-1}

1 atm = 760 mm Hg

= 760 torr

STP = 0.000°C and 1.000 atm

Faraday's constant, $\mathscr{F}$ = 96,500 coulombs per mole of electrons

CHEMISTRY

Part A

Time—40 minutes

YOU MAY USE YOUR CALCULATOR FOR PART A.

CLEARLY SHOW THE METHOD USED AND STEPS INVOLVED IN ARRIVING AT YOUR ANSWERS. It is to your advantage to do this, because you may earn partial credit if you do, and you will receive little or no credit if you do not. Attention should be paid to significant figures. Be sure to write all your answers to the questions on the lined pages following each question in the booklet with the pink cover. Do NOT write your answers on the green insert.

Answer Question 1 below. The Section II score weighting for this question is 20 percent.

1.

$$Ag^+(aq) + 2NH_3(aq) \longleftrightarrow Ag(NH_3)_2^+$$

The complexation reaction above takes place when a solution of silver nitrate has ammonia bubbled through it. The formation constant for the complex is 1.7×10^7 at standard temperature and pressure. Using this information, answer the questions below.

(a) Write the mass action expression for the formation of the complex.

(b) The K_f for the complex is rather large. What does that mean for the system when it reaches equilibrium?

(c) What is the concentration of Ag^+ at equilibrium, assuming that concentrated ammonia was added to 0.100 M $AgNO_3$ to produce an equilibrium concentration of $[NH_3] = 0.20$ M? Neglect any volume change from the addition of the ammonia.

(d) How would the addition of a dilute solution of HCl affect the system?

Answer EITHER Question 2 OR Question 3 on the next page. Only one of these two questions will be graded. If you start both questions, be sure to cross out the question you do not want graded. The Section II score weighting for the question you choose is 20 percent.

2. State the most common oxidation number(s) for each of the following elements, and give an example of a compound in which an atom of the element has that oxidation number.

(i) Li
(ii) Sr
(iii) Al
(iv) Ag
(v) N
(vi) O
(vii) F
(viii) Zn
(ix) S
(x) H

3. Answer the following questions about heat and boiling points.

(a) How much heat is released when 4.50 g of methane is burned in a constant-pressure system?

$$CH_4(g) + 2O_2(g) \rightarrow CO_2(g) + 2H_2O(l)$$
$$\Delta H = -890 \text{ kJ}$$

(b) List the following substances in order of increasing boiling points. Explain.

(i) $BaCl_2$
(ii) H_2
(iii) CO
(iv) HF
(v) Ne

CHEMISTRY

Part B

Time—50 minutes

NO CALCULATORS MAY BE USED WITH PART B.

Answer Question 4 below. The Section II score weighting for this question is 15 percent.

4. Write the formulas to show the reactants and the products for any FIVE of the laboratory situations described below. Answers to more than five choices will not be graded. In all cases a reaction occurs. Assume that all solutions are aqueous. You do not need to balance the equations.
   (a) Calcium turnings are added to water.
   (b) A solution of lead nitrate is mixed with sodium iodide.
   (c) Powdered magnesium carbonate is strongly heated.
   (d) Aqueous potassium permanganate is reacted with hydrogen peroxide in an acidified solution.
   (e) Octanol is burned in air.
   (f) A copper wire is placed in a silver nitrate solution.
   (g) Iron filings are added to a solution of iron (III) nitrate.
   (h) Ethane is burned in a limited supply of oxygen.

Your responses to the rest of the questions in this part will be graded on the basis of the accuracy and relevance of the information cited. Explanations should be clear and well organized. Examples and equations may be included in your responses where appropriate. Specific answers are preferable to broad, diffuse responses.

Answer BOTH Question 5 AND Question 6. Both of these questions will be graded. The Section II score weighting for these questions is 30 percent (15 percent each).

5. Answer the following question about laboratory experimentation and the ideal-gas law equation.
   (a) Oxygen gas evolved from heating $KClO_3(s)$ is collected over water in a bottle. The total volume of gas in the bottle is 150.0 mL at 27.0°C and 810.0 torr. Calculate the partial pressure of the collected $O_2(g)$. The partial pressure of pure water at 27.0°C is 22.4 torr.
   (b) The quantity PV/RT can be used to show whether 1 mol of a gas acts like an ideal gas as the pressure is varied over a wide range.

(i) What is the value of PV/RT for 1 mol of an ideal gas?

(ii) When will PV/RT for a gas be greater than 1?

(iii) When will PV/RT for a gas be less than 1?

6. Write the answer to the following questions about subshells.

(a) An orbital diagram is useful and informative, but it is cumbersome, as well. More commonly, a shorthand notation system is used also to describe electron configurations. This notation uses the nl symbol for each subshell (such as $1s, 2s, 2p, 3s, 3d$), with the number of electrons occupying the orbital set indicated with a superscript. Write the shorthand configuration for the following electron configurations.

(i) O

(ii) Sr

(iii) V

(b) Provide written analysis for the following statements.

(i) Predict the number of subshells in the fourth shell—that is, for $n = 4$.

(ii) Give the label for each of these subshells.

(iii) How many orbitals are in each of these subshells?

Answer EITHER Question 7 OR Question 8. Only one of these two questions will be graded. If you start both questions, be sure to cross out the question you do not want graded. The Section II score weighting for the question you choose is 15 percent.

7. Answer the following questions about equilibrium.

(a) Write the equilibrium-constant expression (K_{eq}) for each of the following heterogeneous equilibria.

(i) $H_2(g) + I_2 \rightleftarrows 2HI(g)$

(ii) $H_2(g) + Br_2 \rightleftarrows 2HBr(g)$

(iii) $(CH_3)_4Sn(s) \rightleftarrows (CH_3)_4Sn(g)$

(iv) $Ag(CN)_2^-(aq) + AgI(s) \rightleftarrows I^-(aq) + 2AgCN(s)$

(b) Predict the change in solubility of $Mg(OH)_2$ when the following substances are added to a saturated solution of $Mg(OH)_2$.

(i) NaOH

(ii) HCl

(iii) $MgCl_2$

8. Answer the following questions about entropy.

(a) Given the ΔG value for the following phase changes at 1 atm, predict whether each change below is spontaneous.

(i) At 283 K, $\Delta G = -250$ J/mol for $H_2O(s) \rightarrow H_2O(l)$

(ii) At 273 K, $\Delta G = 0$ J/mol for $H_2O(s) \rightarrow H_2O(l)$

(iii) At 283 K, $\Delta G = 210$ J/mol for $H_2O(s) \rightarrow H_2O(l)$.

(b) Choose the sample of matter that has greater entropy in each pair, and explain your choice.

(i) 1 mol of NaCl(s) or 1 mol of HCl(g) at 25°C

(ii) 2 mol of HCl(g) or 1 mol of HCl(g) at 25°C

(iii) 1 mol of HCl(g) or 1 mol of Ar(g) at 25°C

(iv) 1 mol of $N_2(s)$ at 24 K or 1 mol of $N_2(g)$ at 298 K

ANSWERS AND EXPLANATIONS

Multiple-Choice Questions

1. **(D) is correct.** This is a mixture of a weak acid and a strong base, so at the equivalence point the mixture will be basic, with a pH greater than 7.

2. **(A) is correct.** Both NaCl and HCl dissociate completely, but NaCl will have no effect on the pH of the solution. Since you are doubling the volume of the HCl solution by adding the salt water, the concentration of HCl will be cut in half, to 0.1 M. HCl is a strong acid, so $[H^+] = 0.1$ M and pH $= -\log[H^+] = 1$.

3. **(C) is correct.** This is a mixture of a strong acid and a strong base, so at the equivalence point, they will have completely neutralized each other, and only salt water will be left. So the solution will be neutral, and the pH will be 7.

4. **(B) is correct.** This is a mixture of a strong acid and a weak base, so at the equivalence point, the mixture will be acidic with a pH less than 7.

5. **(D) is correct.** For the universe, $\Delta S°$ total $= \Delta S°$ system $+ \Delta S°$ surroundings and is always > 0.

6. **(E) is correct.** By definition, the free energy of formation of pure elements is zero.

7. **(B) is correct.** The $S_f°$ at the standard state 298 K indicates the amount of disorder in a substance.

8. **(C) is correct.** A negative enthalpy change is the definition of exothermic.

9. **(E) is correct.** Bromine is one of the only liquids on the periodic table at room temperature.

10. **(B) is correct.** Chlorine has a characteristic green-yellow appearance.

11. **(C) is correct.** Fluorine has a characteristic yellow appearance.

12. **(A) is correct.** Iodine has a characteristic green appearance.
In terms of periodic trends, the physical appearance of the halogens should vary slightly from the top of the group to the bottom of the group. Br_2 does not fit in the trend due to its liquid state, but the other three gases transition from yellow to green-yellow to green as they go down the group. For a set of questions like the preceding four, if you can remember the appearance of one or two of the elements, you can figure out the other two.

13. **(D) is correct.** Transition state theory is the theory that incorporates the activation energy. Activation energy is the minimum energy needed to progress from reactants to products via the transition state.

14. **(C) is correct.** VSEPR is the theory used to determine, predict, or explain molecular geometry. Molecular shapes are defined by electron pair repulsion, so they are as far apart as possible.

15. **(B) is correct.** The kinetic molecular theory is used to explain the effects of temperature on reaction kinetics. Kinetics states that average kinetic energy is proportional to temperature.

16. **(E) is correct.** Quantum theory best explains paramagnetism. Hund's rule was used for the theory for filling orbitals before electrons were discovered.

17. (B) is correct. Sodium gives an emission spectrum of two lines in the visible range near 590 nm.

18. (A) is correct. Nonmetals like sulfur, carbon, and nitrogen form acidic oxides.

19. (D) is correct. In practicing oxidation-reduction reactions, you have begun to analyze what reacts and what does not react. You are given that copper does not react with hydrochloric acid, whereas manganese does. This means that manganese is higher in activity series than is copper.

20. (A) is correct. Determine the limiting reactant, and then complete the math to calculate the amount of $H_2(g)$ produced.

$$4.73 \text{ g Mg} \times \frac{1 \text{ mol Mg}}{24.3 \text{ g Mg}} = 0.195 \text{ mol Mg}$$

$$1.83 \text{ g H}_2\text{O} \times \frac{1 \text{ mol H}_2\text{O}}{18.0 \text{ g H}_2\text{O}} = 0.102 \text{ mol H}_2\text{O}$$

H_2O is limiting, therefore:

$$0.102 \text{ g H}_2\text{O} \times \frac{1 \text{ mol H}_2}{2 \text{ mol H}_2\text{O}} \times \frac{2.016 \text{ g H}_2}{1 \text{ mol H}_2} = 0.102 \text{ g H}_2$$

21. (B) is correct. The chemistry of nonmetals provides concepts on periodic trend and details of specific elements such as oxygen. OF_2 is the only compound listed that contains an oxygen atom in the +2 oxidation state.

22. (B) is correct. Chemical thermodynamics provides details on the molecular interpretation of entropy. The reaction, which produces an increase in the entropy of the system, is CO_2 going from solid to gas.

23. (B) is correct. Its subshells are labeled 4s, 4p, 4d, and 4f. The number given in the designation of a subshell is the principal quantum number, n; the following letter designates the value of the azimuthal quantum number, l.

24. (D) is correct. Chemical thermodynamics provides analysis of the different components for ΔS. From the given information, you can determine that $\Delta S > 0$ for the dissolution process.

25. (E) is correct. Acid-base equilibria provide comparisons of the relative strengths of acids and bases. From the given binary compounds listed, H_2S is the most acidic.

26. (E) is correct. A catalyst increases the rate of a reaction by decreasing activation energy of a reaction.

27. (E) is correct. Deviations occur in the ideal-gas law because molecules are not ideal. Gas molecules have a definite volume and have interactions between the molecules. Temperature increases the deviations because the molecules are moving faster within their system.

28. (C) is correct. Only III is correct. Ionic solids have formula units in the point of the crystal lattice.

29. (D) is correct. Organic chemistry is the chemistry of life. A compound with a —COOH functional group is a carboxylic acid.

30. (B) is correct. Polar-covalent molecules such as SO_2 tend to crystallize in a molecular crystal lattice.

31. **(A) is correct.** In Chemical kinetics there are factors that affect reaction rates. A burning splint will burn more vigorously in pure oxygen than in air, because oxygen is a reactant in combustion, and the concentration of oxygen is higher in pure oxygen than it is in air.

32. **(D) is correct.** Molecular geometry and bonding theories provide comparisons of hybrid orbitals. The hybridization of nitrogen in NF_3 and NH_3 are both sp^3.

33. **(E) is correct.** The molarity of the solution can be determined by converting the mass to moles and dividing by the volume of solution.

$$\frac{1.25 \text{ g}}{250 \text{ mL}} \times \frac{1 \text{ mol}}{40.0 \text{ g}} \times \frac{1000 \text{ mL}}{1.0 \text{ L}} = 0.125 \text{ } M$$

34. **(D) is correct.** The chemistry of nonmetals provides information about many nonmetals such as hydrogen and oxygen. The correct response is the one that is incorrect, that the H—H is bond is weak.

35. **(C) is correct.** The chemistry of nonmetals provides information about many nonmetals, such as hydrogen and oxygen. Be careful of the numerous distracters in the answers in this question about which is the correct mixture for water gas. The answer is CO gas and H_2 gas.

36. **(B) is correct.** Solution: Let the rate be expressed as follows: rate = $K[A]^n[B]^n$.

37. **(C) is correct.** The reaction rate is not constant due to the change in [A] over the course of the reaction. If the decrease in [A] were constant (set decrease in the concentration), then the reaction rate would be constant. At the beginning of the reaction, the rate of decrease in [A] is much larger than the decrease in [A] further into the reaction.

38. **(A) is correct.** In aqueous reactions and solution stoichiometry, you learn about acid-base reactions and precipitation reactions. A neutralization reaction between an acid and a metal hydroxide produces water and a salt.

39. **(B) is correct.** The correct valence-electron configuration is $2s^22p^6$.

40. **(A) is correct.** Of the following molecules, the one with the largest dipole moment is HF.

41. **(E) is correct.** Total heat = heat required to raise temperature of water + heat required to vaporize water.

= (100 g)(4.184 J/g-°C)(1 kJ/1000 J)(100°C − 40°C) + (100 g)(2.26 kJ/g)
= 251 kJ.

42. **(A) is correct.** Chemical equations have many parts to help it balance. This question asks about the status of coefficients. The correct coefficients are 2, 3, 1, and 6.

43. **(C) is correct.** Electrochemistry leads to oxidation-reductions reactions. Remember that redox reactions include transfers of electrons between species. In this case, only Cu + S → CuS is a redox reaction, since the oxidation states of copper go from 0 to 2+ and sulfur's go from 0 to 2−.

44. (C) is correct. VSEPR theory states that XeF_4 is a square planar molecule with two unshared pairs of electrons on the central axis of the molecule. The XeO_4 molecule is a square planar molecule that has 4 double bonds. The $XeOF_4$ molecule is a square pyramidal molecule that has the oxygen double bonded on the central axis. The only molecule that has any polar tendencies is the $XeOF_4$.

45. (A) is correct. In addition to measurement, there is also dimensional analysis. The volume of samples may be calculated using conversion factors.

46. (B) is correct. The properties of water (both physical and chemical) are central to many themes. Water cannot be decomposed into oxygen and hydrogen gases.

47. (D) is correct. $C_6H_5NO_2$—formula weights are determined by adding together the weights of each atom. The mass of the molecule is calculated as:

$$(6 \times 12.0 \text{ amu C}) + (5 \times 1.0 \text{ amu H}) + (1 \times 14.0 \text{ amu N})$$
$$+ (2 \times 16.0 \text{ amu O}) = 123 \text{ amu.}$$

48. (D) is correct. The ionization energy increases as you move left to right across a row. It decreases as you move from the top of a group to the bottom. Note that Na, P, and Ar are in the raw row. Because Ne is above Ar in group 8A, you expect Ne to exhibit the greater first ionization energy. K is the alkali metal directly below Na in group 1A, so K < Na. From these observations, you can conclude that the ionization energies follows the order K < Na < P < Ar < Ne.

49. (C) is correct. Calculating atomic weights is critical to understanding atomic mass scale average atomic masses.

50. (B) is correct. The theory of matter also discusses composition and proportions. This question offers multiple proportions.

51. (A) is correct. The periodic properties of the elements are central to chemistry. Understanding the patterns and trends of the periodic table will help you dramatically.

52. (B) is correct. The pressure of the gas increases, and the number of moles of gas present increases. Injecting more gas into the cylinder while keeping the volume and temperature the same will result in more molecules—and so a greater mass and greater number of moles of gas. The average distance between atoms must decrease, because their number per unit volume increases. Correspondingly, the pressure increases.

53. (B) is correct. Thermochemistry establishes the use of the first law of thermodynamics. You should be able to relate ΔE to heat and work.

54. (B) is correct. An electron in a stable Bohr orbit does not emit radiation continuously. For a Bohr model, an electron may remain in an orbit indefinitely, and the hydrogen atom absorbs radiant energy in multiples of $h\nu$. Electrons may decay into the nucleus. What is not possible in the Bohr model is that the model cannot account for the *ionization* of an electron.

55. (D) is correct. Electrochemistry details spontaneity of redox reactions. You can use the equation $\Delta G = nFE$ to determine the spontaneity of the reaction.

$$\Delta G = (2e^-)(96,500 \text{ J/V mol})(0.82 \text{ V})$$
$$\Delta G = 160,000 \text{ J/mol} = 160 \text{ kJ/mol}$$

56. (E) is correct. Chemical kinetics involves the use of catalysis. It will be useful to review the different forms of catalysts, such as enzymes.

57. (C) is correct. Chemical kinetics leads the change of concentration with time. You should be able to determine first-order and second-order reactions.

58. (B) is correct. Free energy and temperature play a role in chemical thermodynamics. Be sure you assess the different answers to see that different variations of temperature are given. Here the reaction is spontaneous only at high temperatures.

59. (E) is correct. Size increases down a family. Thus, after observing the trends in the periodic table of elements, you can determine that Ba^{2+} has the largest ionic radius.

60. (A) is correct. Acid-base titrations can be done for a variety of experiments in aqueous solution. Practice calculating the concentration of samples made.

61. (E) is correct. Increasing temperature causes the vapor pressure to increase. Thus, water will boil when the vapor pressure is equal to the atmospheric pressure. So if the atmosphere pressure is lowered, then water will boil at a lower temperature.

62. (D) is correct. Chemical kinetics provides information on how temperature and rate are connected. Given that the reaction is exothermic, the following statements are correct: the reverse reaction has activation energy greater than 50 kJ/mol, and the reaction rate increases with temperature.

63. (E) is correct. According to the ideal-gas equation, from the given answers the only true statement is that the volume of a gas decreases by a factor of 2 when the pressure is doubled, if all other variables are held constant.

64. (A) is correct. For a spontaneous reaction, ΔG is always negative. From the equation $\Delta G = \Delta H - T\Delta S$, you can see that the conditions that will make ΔG always negative are when ΔH is negative and ΔS is positive.

65. (E) is correct. To determine the density, you must use the formula density = mass/volume. Thus, the density of the sample would be 7.50 grams/2.5 ml, which equals 3.0 grams/ml. Note that distracters relate to significant digits. The volume has only two significant digits (2.5 l), so the final result of 3.0 grams/ml is limited to two significant digits.

66. (A) is correct. In XeO_4, the oxygen has an oxidation number of $2-$. Since there are four oxygen atoms the overall negative charge is $8-$. In order to have a neutral molecule, the oxidation number/charge on Xe has to be $8+$.

67. (E) is correct. The alkali metals are strong reducing agents. Some alkali metals include Li, Na and K. They are not strong oxidizing agents. They give up their single valence electrons easily, so they are easily oxidized.

■ **68. (E) is correct.** These numbers are listed traditionally in the order n, l, m_p m_s. Since l can be no greater than n–1, answer E represents the quantum numbers that are incorrect.

■ **69. (D) is correct.** Fe^{3+} cannot be oxidized any further, and therefore it can neither cause reduction nor be a reducing agent.

■ **70. (C) is correct.** Remember an alpha particle is also known as a helium nucleus (^4_2He). Also, when writing balanced nuclear equations, the mass numbers for all reactants must equal the mass number for all products; the same applies for the atomic number.

■ **71. (C) is correct.** There are biological effects of radiation. In terms of tissue damage, you must remember each level of radiation. A sheet of paper and heavy clothing can stop alpha and beta radiation, respectively, whereas gamma radiation needs a sheet of lead or other type of blockage. A low dosage version of gamma radiation is used for some cancer radiation therapies.

■ **72. (C) is correct.** Organic and biological chemistry directly link to many of the subjects you have previously studied. Alkanes = single bonded carbons, alkenes = double bonded carbons, alkynes = triple bonded carbons. Aromatic hydrocarbons are cyclic structures and olefins are specialized hydrocarbons.

■ **73. (E) is correct.** The colors of ionic solutions of these metals are due to the variety of charges that they take. "Transition" metals are known for their magnetic properties due to their partially filled d-shells.

■ **74. (E) is correct.** When Q = K, equilibrium is achieved. When Q < K, there is too much reactant, and when Q > K, there is too much product.

■ **75. (E) is correct.** Calcium hydroxide is only slightly soluble due to its low K_{sp}. Since the original solution is saturated, the addition of the common ion forces the equilibrium back to the reactants, thus forming the white precipitate of calcium hydroxide.

Free-Response Questions

Part A

1. (a) The mass action equation for the complexation equilibrium is just like any other equilibrium expression, K = products / reactants.

$$K = [Ag(NH_3)_2^+]/[Ag^+][NH_3]^2$$

1. (b) When K values are larger than 1, the products are favored at equilibrium. Since this system has such a large K value, the concentration of the products will be greater at equilibrium than when the reaction initially starts.

1. (c)

Plan: Since the K_f is such a large number, you can assume that initially all of the Ag^+ has been converted to the complex form. This should be approached as a dissociation of Ag^+ problem and not a formation of the complex problem.

Solve: Due to the large K_f, initially all of the Ag^+ is converted to the complex. Due to this, it would be better to determine the $[Ag^+]$ at equilibrium as a dissociation reaction.

$$Ag(NH_3)_2^+ \longleftrightarrow Ag^+(aq) + 2NH_3(aq)$$

$$K_{dissociation} = 1/K_{formation} = 1/1.7 \times 10^7 = 5.9 \times 10^{-8}$$

	$Ag(NH_3)_2^+ \longleftrightarrow$	$Ag^+(aq)$	$+ 2NH_3(aq)$
I	0.100	—	—
C	$-x$	$+x$	
E	$0.100 - x$	x	0.20

Since the concentration of Ag^+ will be small (K_d favors the reactants), so the change in the complex's concentration can be ignored or neglected. Therefore, the $[Ag^+]$ can be determined by:

$$K_d = [Ag^+][NH_3]^2/[Ag(NH_3)_2^+]$$
$$5.9 \times 10^{-8} = [x][0.20]^2/[0.100]$$
$$(5.9 \times 10^{-8})(0.100)/(0.04) = x$$
$$1.48 \times 10^{-7} \text{ M} = x = [Ag^+]$$

1. (d) The addition of dilute HCl will affect the equilibrium position by shifting it towards the reactants. The Cl^- ions will precipitate any silver that is not complexed, thus reducing the concentration of the $[Ag^+]$. The H^+ will react with the NH_3, to create the NH_4^+, thus reducing the $[NH_3]$. Since there is a reduction of reactants, Le Châtelier's principle states that the equilibrium position will be shifted towards the reactants.

2. Solution
Analyze: You are to determine the most common oxidation number(s) for ten elements.
Plan: Remember, oxidation numbers are usually based on the number of valence electrons, metals want to lose electrons to gain the noble gas configuration before it, and nonmetals want to gain electrons to gain the noble gas configuration ahead of it.
Solve
(i) +1: LiF. All atoms in group 1A have a +1 oxidation number.
(ii) +2: SrO. All atoms in group 2A have a +2 oxidation number.
(iii) +3: $AlCl_3$
(iv) +1: AgCl or Ag_2O
(v) −3: NH_3, +5:NO_3
(vi) −2: CaO
(vii) −1: HF
(viii) +2: ZnS
(ix) +6: SF6, −2: H_2S
(x) +1: HCl, −1: NaH (only with metallic elements)

3. (a) Solution

Analyze: Your goal is to calculate the heat produced when a specific amount of methane gas is combusted.

Plan: According to the problem, 890 kJ is produced when 1 mol CH_4 is burned at constant pressure ($\Delta H = -890$ kJ). You can treat this information as a stoichiometric relationship: 1 mol $CH_4 \approx -890$ kJ. To use this relationship, however, you must convert grams of CH_4 to moles of CH_4.

Solve: By adding the atomic weights of C and 4 H, you have 1 mol $CH_4 = 16.0$ g CH_4. Thus, you can use the appropriate conversion factors to convert grams of CH_4 to moles of CH_4 to kilojoules.

Heat =

$$(4.50 \text{ g } CH_4)(1 \text{mol } CH_4/16.0 \text{ g } CH_4)(-890 \text{ kJ}/1 \text{ mol } CH_4) = -250 \text{ kJ}$$

Check: The negative sign indicates that 250 kJ is released by the system into the surroundings.

3. (b)(I–v) Solution

Analyze: You need to relate the properties of the $BaCl_2$, H_2, HF and Ne to the boiling point.

Plan: The boiling point depends in part on the attractive forces in the liquid. You need to order these according to the relative strengths of the different kinds of forces.

Solve: The attractive forces are stronger for ionic substances than for molecular ones, so $BaCl_2$ should have the highest boiling point. The intermolecular forces of the remaining substances depend on molecular weight, polarity, and hydrogen bonding. The molecular weights are $H_2(2)$, CO(28), HF(20), and Ne (20). The boiling point of H_2 should be the lowest, because it is nonpolar and has the lowest molecular weight. The molecular weights of CO, HF, and Ne are roughly the same. Because HF can hydrogen bond, however, it should have the highest boiling point of the three. Next is CO, which is slightly polar and has the highest molecular weight. The predicted order of boiling points is therefore

$$H_2 < Ne < CO < HF < BaCl_2$$

Check: The actual normal boiling points are H_2 (20 K), Ne (27 K), CO (83 K), HF (293 K), and $BaCl_2$ (1813 K), in agreement with your predictions.

Part B

4. (a) The reaction is K + H_2O → KOH + H_2, but this is not the net ionic equation, since the KOH is an aqueous solution. The final answer is actually:

$$K + H_2O \rightarrow K^+ + OH^- + H_2$$

(b) The reaction is $Pb(NO_3)_2 + NaI \rightarrow PbI_2 + NaI$. It is a double-replacement reaction that forms a PbI_2 precipitate (you must remember the solubility rules.) Removing the spectator ions from the reaction, the final answer is actually:

$$Pb^{2+} + I^- \rightarrow PbI_2$$

(c) The reaction is $MgCO_3 \rightarrow MgO + CO_2$. This is a decomposition reaction that starts with a solid and produces a solid and a gas. Due to this, there are no spectators involved in the reaction.

(d) The reaction is a redox reaction. The best way to solve this is to remove the spectator ion, K^+ and determine what the reactants will produce in terms of the redox rules. The bromide ion (Br^-) will be oxidized to form Br_2, and the H_2O_2 will be reduced to form H_2O and O_2. In order to follow the "acidified solution" part of the reaction; H^+ must be included on the reactant side of the equation. Therefore, the final answer is:

$$Br^- + H_2O_2 + H^+ \rightarrow Br_2 + H_2O + O_2$$

(e) The reaction is a complete combustion of an alcohol. From your organic studies, you should remember that "octane" means that there are 8 carbons, all single-bonded to each other and to hydrogen, C_8H_{18}. Since the ending is "-ol", you should remember that the compound is an alcohol, so one of the H's has been replaced by the —OH group, $C_8H_{17}OH$. When air is mentioned in a reaction like this one, the expected reactant is O_2. Complete combustions always have CO_2 and H_2O as products. Therefore, the actual answer is:

$$C_8H_{17}OH + O_2 \rightarrow CO_2 + H_2O$$

During the AP Chemistry Exam, if you can't remember the formula for octanol, at least write down the products ($CO_2 + H_2O$), since you will be able to receive partial credit.

(f) The reaction is $Cu + AgNO_3 \rightarrow Cu(NO_3)_2 + Ag$. This is a single replacement reaction that includes spectators, NO_3^-. Remove the spectators and the final answer is:

$$Cu + Ag^+ \rightarrow Cu^{2+} + Ag$$

(g) This is another redox-type reaction. So just like problem (d), remove the spectator ion, this time it is NO_3^-. The Fe is oxidized to Fe^{2+} and the Fe^{3+} is oxidized to form Fe^{2+}. Therefore, the final answer is:

$$Fe + Fe^{3+} \rightarrow Fe^{2+}$$

(h) This is an incomplete combustion reaction due to the limited supply of oxygen. You should remember from organic that ethane is C_2H_8 and that the limited supply of oxygen is represented as O_2. The products of the reaction are CO and H_2O. Therefore, the final answer is:

$$C_2H_8 + O_2 \rightarrow CO + H_2O$$

5. (a) Solution

Analyze: You are given the volume [150.0 mL] and temperature [27.0°C] of oxygen gas in a bottle containing water, and the total pressure in the container is 810.0 torr. You are asked to calculate the partial of oxygen gas in the bottle. In addition, you are told that the partial pressure of pure water vapor at this temperature is 22.4 torr.

Plan: A gas collected over water contains both water vapor and the gas. Thus, the measured pressure is a sum of the partial pressures of oxygen gas and water vapor. The partial pressure of water vapor is given in the question. You can use Dalton's law of partial pressure to solve for the partial pressure of oxygen gas.

Solve: A gas collected over water contains water vapor. Thus, the measured pressure in a sum of the partial pressures of oxygen and water above the water.

$$P_{total} = P_{O_2} + P_{H_2O}$$

Solving for P_{O_2} gives

$$P_{O_2} = P_{total} - P_{H_2O} = 810.0 \text{ torr} - 22.4 \text{ torr} = 787.6 \text{ torr}$$

Check: The partial pressure of oxygen gas must be less than the total pressure, which is confirmed by calculation.

5. (b) Solution

Analyze: You are told that the ratio PV/RT can be used to demonstrate whether one mole of a gas acts like an ideal gas. You are asked what is the ratio for one mole of an ideal gas. You are asked what is the ratio for one mole of an ideal gas and when is the value greater than one or less than one.

Plan: The ideal-gas law equation is $PV = nRT$ and can be rearranged to $n = PV/RT$. For a given temperature, the value of the ratio depends on how the experimental values of P and V compare to those expected for an ideal gas. You can analyze how factors such as the size of particles and intermolecular forces affect P and V.

Solve

(i) $PV = nRT$ for an ideal gas. The ratio PV/RT equals n, which has the value of one for 1 mol of an ideal gas.

(ii) The observed value of PV is greater than the ideal value of PV for a gas when the observed volume—that is, the measure volume—is larger than the ideal volume. This happens when the gas molecules occupy a significant portion of the volume of the container. When this is the case, not all the volume of the container is available to the gas molecules, because the gas molecules exclude space for each other. Thus the gas molecules have an ideal volume that is less than the observed volume. This behavior of gases occurs at very high pressures.

(iii) A gas shows this behavior if it is not an ideal gas and if the following relation exists.

$$PV_{experimental} < PV_{ideal}$$

The observed pressure will be less than the ideal pressure when gas molecules are attracted to each other and do not collide with the walls as frequently as in the ideal case.

6. (a) Solution

Analyze: You are given information on how to write the complete electron configuration for elements and asked to write the complete shorthand notation for all electrons possessed by O, Sr, and V.

Plan: First, determine the number of electrons possessed by each atom. Then, using the Aufbau principle and Hund's rule, place electrons in the appropriate subshells.

Solve

(i) O: $1s^2 2s^2 2p^4$; or $[He]2s^2 2p^4$, where $[He]$ is used to describe the He core electron configuration $1s^2$.

(ii) Sr: $1s^2 2s^2 2p^6 3s^2 3p^6 4s^2 3d^{10} 4p^6 5s^2$; or $[Kr]5s^2$, where $[Kr]$ is used to describe the Kr core electron configuration.

(iii) V: $1s^2 2s^2 2p^6 3s^2 3p^6 4s^2 3d^3$ or $[Ar]4s^2 3d^3$, where $[Ar]$ is used to describe the Ar core electron configuration.

Check: The number and types of electrons agree with the assignments. Always count the total number of electrons in the shorthand notation to confirm that it agrees with the atomic number of the element.

6. (b) Solution

(i) There are four subshells in the fourth shell, corresponding to the four possible values of l (0, 1, 2, and 3).

(ii) Thee subshells are labeled $4s$, $4p$, $4d$, and $4f$. The number given in the designation of a subshell is the principal quantum number, n; the following letter designates the value of the azimuthal quantum number, l.

(iii) There is one $4s$ orbital (when l = 0, there is only one possible value of m_l: 0). There are three $4p$ orbitals (when l = 1, there are three possible values of m_l: 1, 0, and −1). There are five $4d$ orbitals (when l = 2, there are five allowed values of m_l: 2, 1, 0, −1, −2). There are seven $4f$ orbitals (when l = 3, there are seven permitted values of m_l: 3, 2, 1, 0, −1, −2, −3).

7. (a) Solution

Analyze: You are given four reactions describing different equilibrium conditions and asked to write the expression for K_{eq}.

Plan: According to the law of mass action, K_{eq} involves a ratio of the concentration of products to reactants. The concentration of each substance is raised to a power equal to the stoichiometric coefficient in front of it in the chemical reaction describing the equilibrium.

Solve: Remember that only gases and solutes are shown in the equilibrium-constant expression.

(i) $K_{eq} = [HI]^2/[H_2]$

(ii) $K_{eq} = [HBR]^2/[H_2]$

(iii) $K_{eq} = [(CH_3)_4Sn(g)]$

(iv) $K_{eq} = [I^-]/[Ag(CN)_2^-]$

7. (b) Solution

Analyze and Plan: You are asked to predict the change in solubility of magnesium hydroxide when three different substances are added to a saturated solution. You can use Le Châtelier's Principle to make predictions.

Solve: The equilibrium of the slightly soluble salt $Mg(OH)_2$ is described by

$$Mg(OH)_2(s) \rightleftarrows Mg^{2+}(aq) + 2OH^-(aq)$$

(i) Adding NaOH, which contains an ion common to $Mg(OH)_2$, drives the equilibrium to the left, thus decreasing the solubility of $Mg(OH)_2$.

(ii) The proton from HCl reacts with the OH^- ion to form water. This removes OH^-, thus increasing the solubility of $Mg(OH)_2$.

(iii) $MgCl_2$ drives the equilibrium to the left and decreases the solubility of $Mg(OH)_2$.

8. (a) Solution

(i) The reaction is spontaneous since $\Delta G < 0$. You expect this because ice spontaneously melts at 283 K (10°C).

(ii) The system is at equilibrium because $\Delta G = 0$; there is no net reaction. Ice and water coexist at the melting point of ice 273 K (0°C).

(iii) The reaction is not spontaneous because $\Delta G > 0$. Ice does not spontaneously melt below its melting point, 273 K.

8. (b) Solution

Analyze and Plan: You need to select the system in each pair that has the greater entropy. To do this, you examine the state of the system and the complexity of the molecules it comprises.

Solve

(i) Gaseous HCl has the higher entropy because gases are more disordered than solids.

(ii) The sample containing 2 mol of HCl has twice the entropy of the sample containing 1 mol.

(iii) The HCl sample has the higher entropy, because the HCl molecule is capable of storing energy in more ways than is Ar.

(iv) The gaseous N_2 sample has the higher entropy, because gases are more disordered than solids.